FIFTY-FIVE "BAD" BOYS

On Child
Psychology

RECONSTRUCTING BEHAVIOR IN YOUTH
A STUDY OF PROBLEM CHILDREN IN FOSTER
FAMILIES
by William Healy, M.D., Augusta F. Bronner, Ph.D.,
Edith M. H. Baylor and J. Prentice Murphy

THE CHILD IN AMERICA
BEHAVIOR PROBLEMS AND PROGRAMS
by William I. and Dorothy Swaine Thomas

TOWARDS A NEW EDUCATION
Edited by William Boyd, M.A., B.Sc., D. Phil.
With an Introduction by Sir Michael Sadler

A MOTHER'S LETTERS TO A
SCHOOLMASTER
by Rita Scherman
WITH AN INTRODUCTION
BY JAMES HARVEY ROBINSON

THESE ARE BORZOI BOOKS PUBLISHED BY
ALFRED·A·KNOPF
AND FOR SALE AT THE BETTER BOOKSHOPS

NEW YORK·ALFRED·A·KNOPF

FIFTY-FIVE "BAD" BOYS

BY

SAMUEL W. HARTWELL, M.D.

DIRECTOR OF THE WORCESTER
CHILD GUIDANCE CLINIC

WITH AN INTRODUCTION BY

WILLIAM HEALY, M.D.

1931

NEW YORK · ALFRED · A · KNOPF · LONDON

NEW YORK
ALFRED A. KNOPF INC.
730 FIFTH AVENUE
§
LONDON
ALFRED A. KNOPF LTD.
37 BEDFORD SQUARE W.C.I
§
TORONTO
LONGMANS, GREEN & COMPANY
128 UNIVERSITY AVENUE

Dedicated to the
FIFTY-FIVE BOYS

ACKNOWLEDGMENT

The Author wishes to express his most sincere appreciation and acknowledgment to Dr. William Healy and Dr. Augusta Bronner for their cooperation and the encouragement they have given him both in the treatment of these boys and in the preparation of the manuscript.

Also, to Miss Harriette Wilinsky for invaluable help rendered in the reading and revision of the manuscript.

PREFACE

HIS book is an attempt to discuss and to describe the psychiatric study and treatment of problem boys and to interpret the results obtained by psychotherapeutic endeavours with them. Throughout the book two practical plans of treatment which seemed useful to the writer are outlined and emphasized. A large part of the book is taken up with the reports, given in some detail, of a series of cases in which an attempt to carry out these plans has been made.

The cases form a chronological series in the respect that all the boys with whom the writer began any degree of psychotherapeutic endeavour at the Judge Baker Foundation during a certain period of five months are included.

The ideas and plans here described have gradually developed through trying to understand, during a period of many years, how accepting the writer as their friend has helped children who were unhappy, worried, misbehaving, and generally poorly adjusted to life. Later, for a period of two years, under the direction and encouragement of Dr. Healy and Dr. Bronner, the writer has had the privilege of intensively studying, treating, and following this series of cases. About one-half of the group are still, two years later, under the writer's observation and are seen by him occasionally; and at times a few cases are still seen regularly.

The opening chapters are written and the cases reported in somewhat informal fashion. Often the personal pronoun is used. Thus the implication is avoided that others with whom the writer has

ix

been associated necessarily endorse the ideas expressed; and, more important still, the reader may thus gain some idea of the personality of the one administering the treatment, a thing absolutely necessary for the intelligent evaluation of the methods used, the ideas advanced, and the results obtained.

There cannot be the slightest doubt that if psychotherapy extends hope of help or cure to anyone, it does so especially to children. Most of the things that act as an etiological factor in functional mental diseases, personality difficulties, or misconduct tendencies have their origin at an early age. If these can be found out, faced, and understood by the psychiatrist and the patient at the time the damage is being done, or soon after, the hope of cure is greater.

Many psychiatrists studying and treating children in private practice or in institutions and clinics express the wish that the detail and technique of treatment be more frequently reported. It is not easy to report cases or interpret results in a way that will be helpful and not be misinterpreted. Until longer clinical experiences have taught more exact methods of treatment and longer clinical thinking has given us more exact terms in which to describe them, we should constantly be trying to interpret our results in a practical but painstaking way. We should be separating our theories of what we think should happen from our knowledge of what does happen.

The only reason that these cases are here reported and this book is written is that the ideas and plans here described have seemed to be helpful, both in the treatment and in the understanding of the successes and failures that have resulted.

CONTENTS

CONTENTS

INTRODUCTION

ORIGINALITY based on sound fundamentals is not so common in any field that it should be lost to the world. And where the behaviour problems of child-life are concerned, extraordinarily numerous as they seem nowadays, methods of treatment have not yet been developed to the stage where anything that savours of improvement in technique should be overlooked. Indeed, most of those who are professionally active with these problems have too few years in retrospect to be able to know very well their own results as related to special forms of treatment. Hence our interest in this setting forth of principles and case studies.

When the author of this book, physician and psychiatrist, began to work with this series of cases, we begged him, having previously observed his unsparing devotion to his chosen field and having learned something of the originality of his methods, to register carefully his actual procedures and the responses which they evoked. Now we have them before us, written so that he who runs may read.

The whole book represents a freshness of approach that is decidedly welcome, especially as it is based on long experience. Dr. Hartwell very frequently had the problems of child-life turned over to him, either by parents themselves or by juvenile-court judges, while he was engaged in the general practice of medicine. Then, during his two years and more of war service and later, he has been much sought out by those who have perceived that he possessed qualities necessary for sympathetic understanding of human lives. So it is plain that his equipment at the time of the study of these cases consisted in a certain innate gift, together with what had been learned from much endeavour to straighten out the personal troubles of fellow-beings.

However, the reader will see that originality for this psychiatrist is no fetish; he never fails to be a diligent reader of modern psychiatric theories, nor is he ever unwilling to feel that he can learn from many sources. He has grown much from time to time, even while he has been at work with these boys.

Realizing the practical implications of the close contacts and of the deeper understandings which were part and parcel of Dr. Hartwell's method, we naturally wanted to know how they worked. We did not discern at first that this man had principles definitely formulated; it came out later that for many years he had used a specific plan of attack. In this book he has attempted to set forth his system, if it may be so called.

A lot of common sense must be embodied in good psychiatry, in the treatment of the mental life of a human individual. And it is just the mental life of these youngsters that, for the most part, comes into view when their personality and conduct disorders are understandingly faced. As our author points out, it is not only technical understandings but plenty of sympathetic appreciations of situations that are required for helping anyone to adjust himself to his surroundings with happiness of spirit and with satisfactory social behaviour.

That such work as Dr. Hartwell's demands sympathy and devotion and industry goes without saying, but, then, to my mind, so does all well-conducted effort aimed at the solving of the problems involved in such examples of behaviour tendencies as are exemplified in this book. It may be rare to find anyone willing to give so much time and energy to the effort, but yet in measure this is always necessary, particularly if one is blazing trails, as Dr. Hartwell has done in setting forth on his adventures with these young people.

The book speaks for itself in making manifest the personality of the author through its forthright statements of underlying principles as well as of attitudes taken and endeavours made. And it is particularly interesting in this day of many theories about the developmental bases of human behaviour trends that this psychiatrist did not enter the lists as knight-errant of any school or theory. He is a free lance, seeking first of all to discover in boyhood life whatever there may be that can be assailed as causative of trouble.

But beyond this, in all instances, he seeks whatever can be discovered that is good and hopeful in youthful life; anything upon which to build loyalties; anything there may be that can be reckoned as assets, whether in terms of abilities or interests or affectional tendencies—anything and everything that can be utilized for the purpose of reconstructing behaviour trends. Consideration of absence of loyalties, of distorted conceptual and emotional life, of untoward family conditions and attitudes, of bad companionships, are all only negative phases of this study of a young problem individual. It is the part of the wise therapeutist equally to discover the more positive features of the situation or of the personality. It is undoubtedly Dr. Hartwell's insistence to himself on these more constructive aspects of the total situation—and he always does insist that they exist in every case—that leads him to his optimistic, thorough-going therapeutic endeavour.

It is to be hoped almost more than anything else that there will be many parents who will have deep appreciation of the principles which are here set forth and of their working values. Here we have a very practically minded man showing that better attention to what is known about the bearings of mental life upon behaviour has immense values for dealing with young people when they present behaviour difficulties. Would it not aid rehabilitation of much that goes wrong in family life, even with such families as are herein portrayed, if such a book as this should be widely enough read?

In all fairness, it must be stated that the cases that Dr. Hartwell was asked to work with were never the simple and easy problems that came to the clinic. His energetic willingness was taken advantage of only whenever the situation or the personality seemed particularly difficult. This makes his results all the more striking and his failures, as any reader can see, the more understandable.

It is a remarkable assortment of human lives and situations that is presented in these short case studies. The background of behaviour problems in unfortunate experiences and circumstances stands out most clearly and almost picturesquely. Probably many will seize upon these stories, given in their high lights and not with the fullness of detail that many of us of a scientific bent might desire, to the exclusion of attention to the principles of understanding and treatment that are also equally clearly set forth. But we hope not, for it is just the appreciation for the need of these deeper understandings that is so necessary if we are ever to have better handling of young people's lives.

I, for one, have to confess that I do not always altogether agree with Dr. Hartwell's categories, and I sometimes perceive a certain illogicalness in his statements and interpretations. But what of it?—he honestly and trenchantly gives what he conceives to be the essence of the situations and he is never afraid to tell of failures. He has produced a most interesting book, which will be revealing to many of what there is that may be going wrong with the ideational and emotional life of young people who present behaviour problems. And what one man has been able to accomplish in the endeavour to swerve such lives into better paths cannot be denied in the face of the facts given.

It is my feeling after many years of actual work with or directing work with problem children that we have still very much to learn about what can be achieved in struggling against undesirabilities of behaviour responses. Consequently all sorts of reasonably promising methods should be tried and evaluated. Attempts to stem the constantly flowing tide of misbehaviour tendencies in the young people of America are none too successful. It is apparent that many preconceptions concerning the possibilities of corrective treatment lead in large measure to failure. Therefore I still welcome the presentation of what appear to be at all useful devices of psychotherapy for conduct disorders.

It is because the antisocial behaviour of the types illustrated by this series of fifty-five boys concerns society so deeply, as well as involves the happiness of these young individuals, that I am challenged by the rugged honesty of this presentation of what one man, using a special method, has accomplished or was unable to accomplish. There is a lesson in both successes and failures.

WILLIAM HEALY

PART I

FIFTY-FIVE "BAD" BOYS

CHAPTER I

THE PROBLEM

HE psychiatrist dealing with children and with youth has two very important tasks, inseparably linked and yet distinct from each other. He must try to help to a better footing the child who has already stumbled on the rocks of life, and he must try to understand him and his problems so that he may be able to keep others from losing their balance and similarly falling by the wayside.

In so far as he may help to better mental life, or to better living and make it more happy, his duty is therapeutic. In so far as he can understand the reasons for his successes and failures in this attempted therapy, his duty is educational. The psychiatrist is a specialist in the understanding of mental life. There is nothing mysterious about what he is trying to do. He is trying to change, influence, educate, or treat, if you will, the young individual so that he may live happily in his environment without making others unhappy.

It is most certainly desirable that there should be nothing secret about anything he attempts to do in the way of therapeutics. The same cannot always be said of the analysis of the case. It is true that the psychiatrist reads from a wonderful book that is closed to many people. He opens for study and understanding the most important book of all, the book of the human mind in its formation. He may not read aloud to all, but he must interpret to all what he

3

has learned from it. He must understand thoroughly what he learns, and he must understand thoroughly those whom he would teach. To the average mother and her child he may not read in frank detail that most vital chapter that tells of the psychopathological situation often developing from the parent-child relationship, without danger of doing them harm, but if he understands that mother and her child, he may impart his knowledge in such a way as to do them incalculable good.

What we know about treatment must be taught freely to anyone who has to do with children. The flamboyant public display of theories concerning the human mind and of personality in the making is not psychotherapeutic instruction. Theoretical and didactic answers to the sincere questions of teachers, social workers, and parents are often loosely optimistic, but offer little practical definite instruction in the treatment of the individual problem child and do not constitute true psychotherapeutic advice. We should not forget that these answers are frequently accepted and acted upon earnestly and sincerely by others, and that they contribute to the misjudgment of this very important branch of human endeavour. Popular magazine articles and lectures dealing with serious and complicated mental and behaviour problems frequently have this very grave fault.

Those to whom the world is looking for advice and instruction as how best to help children to win mental health and good adjustment to their environment have a serious responsibility. No true physician has ever withheld an iota of laboriously obtained knowledge that would tend to improve the health of the individual or the community, and no true psychiatrist will ever withhold any of his knowledge that will increase the chance of happiness for children. The danger is not in that direction. It lies rather in this: that the psychiatrist may give instructions before he is sure that they are practical, or that he may advance prognoses based on theory only. Because his interpretation of maladjustment sounds convincing, too much reliance may be placed on what he says about theoretical methods of treatment.

It must not be forgotten that there is a great difference between the fields of physical health and mental health. Generalizations can often be made in the physical field—what is good physical treatment and hygienic routine for one will be good for a large part of any group—but in the mental field generalizations are dangerous, and within wider limits every child is a law unto himself. Each child must be understood individually if he is to receive fundamental help.

Social workers, teachers, court officials, probation officers, and parents are constantly asking for suggestions as how best to modify personality trends of children and of adolescents. Psychiatrists often give only vague answers to these questions. We should be very certain of the suggestions we give. We should know more about the final results of the various forms of the treatment we use. By keeping good records and following cases thoroughly, we should know when we have succeeded and when we have failed, and we should forever be attempting to understand how these things have happened. We should think of those children as our successes who, despite early unfortunate behaviour and abnormal mental life, later become happy and well adjusted, and we should think of those boys and girls as our failures who, despite our elaborate causative interpretation and efforts to help them, become unhappy and maladjusted adults. We must try to discover why we get these different results.

Our social customs and civilization create an environment that demands complex adaptations on the part of every child. No child makes these without some help. The child must be educated in such a way that his primary instinctive behaviour is modified. In this process many adjustments are to be made which are quite at variance with the instinctive impulses he develops very early or brings with him when he is born. The psychiatrist is trying to do this for those children who have not yet been adequately helped to make these adjustments.

Before attempting to describe therapeutic procedures one must make clear his meaning of the word "therapy" as it is to be used. The particular type of psychotherapy I have attempted in the cases reported may be defined as: *a definite planned attempt to influence towards normal and healthy trends the mental life and behaviour of the one being treated, by introducing into his environmental values the person and personality of the psychiatrist, who carries with him a knowledge about and an understanding of the mental life of the patient.*

This definition allows broad scope for what the psychiatrist may do or say in the course of treatment, but it definitely limits and clarifies the endeavoured psychiatric goal.

Psychotherapy, by its very nature, must always remain in the mental realm and must always involve to a greater or lesser degree the emotional responses of both the psychiatrist and his patient. Therefore it must be considered an art, rather than a science; yet if one is to think clearly about any subject, certain definite principles must form the basis of one's thinking. Four general principles are assumed for the purpose of this study:

1. The specific mental reactions of a child to his experiences and to his environment are of greater importance for his adjustment to life than the experiences and environment per se. The way the child interprets his experiences and *feels* about things is more important than the experiences and things themselves. Therefore, if we are to modify the behaviour and emotional habit patterns of

children in the direction of normal and healthy reactions, we may do it best by altering the way they feel about things. Often, of course, changing the environment acts as a corrective measure and alters the mental life, but this is usually because in the new environment the child finds some desirable person whom he admits into his environmental values and who consequently influences his emotional responses.

2. In the final analysis the behaviour of all human beings, both children and adults, is their attempt to attain happiness. All their behaviour and their mental life is, as far as they are able to control it, a striving towards this end. Unless one understands the child in terms of this desire for happiness, one does not understand him at all. We must answer the question: "Why does the child feel and act as he does?" If the answer is to be of any practical value in altering the child's behaviour, we must give it in terms of effort to be happy or to escape unhappiness.

3. A child's mental life is to a large extent developed, shaped, directed, and given force by the sum total of his experiences and of his mental responses to them. He does not bring with him, in unchangeable form, any large part of his emotional life when he is born. It evolves from his experiences and is altered as life progresses.

4. In a child's environment the *people* whom he knows and to whom he responds are given much more emotional value than objects or happenings; his developing mental reactions will be formed, directed, and changed by his contact with other human beings whom he has accepted in his dynamic life, much more than by things he sees or by happenings that do not involve people to whom he gives emotional response. If we would know the child subjectively, we must investigate the people the child has loved and hated, rather than the sort of house he has lived in. We must

realize, however, that the child may be surrounded by any number of fine people and not receive one of them into his life. Any person with whom the child has any close association and for whom he develops a dynamic personality response, either positive or negative, acts either for good or ill in that child's developing mental life. Thus the establishment of any degree of psychiatric rapport is a profound experience for the child and should always be so considered.

CHAPTER II

THE PLAN

HE first of the two plans used in the treatment of these boys was an attempt to formulate and to describe a systematic and usable plan of mental approach to the study of each child on which might be based both the understanding and the treatment of the case.

In my experience the results obtained from thinking about problem children and working with them have always seemed far ahead of the understanding of how they were obtained. Very frequently theoretical thinking about the dynamics has failed to assist in this understanding. Gradually the belief has developed that the trouble lay not in superficial or in insufficient thinking, but in *mixed* thinking.

When a child is studied and treated, the problem should be considered in three ways: first, understanding the child; second, planning what to do for him; third, administering psychiatric treatment itself. Systematically and planfully to divide the thinking in these ways always adds to the *understanding* of the final results and often to the attainment of the results themselves.

When I study and try to help a child, I *think about* him, I *think for* him, and I *think with* him. Before describing what I mean by these terms it may be wise to state that by this I do not mean that I think about him first; then, when that is over, that I think for him; and finally that I think with him. Rather it is that I try always to know, as I proceed to work with him, in which particular one of these categories of thinking any idea may belong. I find that a failure to obtain or to understand results has happened most frequently when this kind of idea-sorting has not been done; in other words, when the thinking has been mixed.

Thinking About the Child. In thinking about the child I may consider all that is known of his history, all that has been observed, and all that has been told me by the child himself. I may have opinions and I may try to develop theories and to think about them. I may do this freely, for I do not *think about* the child aloud. In this department of thinking one may hope to improve one's own understanding and hope to systematize the knowledge that the study of various children may bring.

The *thinking about* the problem is the mixing, fusing, and crystallizing of the objective facts known about a particular child with one's own knowledge and theories about such problems in general. The success of the constructive *thinking for* and the therapeutic *thinking with* largely depends on the success of this thinking. But the failure in many seemingly hopeful cases may be, and probably often is, caused by carrying over into the constructive and therapeutic thinking too much of the theoretical *thinking about* the problem.

Thinking For the Child. By this is not meant doing the child's thinking for him, but constructively thinking and planning to give him help. It is in this field that one may make definite plans to influence the child towards a healthy mental life, by altering either his environment or his emotional responses to it. One must always *think for* the child and be sure he has some plan for giving him help while *thinking with* him, before deciding to explore deeply into his mental life or to establish a deep rapport. It is to be questioned whether one is ever justified in exploring the instinctive and mental life of problem children simply in search of dynamisms, unless one feels that the problems will be better handled if discovered, for the child has already made some sort of an adjustment, and even though this be an undesirable one, it may easily be better than another that will spontaneously develop after the exploration if the psychiatrist has given no help.

Thinking With the Child. This implies some definite degree of rapport. The depths of the therapeutic *thinking with* should be in direct proportion to the depths of the rapport. Simply listening to a child's story and talking with him in the absence of a definite and positive rapport does not mean that he is being, or that he needs to be, *thought with.* If it seems therapeutically advisable to attempt to explore the child's mental life, and if this is successfully accomplished, one may then freely and sincerely discuss anything in the child's mental life that should be dealt with.

The psychiatrist *thinks with* the child when he seriously discusses with him things about which it is desirable for the child to accept the psychiatrist's ideas and emotional attitudes.

When *thinking with* the child, there may be things about which I wish to reason with him; there may be things he does not know, of which I inform him; there may be things of which he does not appreciate the importance, and I evaluate them for him; there may be things the reality of which he has denied, and I help him face them; or there may be things he has forgotten, and I help him to remember. Even if I make a poor interpretation in my *thinking about* and have a poor plan in my *thinking for,* I may still get excellent results, for I am *thinking with* the child; that is, he and I are thinking similarly and simultaneously. His thinking may influence and help me to do more intelligent and constructive thinking, and at the same time it may actually be of therapeutic value.

This plan of separating the various parts of the entire problem into these divisions, and of always trying to know in which part of the thinking any idea belongs, has these advantages: it avoids haphazard approaches and prevents the fixing of one's thoughts on some particular phase of the problem to the exclusion of others; it allows the credit for successes and the blame for failure to be attributed to the just source. Failure in *thinking about* may be attributed to the lack of knowledge and skill of the psychiatrist; failure in *thinking for* may be borne in part by the parents, teachers, and social workers; failure in *thinking with* is due most frequently to the lack of the necessary rapport, for which either the psychiatrist or the child may be blamed. In this way the plan presents a systematized method for considering all cases, so that they may be grouped and evaluated from the standpoint of success and failure.

The second plan in the treatment is an attempt to distinguish degrees or depths of rapport that are reached between the child and the psychiatrist. Since this mutual response is the very essence of any mental therapeutics, such a distinction is desirable. This is possible because each depth of rapport to some extent carries with it general forms of emotional and behaviour responses, by which it may be objectively recognized, and the responses to the different degrees of rapport are sufficiently definite and distinctive to be partially predicted. Consequently the psychiatrist can select and attempt to effect for each case the most desirable degree of rapport.

A highly personal matter is now being discussed, and this is as far as a general hypothesis can go. The rapport established and the responses elicited are so largely conditioned by the entire mental reactions of the individual treating the child that no two people will agree on just what rapport itself is. Much less will they agree on its division into types or classes. What is true for one person is not true in detail for anyone else. The hypothesis is this only: it is always therapeutically desirable, and almost always possible, for each psychiatrist thus to classify his own cases.

Degrees and types of responses become objective only as one observes his own and the child's emotional responses while thinking of the subject in this way. Many people who work with children—teachers, and social workers, and parents sometimes—have been trained to consider it best to adopt but one type of behaviour towards all children. To do this they try, as far as they consciously can, to respond emotionally to every child in the same way. Those whose mental reactions are thus conditioned and controlled will not readily observe different types of responses in children because they themselves by their own monotone patterns discourage their manifestations.

It is very difficult to understand and to describe the mental responses to very simple human contacts. It is much harder to do so for such complicated ones as occur in the prolonged associations of a child with an adult who is deliberately trying to alter the child's personality and behaviour. The mental reactions to such contacts are, however, the things we stimulate purposively. We must attempt to understand them. Gradually, through considerable experience, I have discovered that I make four distinct degrees of rapport with children. It is likely that if others were to describe their personal contact with children quantitatively and qualitatively, they would not interpret or group them in this way, but I recognize them clearly in my own work as very definite states. I find it possible to classify definitely the rapport between me and each child with whom I am working in one of these four groups. From my experience phrases descriptive of these degrees of rapport have gradually evolved.

Before describing these degrees of rapport let me point out the fact that the child usually seems to pass from the more superficial rapports to the deeper ones in regular order and to carry with him the responses that have already occurred. Practically, this does not always happen, for often a lonesome, frightened, and unloved child is so eager for help and for human friendship that he enters the more profound types of rapport almost at once.

It must be understood that only the positive or the obviously desirable types of responses are now being considered. There are many negative ones that might be classified and studied by anyone who was *thinking about* children, but to *think for* a child who showed these negative types would probably be futile, and to attempt to *think with* him would certainly be harmful.

The most superficial of these positive responses will be called the rapport of *"friendly belief."* In this state the child thoroughly believes in me and thinks I have a knowledge that may help him. The child is willing to talk to me because someone in his environment wants him to talk, or because he thinks that since I am a doctor, it is my prerogative to expect his confidence and his duty or privilege to give it. He usually hopes to gain something. He asks only a few questions and these are of intellectual interest. The spontaneous statements he makes are largely in regard to things already known. (The spontaneous questions and statements made by the child are, incidentally, the best indication of the degree of rapport that has been attained.)

In this superficial rapport of *friendly belief* he listens to the things said because he is talking to a doctor, an older and more experienced person, or he may listen and talk only because he is in trouble and wishes to get out of it. If he is told anything that he is to accept, he must at the same time be given what he considers valid reasons for accepting it. At this stage he has no special interest in the psychiatrist's personality, and what is said to him or done for him he considers in terms of himself. He does not wish to end interviews hastily and is willing, but not anxious, to return.

This rapport might be said to correspond loosely with that established between an average normal child and a teacher whom the child respects and believes is interested in his welfare. The therapeutic procedure for this type of response is good advice and counsel, always backed by reasons that the child understands and accepts, instructions concerning things about which the child is ignorant, but about which there is no present or possible future conflict or repression. Encouragement may be given, successes and good characteristics pointed out, if he recognizes them as such. Confessions and confidences concerning things of emotional value to the child should not be sought in this superficial type of response.

The second degree of rapport will be called the rapport of *"personal trust."* In addition to believing in me, the child now *trusts* me in regard to *personal* matters. He is now somewhat interested in me as a person, yet he still thinks of things said and done in terms of himself, and his own emotional reactions are still more important to him than those of his "trusted friend." He is frank as far as he has ever consciously wished he might be or thought he ought to be with someone he could trust. He is slightly more suggestible now and is willing to accept opinions and ideas when they are based on my view-point. He asks more questions of an intimate nature and these questions show the *direction* of his emotional, ideational, and instinctive life, but they do not frankly reveal the whole of it.

In a general way the therapeutics that may be successfully carried out in the stage of *personal trust* are similar to those of the first stage—*friendly belief*. The child, however, is now more suggestible and is to a greater extent admitting the psychiatrist into his environmental values. Now things of emotional as well as of intellectual value may be discussed and advised upon. This type of rapport may be compared loosely to that existing between an adolescent child and a young person several years older whom the child admires for his knowledge and experience and by whom he desires to be noticed, appreciated, and advised.

Consider this analogy as an illustration of the difference in the responses occurring in these two degrees of rapport. An experienced football-player is down on his luck to the extent that he has but ten dollars in money and no good friends. This football-player chances to see two evenly matched teams playing a game. At first he has no personal interest in either team, though he has heard of the good reputation of one of them and expects it to win. Soon this team executes some plays of which he approves, and which he believes are the logical ones to use. He decides they know what they are doing, and he now *believes* they will win and watches the game with more interest because of this belief. He watches it more closely, too, because he thinks that he may learn some good points he himself may use later. This man is now in the state of friendly belief towards the team in which he is interested. As the game progresses, he comes to admire his team because they seem to understand football very well. Sometimes they choose a play that he believes unwise and make their downs on it. He ceases to criticize them and comes to the place where he feels that whatever they do is probably best. He now begins to shout for the team and defends them in their playing to his fellow spectators. Finally, one of these spectators offers to bet ten dollars that the other team will win, and our player immediately risks all the money he has on his favourites. He now might be said to be in the state of *personal trust* towards this team.

There is a sharp distinction between the two states of rapport already described and the two yet remaining. The practical importance of this is that there is little danger of doing the child harm if one fails to help him in the first two states; in the latter two there is danger. Only exceptionally is it advisable to go further than the stage of *personal trust* with a child who is to be seen but once or twice.

The third, and therapeutically the most important, rapport is that of *"personality contact."* The child now believes in me, trusts me, and in addition to that he likes me and wants me to understand and to like him. The most essential response is the child's desire and willingness to be understood and the indications of satisfaction he gives from the knowledge of this understanding. He now gives emotional as well as intellectual value to the things I do and say. This is the degree of rapport that is best established with all children who have definite mental, personality, or behaviour problems, the solution of which is obviously necessary to the child's adjustment to life, well-being, and happiness.

I believe that all unhappy children are either consciously or unconsciously desiring this *personality contact* with someone. The child is now interested more in the way his friend *feels* about things than in what he *knows*. He believes that he has an understanding friend and that this friend wants to help because of interest in and liking for him. If the psychiatrist so wishes, a child in *personality contact* will be entirely frank about his behaviour, his past experiences, and his emotional life. He assumes that his confidence will be respected. The questions he now asks and his manner in asking them show very clearly the content of his conscious problems. They point to the source of his conflicts, reveal his instinctive and emotional life, and throw much light on the entire situation. A child is not in this stage of rapport unless he believes that the psychiatrist will be in no way disgusted or shocked by the things he tells. He must also believe he will be liked none the less because he has been frank. The child in *personality contact* feels and usually expresses regret when he knows that the period of treatment is to come to an end. The psychiatrist must never fail to deal with this when *thinking for* the child, for during this association the child has taken him very actively into his environment. The way the psychiatrist responds to the child and the things he does in his presence, as well as the things he says to the child, are going to have a permanent influence on him. These facts should not be forgotten, for severing the *personality contact* may create new problems for the child which are worse and more upsetting to him than the ones that may have been met and solved.

Recently I received a letter from a man, happily adjusted to life now, asking me for advice in regard to his five-year-old boy. I had known this man as a very unhappy and "bad" little boy sixteen years ago. He was a member of a boys' camp, and I was the young doctor in the camp. I have never seen him since. Although I had never thought of such a phrase as *"personality contact"* at that time, this was really established between the boy and myself, although I had no name for it then. I *thought with* and *thought for* and probably did some amateur *thinking about* him. He has written to me occasionally during these years. I have spent probably two hours in answering his letters. This case was not closed, though ordinarily it should have been long ago. But I now feel that harm may yet be done by closing it, so I shall answer his letter, give him the advice, and ask him to report about his boy again.

I believe that every boy and girl who makes *personality contact* with me is either harmed or helped by that contact. The things I say to the child, and of which I convince him, not only will be remembered but also will permanently influence his emotional responses. They will give direction and force to his developing personality traits, and, in this deep state of rapport, they will have some conditioning influence on his entire life. This is especially true if the *personality contact* is made at some critical period in the child's life.

The child in *personality contact* is much more suggestible than in the more superficial states. He receives the ideas of the psychiatrist gladly and is anxious to try them out. In a large measure this desire is based on the feeling that now he is understood and that he has found a friend who, although he knows all about him, still likes him. All the therapeutic procedures of which one has a usable knowledge may be undertaken in this type of rapport. The desirable things in the child's personality may be developed and augmented both by reason and by suggestion. Undesirable things may be attacked in the same way. The most profound things in his conscious mental life may be seriously discussed. One may help him more correctly to understand his environment and his friends, and one may hope to change not only his behaviour, but the fundamental mental responses behind this behaviour. The reactions of a child in personality contact might be said to correspond to those of the normal, *uninhibited* child to a normal, intelligent parent. The difference is, of course, that the child's relations with the psychiatrist are established suddenly, usually under some emotional stress, and that the child realizes that these relations are not permanent.

The last and deepest state of rapport will be called the state of *"dependent attachment."* The child believes in me, trusts me, likes me, wants me to understand him. In addition to this he is *dependent* on me and wishes *very much* to have me like and appreciate him. He is thinking about himself and trying to interpret himself in terms of my personality. He is suggestible to the greatest possible degree. He considers things in the light of my emotional responses to them rather than in the light of his own. He is apt to be more than frank now. In fact one may always place more reliance on what a child says during good *personality contact* than during *dependent attachment*. Several children whom I have allowed and encouraged to make this extreme degree of rapport have later told me, after they had successfully directed their attachment to other people and things, that during the earlier period they reported things about themselves to be worse than they actually were. They did this because of the pleasure derived from proving to themselves that I could still appreciate and understand them even if these things were true.

The child now wishes to be with me as much as possible. Most of these children show a desire for expressions of endearment and signs of affection. Many of them exhibit feelings of jealousy. It should be made clear that allowing or encouraging the child to reach this state of *dependent attachment* should be a measure of last resort, and that its danger should always be kept in mind. It should be used only to accomplish therapeutic results in cases that seem hopeless otherwise, and in cases where it will be entirely possible for the child eventually to re-transfer to some other desirable person or persons in his environment whom he does not at the time accept for some reason. No doubt there is a sexual element in this response, but in children it is usually unconscious and quite the same as that found in the parent-child relationship. There are two groups of children only with whom the rapport of *dependent attachment* should be encouraged, and with these only after other methods have failed. These two groups are quite closely related. It is fortunate that they are the ones who reach out for help the most and also that they are the ones least likely to be harmed by the establishment of a deep and dependent rapport. The first group are children who feel themselves entirely inferior. The second group are those who have no loyalties in life and who develop none in response to whatever help and suggestions are given during personality contact. When I do anything to help these children who make a *dependent attachment* to me, it seems to be in one of two ways. Either I am myself the person who does not believe the child to be inferior and can make him understand and appreciate this, or

I am the person towards whom the child develops his much needed loyalties. It then becomes possible for me to use the same therapeutic methods and to have the same influence with this child as I do with one in personality contact. In other words, the child who will not accept me into his environmental values, even though he be in *personality contact,* will sometimes do so after he has made *dependent attachments.*

There is sometimes a practical and direct mechanism by which permanent results are effected in this deep rapport. Good physical results may be obtained sometimes by holding a child in a dentist's chair until the child finds by experience that the dentist does not hurt him so much as the toothache does and will then sit still without being held. Similarly, if some children in their unhealthy quest for happiness are made even for a short time to experience more normal emotional reactions, they come to understand and to feel that this new way will give them greater pleasurable returns after all. Sometimes a child establishes more normal and healthy personality traits simply through the concrete experiences in normal living that he has during his period of *dependent attachment,* but this does not often happen.

It must be remembered that the child in *dependent attachment* is in an abnormally suggestible state. One may not be quite so sure of permanent results when they are obtained in this rapport as when they are reached in the less profound one of *personality contact.* This, of course, is partly due to the difficulties that may arise when the psychiatrist to whom the child has formed this attachment steps out of his environmental values after the treatment is ended.

A child in *dependent attachment* wants his psychiatrist to be his best friend. He wishes to please him more than he wishes to do anything else. Out of loyalty to his friend he is perfectly willing to alter his emotional life as far as it is possible for him; or if he believes that his friend feels him to be superior, for a time he does not care what others think. This temporary superiority becomes therapeutically useful.

This rapport might be compared to that existing between a spoiled and protected child and a parent who has allowed a feeling of complete dependence to develop, with this difference, of course: that, while poorly adjusted or unwise parents often obtain pleasurable emotional reactions themselves from this attachment and wish to continue it, the psychiatrist uses it only as a first step to constructive character development in a seriously maladjusted child.

The analogy of the football-player might be extended to include these two more profound states of rapport. He has lost his position on the team with which he formerly played, either because of poor playing (behaviour) or because he could not agree with the players and would not co-operate with the team (personality). After he watches the game longer, he becomes so impressed with his favourite team's playing and their understanding of football that he believes them to be as good or better than he, and he wishes that he might be a member of this team. He is permitted to join it. He responds to the spirit of the team, loses some of his conceit, and in other ways is a more efficient player than ever before. His new captain soon sees his abilities and takes advantage of them. He now may be said to be in *personality contact* with the team. They try him out and he cannot "make" the team. Still for some reason— perhaps because they are more kind to him and less critical of his faults than his former team-mates—he still wishes to stay with them. If he stays with them, though he must be on the side-lines and can have little hope of getting into the game, he may be said to be in *dependent attachment*. Now the team's success will bring him happiness and satisfaction because of his affection for and loyalties to them.

One should do very much *thinking about* and *thinking with* a child before he includes in his *thinking for* a plan to allow this *dependent attachment* to occur. I may say, however, that some of my best results, in apparently hopeless situations, have been obtained by this method. The misunderstood, unhappy, and unloved child who is seemingly destined for failure may sometimes be surprisingly helped.

This arbitrary plan of differentiating the degrees of rapport I obtain with children, has the following advantages for me:

It enables me better to understand the real reason for successes and failures. If I have made a correct estimate of the degree of rapport desirable and have failed to obtain it, this is likely to be the reason for my failure to help the child. Confidence should not be lost in the concrete methods that have been used or in the things that have been said to him. For unless one can evaluate the personal element that enters into the total equation, one will never be able to separate successful psychotherapeutic methods from unsuccessful ones.

It aids in prognosis. The ultimate solution of every individual's problems is determined largely by the people he admits into his dynamic mental life, and the degree to which he responds to and is influenced by them.

It offers a somewhat systematic method of interpreting results in every case and it points out the possibility of a systematized approach and planned therapy for every case.

CHAPTER III

THE TECHNIQUE

HE intricate mental reactions that occur between two human beings when they enter one another's dynamic environment do not readily lend themselves to description. Much less is it possible to describe the essentials, or the technique, if one wishes to use the word, for obtaining and directing these responses in a way that will make them therapeutically useful.

Yet there are some concrete methods, things that one may try to do or may avoid doing, that do lend themselves to description. But, while considering these concrete methods, we must always keep in mind the fact that these things are *not* the essentials. Behind them all is that essential and potent something which for want of a better term we may call "personality response."

This chapter is a description of some of the methods used and a discussion of the beliefs and ideas on which I based my attempts to establish psychiatric rapports with the children whose cases are here reported. They are given rather as aids to the reader in evaluating the psychotherapy than as methods and ideas that others may use.

It may be unwise for anyone to describe his methods in attempting to establish rapport with the child. The various ways in which the idea "establishing rapport" is expressed show very clearly how differently it is understood by various people. Some say: "getting the child's confidence"; some say: "making the child like you";

some say: "talking therapeutically with the child"; some say: "getting under the child's skin"; some say: "getting the child to be frank"; some say: "bringing the child to his senses"; and some say: "getting an influence over the child." These phrases but show the great divergence of thought as to what actually happens between the child and the adult who attempts to help him.

Any plan or method of one's own developing is much more likely to be successful than a method that one has borrowed from someone else. Everyone working with children knows the frequent failures that occur when he attempts to use others' methods of approach or of treatment.

These methods and ideas are discussed under various headings. They are not discussed in the order of their relative importance, but rather in the general order of their chronological appearance, as the child is seen, studied, and treated.

Being Sure that the Child Understands Who the Psychiatrist Is. This is important and should never be neglected. Before a child is asked to co-operate with the psychiatrist, even to the extent of the physical examination (during which a very good superficial rapport may often be established), he should be told, in a way that he can understand, with whom he is talking and the reasons for the interview. Considerable time may have to be spent with the child to do this. One must dispel any suspicions the child may have that the psychiatrist is a detective or the individual who will control him, assign punishment, or make an unwelcome change in his environment.

If the psychiatrist puts himself in the child's place and thinks how the entire procedure appears to him, he can surmise what questions the child would like to ask. These are, usually, the ones that may best be discussed first. For example, one of the first questions to which delinquent or misbehaving children will frequently respond is whether or not it is best or easier to talk about one's troubles with the doctor or with the policeman or with others who are in authority. This is something about which the child is thinking and about which he is apt to have ideas that he is willing to express.

The Physical Examination. Personally, I believe that it is much the best for the psychiatrist himself to make the routine physical examination. I also believe that when the establishment of psychiatric rapport is important, or difficult to obtain, the physical examination should not be made until a friendly acquaintance has been reached. The examination itself presents many opportunities for the initiation of a good rapport, and these opportunities may be lost in the process of a routine examination before the child feels acquainted.

The Child's Behaviour during the Interview. One must be sure the child is physically comfortable during interviews. The child must not be hungry, ill, or in pain, and he should know where the toilet is. He should have a comfortable chair. The child must know that he will not be criticized or punished at home for being detained by the interview.

I prefer that the child sit still and look at me when we are talking, but I never scold him or try to make him do it. If he is hanging his head or speaking in a low or mumbling voice, he is seldom told not to do so, but an earnest effort is made to remove the inhibitions that are causing this behaviour. Going to lunch, attending a baseball game, or going for an automobile ride or a walk with the boy will often entirely change his manner in future interviews. I let him know, without scolding him, what I think is proper concerning his general behaviour in my presence and elsewhere.

Making Notes in the Child's Presence. It is best to make notes immediately after the child has left, and especially before another child is seen. It is not usually advisable to take notes in the child's presence. Sometimes one may frankly write down just what the child says, as, for example, when he tells of his dreams, but if it embarrasses him in any way one should not even do this. Essential details are not easily forgotten if one is really *thinking about* the child when one is talking with him. Even if they are, getting the details into the written record is secondary to the importance of establishing the desired rapport.

Knowing the Child's First Emotional Attitude towards the Psychiatrist. This is very important. The psychiatrist may know exactly what should be said to the child, but if he says it while there is the feeling of ridicule, dislike, contempt, or fear of him in the child's heart, not only will he fail to help the child, but also he is apt to find the child taking the same emotional attitude towards the things said that he has toward the one saying them.

A distracted mother once said to me: "I tell Willie over and over again that I don't see how he can be such a bad boy when his uncle John talks to him so much about being good and sets such a good example for him every day. I make Willie stay with him a lot, too, for his uncle John is such a good man and tells him so many times what he ought to do that I am sure he will influence him somewhat, after a while."

It was hard to understand Willie and his bad behaviour, all of which seemed to be without any drive or reason whatever, as far as we could judge from reports given of the boy. However, when Willie was given an opportunity to talk confidentially, he made the reason evident. He said he believed his uncle John was a "hypocrite and a snoop." Willie did not really want to be bad. He did not have any temptation to do bad things, particularly. But he did want one thing very much, and that was not to be or feel like his uncle John and not to do anything his uncle John wanted him to do. With the emotional attitude Willie assumed towards his uncle, it would have been therapeutically better for the uncle to have told Willie to be a bad boy. Personally, when I am not able to get any positive rapport with the child, or if he is not at least neutral in his emotional attitude towards me and if he cannot be changed in this attitude by ordinary friendly association, such as may be had during the physical examination, I do not undertake either psychiatric exploration or psychotherapy.

Taking the Interview Seriously. Interviews should always be taken seriously, though one should never wear a long face when talking with children. One should smile frequently. The child must not feel that he is considered unimportant or in the way. This is especially true of first interviews. It is unwise to allow interruptions to occur, or to permit oneself to be distracted by anything that does not directly concern the child. Usually each child, like the average adult, enjoys feeling that the doctor is especially interested in his particular case.

Knowing Personally of the Child's Environmental Problems. In complicated or important cases, if the child says or implies that he wants the psychiatrist actually to see for himself the environmental situation he describes, the psychiatrist should do this, if possible. This wish on the child's part is a compliment to the psychiatrist and a favourable symptom. We grant that the psychiatrist's estimation of the situation may not be so good as that of the social worker who may already have reported it. Still, if the child who is trying to meet and to solve his problems knows that his friend has seen his home, his parents, or his teachers, he not only appreciates his friend's interest but he develops more confidence in his friend's understanding of his problems. Doing this for the child is often the very thing that finally establishes one fully in the child's environmental values. A child who is at all loyal to his parents will more readily develop loyalties to a new friend if his parents have met and approved this friend. If a poor handling of his father-mother relation enters into the child's problems, one can give little help in working out the situation without seeing and knowing the parents and the child as they respond to their home situation and to one another.

Using the Child's Vocabulary. Some children are so conditioned by their environment or so limited in their ability to express themselves that if they are to become entirely at ease and frank, they must use slang and vulgar expressions or even profane words and phrases to express their emotions and to make their meaning clear. The same thing, in a different way, may be true of the spoiled child who has a tendency to talk in over-affectionate terms or to use "baby talk" when he becomes frank and friendly.

It is usually best not to discourage this, especially at the beginning of the acquaintance; and often, if one can do so in an objective and unselfconscious way, it is well, at first, to adopt the same way of expressing oneself as that used by the child. This is a matter to be decided for each case, however, for if the child suspects that the psychiatrist is affecting this method of expression, he will feel that the psychiatrist is doing it either to patronize him or to mock him or for some other uncomplimentary reason, and the child will think contemptuously of it. Of all the therapeutically negative emotional reactions the child may have, a feeling of contempt or of ridicule for anyone who is trying to help him operates most fatally against a good rapport and therapeutic results.

Sometimes it is possible to establish rapport with the "tough" and "wise guy" boy by outdoing him and beating him in the use of brazen and profane language.

The use of vulgar or common expressions in discussing sex matters with children is nearly always necessary and wise. Usually, if the child is in good rapport, he can be guided later into using more conventional terms although he starts with the common ones first. This is less embarrassing to the child than beginning with terms he does not understand and adopting the common ones later. This is a very important point in technique.

The Feeling of Being Understood. The most important single thing in obtaining a good psychiatric rapport with a child is to establish in him the belief and the feeling that the psychiatrist understands him. If a child is unhappy, if he is maladjusted, if his environment is such that he cannot possibly face it in a healthy way, the thing that will most often cause him to reach out and take someone into his life is the belief that *that* person understands him. The statements and behaviour of all the children I have known and helped tend to strengthen this opinion.

If a psychiatrist is sympathetic and appreciative before convincing the child that he understands him, the child is apt to feel that the psychiatrist is insincere and to classify him with others who have done the same thing and have failed to help him with his problems. There are some very interesting mental dynamisms effecting this almost constant response. To understand them is of the greatest importance in *thinking about* and in dealing with unhappy and delinquent children. To understand the child, not only must one know about his behaviour and his emotional responses, but one must also be able to put oneself in the child's place, look at life through the child's eyes, and, for the moment, feel exactly as the child does about this whole business of living. If one cannot do this, one does not thoroughly understand the child, and one probably cannot help him.

One must really understand the child before the child will believe that he is understood. Children are not easily deceived, especially in this respect. Very often, delinquent children who are unhappy because of their delinquency and what it has led to, have told, before the psychiatrist sees them, of their misdeeds. If they have reported their behaviour to others who have in no way understood or been interested in how they feel or how they felt at the time of their behaviour, they have usually received little help. Most children who come to believe that the psychiatrist understands their present emotional responses will co-operate in his attempts to understand them further and deeper. They will themselves become interested in the dynamisms conditioning their behaviour.

Gaining the Child's Confidence. This is the thing that many consider the most important of all. Diagnostically and socially it is often essential. My own experience is that if a child tells his real story for any other reason than because he wants me to understand him, much of the therapeutic value of the telling is lost. The story may be true and complete in its behaviour details, but it will probably be lacking in its emotional ones. After all, the therapeutic question is *why* and not *what*. Speaking therapeutically, the depth of the child's confidence should always depend upon the depth of rapport established.

If a child who has become entirely frank with me is not glad of it, I have been a good detective, but I certainly have not established a good therapeutic rapport. Since freely reporting his behaviour and responses carries an emotional value for him, it follows that it is usually unwise from a therapeutic standpoint to encourage or to allow a child who is not in good rapport to tell his story. No one believes more in the constructive value of the "confession," or the "getting it off the chest," or whatever else it may be called, than I; but the therapeutic value of this is largely measured by the circumstances of the telling, by the reasons for the telling, and by the child's attitude towards the person to whom it is told, rather than by what is told. Children who have understanding parents with whom they are willingly and entirely frank seldom become problem children. When a child willingly gives me his full confidence because he thinks I understand him and can help him, he has placed a great responsibility on me. If I have encouraged him to do this without really knowing that in some way I can constructively help him, I may have harmed rather than helped him.

Often in clinics, when a child may be seen but once or twice, the only probability of his receiving personality help is through the therapeutic value of the confession. Possibly one may occasionally be justified in establishing a deep rapport with an unhappy child so that he will tell his real story for this reason alone. But the element of trust always enters into any good rapport, and the child, consciously or unconsciously, is expecting help. When nothing further in the way of social or psychotherapeutic help can be given, to cut him adrift in a sea of troubles and difficulties when he believes that at last he has found an understanding helpful friend may add profoundly to his emotional troubles.

Making the Child Talk about Unpleasant Things. The ideal way is to make him feel like talking about serious and unpleasant topics, not to force him to do so against his will. This is an easy prescription to write, but it is sometimes very hard to fill. With unlimited time it may be done in any case in which good rapport is established. One can, at least, be sure that the child understands why he is being asked to discuss things he wishes to avoid and to forget. During interviews with children I try not to let either my thoughts or the child's wander or lag, but if we are thinking, it is often best to have pauses in the conversation. One may often gauge progress in the establishing of rapport by noting whether the pauses in the conversation are awkward and embarrassing or easy and natural for the child.

Methods of getting uncommunicative and unresponsive children to talk willingly are so individual and so dependent on the interacting of personalities that attempts to describe them are futile. But a psychiatrist must have the ability to make children respond to him if he is to help them.

Scolding or Criticizing the Child. One should not scold or directly criticize the child. This very old form of psychotherapy is not entirely valueless, for it does work sometimes. When it does, it is because the one who has administered it has previously established a good and usually long-continued rapport with the one who is scolded or criticized.

By the time most cases are seen by psychiatrists, scolding and criticism have already been tried. It often happens that the habit of withdrawing from those who administer this type of treatment is already so firmly established that it is likely to be repeated with the psychiatrist. The psychiatrist must wait then until late in his contact with the child before he tries scolding. By that time he will probably understand the child so well that he will feel no inclination to scold or to criticize him.

Personally, however, to all children who have made good rapport and who have developed any feelings of loyalty towards me or any desire that I should like or approve their conduct, I always make it clear just how I feel in an abstract way about behaviour such as theirs. I wait for a favourable time to do this, and I do not over-emphasize its importance.

Children who have reached the stage of *personal trust* often ask personal questions of the psychiatrist. Questions in regard to the psychiatrist's attitude towards their misbehaviour are very frequently asked. Children of different ages and of varying personalities ask them in different ways. A question recently asked me by an eleven-year-old girl is typical. The answer illustrates my attitude in regard to criticizing a child. She said: "Yes, I'll bet you feel just like my mother and father and everybody else does about me and don't like me better than they do either, only you don't want to tell me." I said: "You're wrong there. I like you just as well as I should if you had not done these things which no one likes to see little girls do, but it has been a little harder for me to like you because you did them. You see, you have told me all about how you feel and how it happened, and I believe I understand, and I think if you tell your father and mother about it, they will understand, too. Now, even if you keep on doing them, which I'm betting you're not going to do, I shall still like you, but it's going to be a pretty hard job."

Being Disgusted or Shocked with the Child. A child should never feel that the psychiatrist is disgusted or shocked either by anything he may tell or by anything he may have done. One who understands and likes children seldom experiences these emotional responses towards them. If a child tells me of things he has done or emotions he has experienced which I know have for all time destroyed for him those fine indefinite things we call innocent childhood and happy youth, I am profoundly sorry for him, but it requires no effort to avoid any feeling of disgust or repulsion.

I have had little success in trying to deceive children in regard to anything and I am skeptical of the ability of others to do so. But if one is repelled by the child's behaviour, one should deceive the child to the point of concealing this repulsion. This is particularly true if one is attempting to give the child help. It frequently happens that the child's knowledge that he has disgusted the one to whom he has been confidential means irrevocable failure, as far as that person's helping him is concerned. These emotional reactions on the part of any adult who has established positive rapport are unfortunate when they are real and uncontrollable. They are always to be condemned when they are feigned. Many people at times pretend to be disgusted and shocked when they really are not. I have known fathers who, in their sons' presence, appear greatly shocked and grieved by their behaviour, but who later tell me privately that they themselves did the same things when they were young, and that they think their sons will be, after all, the better and wiser for their experiences. This is an attitude fraught with danger, especially for younger children who have voluntarily become confidential.

When a child becomes thoroughly confidential, there is some strong emotional reason for it. To have a parent or respected person show a child that he feels disgusted or shocked at the child's confessed behaviour, or to have him give the child the idea that his life or character has been permanently damaged or that something has happened that has destroyed any of the former friendly relationship or love existing between the two, is one of the most profound psychic traumas possible for any child to experience. In one short hour all the confidences of the child's life may be destroyed beyond hopes of rebuilding, and when this thing happens between a child and his parents or between a child and a trusted friend, the child is very apt to become distrustful of all the world. An experience like this may be the beginning of the child's resisting his environment or shutting himself away from it.

After all, when most of us think about the regrettable "wickedest" things in our lives, we arrive by some mental process at the belief that in our particular case they were not so bad or disgusting. Were our friends to learn of them in some way, especially were we to confess these things to them, we should not expect them to feel much differently from the way we ourselves do. This is particularly so with children, who have not yet developed their moral apperceptions to that standard which most adults hope their children believe they, as their parents, possess and exemplify.

I have been told that I "sided" with a child or had a bad influence on him because of my refusal to scold or to condemn him or to be greatly upset about his behaviour. Suppose a child does have his first friendly relationships with me on this basis? I still have a chance to do him some good perhaps, really to show him how much I think bad behaviour detracts from his happiness and from that of others; but if I adopt the opposite plan, of scolding from the start, the child builds a barrier against me in his mind that destroys my opportunity of ever doing so.

Not so very long ago a man brought his thirteen-year-old son to me. In spite of my efforts to avoid it, he insisted on describing in detail, in the boy's presence, some very unfortunate habits, and delinquency that accompanied them, into which the child had been drawn. It was quite evident that the father expected me to be greatly upset when he told me these things and to display this state of mind to the lad. He said he had brought the boy to me to get my advice as to what type of punishment he might give that would be severe enough sufficiently to punish the boy and at the same time to correct the behaviour, without bringing any disgrace to the family. I answered, not by suggesting any punishment, but by trying to make him see that he should take a different attitude towards the boy. I was sorry for this afterwards because it, apparently, had lost for me my only chance of attempting to help the lad, who needed help badly. The father said something about men who were dealing with bad boys becoming calloused and took the boy away without my having opportunity actually to talk with him. The boy had been talking to me with his eyes during the entire interview. The next day the lad came back to me without his parents' knowledge. I did not believe then, nor did later developments show, that he came back to me because he thought I would "side with him" in his misbehaviour.

This instance illustrates my point. Since this is not one of the cases reported, perhaps the rest of the story should be told. After talking to him a little while about his mother, I decided with his permission to call her by telephone and tell her of the circumstances. She gave her sanction to this interview and to later ones. It was possible to give this boy help which, I think, will be of lifelong value to him. No one had to make him stop his bad habits. When he understood himself and his habits, what they meant and what they would lead to, he wanted to stop them and he did. More important than this, he came to understand his father better and to take a much better attitude towards him. Perhaps a mistake was made in not deceiving the father in regard to my own attitude in the first interview (he would have been very easily deceived) so that I might have been sure of an opportunity to help the lad, but I do not like to be a hypocrite before a child.

Respecting the Child's Confidence. If a child assumes, as he often does, or is assured that the things he tells the psychiatrist will not be repeated, this confidence should invariably be respected. If a child is in good rapport with him, the psychiatrist will seldom fail finally to obtain the child's consent and co-operation in reporting to the proper persons anything he may confess or reveal, if this is socially necessary or therapeutically wise. If the rapport is not good, the psychiatrist will fail in this effort. This is one of the important reasons why confidences and confessions should not be encouraged or even allowed in superficial or negative degrees of rapport.

No matter who is responsible for the interview, the child is the psychiatrist's patient, and the psychiatrist, as his physician, is highly privileged as well as duty bound to keep the secrets of his patient. My own experience has been that in no cases has good resulted, either for the child or for society, from breaking confidence with the child and reporting any part of the child's story given me in confidence. The child is unco-operative in any social treatment based on information so obtained by others, and he loses faith and confidence in other people in proportion as he loses faith in the psychiatrist. Society gains another suspicious and antisocial member, and the psychiatrist loses his chance of helping the child.

It is dangerous for one who works with children, whether he be psychiatrist, psychologist, judge, social worker, or probation officer, to take pride in getting the child's confidence in any other way than by making the child want to give it, and for any other reason than that he may give the child help. If it is essential that information in the child's possession be obtained from him for social reasons, the psychiatrist is not the one to get it.

The child's knowledge that his confidence is to be respected is a powerful therapeutic weapon, although it may easily be abused.

Answering the Child's Questions. One should truthfully answer all the child's questions with as much completeness as the child is capable of absorbing and of comprehending. Often this is not possible at the time they are first asked, but they should not be forgotten; finally they should be answered. Asking questions is so important, therapeutically, that one should not discourage it by answering with lies. Of course it is often not best to tell the child immediately all the facts one may know about the things he asks, either about himself or about his environment, but every question should be met at first with a truthful attitude. One should aim ultimately to answer frankly and truthfully.

Since this is a question much thought about and much discussed by all who are thinking and working with children, I shall report an example of what I consider a truthful answer to a question obviously hard to meet. It was asked me by a fourteen-year-old girl of superior intelligence who was failing in her school-work. I knew from her family history and from talking with her mother what the answer to the question was. I also felt that from a therapeutic standpoint the girl must ask this question if I was to help her. Finally one day she said to me: "Do you suppose that the stories the girls have been whispering about my mother are true?" She told me that she had observed things that made her fear they were.

This girl was very loyal to her young widowed mother, who was in most respects an excellent mother and loyal to the child. I did not answer the girl's question that day, so I suppose that technically I lied to her. During our next talks we discussed people who did not have good surroundings and training when they were children, people who have very strong temptations in the face of unhappiness, and especially those people who do things they would not otherwise do because of a desire in some way to help those they love. We discussed the fact that, after all, the reasons behind things are more important than the things themselves. We talked also about girls who could not pass in school because their minds were busy with worry and unhappiness; we discussed the fact that sometimes buckling down and trying to help others to be happy was the best way to get passing grades. When I believed the time had come for the answer to her question, I told her what I call the therapeutic truth. I told her that I thought the best thing would be for her to assume that the things she had heard about her mother were true, and that by being loyal to her mother, despite them, she might help her. I told her that some day, when she understood her mother and life better, she might discover that they were not true in the real sense at all, and that, whether they were facts or not, the mother was *her* mother and loved her and needed her. I told her that anyone who understood would admire very much a girl who could be so fine as this. In its final outcome this case represented one of the best psychiatric successes I have ever had. It illustrates very well two points: namely, that asking questions is a most hopeful and helpful symptom, and that a person in good rapport answering them is our best psychotherapeutic weapon. When this intelligent girl first asked me the question, I might have lied and said: "Why, who ever put such an idea into your head? Of course it isn't true. Now, you go home and study your lessons instead of thinking about such terrible things and you will be all right." Or I might have told the naked truth and said: "Oh, you poor girl! I am so sorry for you! Yes, I am afraid it is true. You will just have to make the best of it. There is nothing you or I can do about it. We have to admit the truth, even though it hurts." Either of these answers would have been therapeutically false.

Causing Discouragement, Fear, or Worry. Of those who are sincerely attempting to help children, very few believe that discouragement, fear, or worry is ever desirable, but unless one thinks of the world and understands it in the way the child does, one may very easily prompt these emotions.

There are many ways this may happen. Serious looks or gestures or ambiguous remarks made during a physical examination may do it. Gaining the child's confidential story in regard to his sex habits, but at the same time failing to help him understand and properly to interpret his feelings and experiences, very frequently causes much worry and even fear. Another and more dangerous thing is to elaborate psychopathological theories to a child who is already concerned about himself or to ask unusual and vague questions which the child does not understand, especially if the child is in good rapport with the one asking them. These things often cause serious mental conflicts. If delicate questions are asked, explanations should be made so that he understands the reasons for the questions.

A case that well illustrates this point once came to my notice. Though he knew but little of psychiatry, a judge felt that a certain boy whom he had sentenced to a correctional institution should be given some sort of help that the institution could not give. He asked a psychiatrist who had thought but little about children's problems to see this fifteen-year-old boy. The psychiatrist read the boy's history and the social worker's report and, before seeing the boy, made the statement that he was "clearly a case of 'Œdipus complex.' I think I can straighten him out." He saw the boy for forty-five minutes. In that time he elaborated to him the theory in great detail, imparted a huge amount of bizarre theoretical psychopathological sex information, and told the boy that if he could remember what had been told him, he would be all right and would turn out fine. In fact, he had so much to tell him that the boy himself had no opportunity or inclination to tell the psychiatrist anything. The boy went to the institution, the psychiatrist to his practice. He does not know the rest of the story to this day. In a few days the boy made an unsuccessful attempt at suicide. He was then studied at greater length, and after the study it was felt that the first psychiatrist was crudely correct in his interpretation. However, the practical situation was this: The boy had got into trouble because he had no friends. He had no friends because of his unhappy personality traits. His unhappy personality traits were due to a distorted outlook on life. His distorted outlook on life was caused probably by the unfortunate way in which he had handled his early emotional responses to his parent situation. The boy stated frankly his reason for wanting to kill himself. When he learned that his trouble was caused by being "so rotten and good-for-nothing inside," he thought suicide was the best solution. The psychiatrist who first saw him, knowing that his association with the lad would be brief, should have spent the time available in listening to the boy's story and convincing him, if possible, that there was at least one person in the world who could be interested in him and be his friend without being disgusted with him. Unless one has established a good rapport, it is not desirable to attempt to *think with* the child on a theoretical basis. For it is not so much *what* one says to the child that accomplishes therapeutic results as *the way* one says these things, and how they make the child feel.

Ridiculing or Shaming the Child. One should never under any circumstances use ridicule or try to shame the child or laugh at him. Because of this unfortunate method of dealing with children they will often absolutely and unchangeably put out of their lives people who might otherwise be a great help to them. In *thinking with* children I always try to get the child's own answer to the question *why,* as it applies to his emotional responses or to his behaviour patterns. One question I very frequently ask is: "Why do you so cordially hate your teacher?" The answer in more than half the cases is: "Because she makes fun of what I do in front of the others." If this is not the answer, it often is: "Because she is not fair." This reply is given not nearly so bitterly as the first. Another question I frequently ask is: "Why have you failed to talk with your father and mother about these things with which you have needed help so badly?" and many of the children answer: "I'm afraid they wouldn't understand and would only laugh at me." What makes it seem worse to the child is the fear that others will be told the joke and laugh at him too.

Interest in a Child's Activity. The expression of interest in and knowledge of the things in which a child is interested is a very common, useful, and important way of establishing oneself in the child's dynamic environment. A child will more quickly ask questions of his new friend if contact is established in this way. But he will also evaluate one's ability to answer other questions by the answers to these. One should be very careful about trying to make a child believe that one knows much about his world and interests unless one really does.

At one time I was interested to know why a certain scoutmaster, whom I knew and whom I believed had the personality traits for a good and successful boys' worker, was very unsuccessful in his personal contacts with boys. I discovered that the scouts were contemptuous of him. As one boy said, "He pretends to know all about everything anybody talks about, and I don't believe he ever went on a real camping trip or played a ball game in his life, from the way he goes at it." The scout-master would have made much better contact with his boys and gained their respect more quickly by confessing his ignorance and by expressing a desire to learn. Every child is glad to show and to tell about things he knows or in which he is interested, particularly to anyone who is really sincere and wants to be informed. I have often seen a spoiled or a frightened child who would not talk to me become friendly in the process of explaining to me some mechanical toy which I had failed to operate. A psychiatrist should develop a sincere interest in children's activities, both because it will help him in the understanding of the child and because it will keep him young. Anyone in this day and age who is able to talk intelligently and answer the average twelve-year-old American boy's questions about aeroplane and radio construction and operation has no mean accomplishment, and he will gain much in the boy's estimation by this ability.

Keeping Appointments and Promises. The experience of many years in Boy Scout work, during which I have asked hundreds of boys why they did or did not like their leaders, has taught me that promptness and faithfulness in keeping appointments and promises is one of the most important concrete things one can do to obtain a child's liking and respect, if not *the* most important of all. Broken or neglected appointments are the forerunners of failures to help unhappy children. Vague appointments or vague promises of excursions or recreational activities should never be given to a child. It is much better to say once during the period of acquaintance: "Next Thursday, after school, I will come to your home and we will drive down to the beach" and then really to keep that appointment, than to say at the close of every interview: "We must take a little trip some day" and never do it. In dealing with children, poor excuses are not better than none. Breaking appointments for interviews is dangerous business, for a child may have been looking forward to keeping it and he may have decided that at that time he will tell or discuss things of serious importance to him. If the date is broken, his reasoning is likely to be this: "Well, he doesn't understand me, that's all. He asked me to come, and if he knew how much it meant to me, he would not have forgotten and had another boy come at the same time and then send me away. I thought he did really know how I felt and came very near being fool enough to tell him everything and ask him to help me. Nobody really cares for me anyway."

Knowing the Child in his Natural Environment. Completely to understand the child who is to be treated over a considerable period of time it is very helpful and often necessary to observe his behaviour and emotional reaction in his home or in his group or when he is having a good time. There are many ways of doing this. In suitable cases one may let the parents know that one will welcome a dinner invitation to the home. Outings may be arranged at which several problem children may be present in one group. Picnics to lonely spots where group games may be played are good examples. One of the best possible ways really to know in his everyday behaviour a boy who is interested in athletics is to take him and some of his friends to watch a game which the boys themselves play.

In every case on which considerable time is to be spent, a portion of this time should be devoted to informal interviews. It is usually best to do something or go somewhere that will give the child pleasure. This aids both in understanding the child and in establishing good rapport. Unless the child himself takes the initiative, it is better not to discuss his problems directly at such times. Reserve this for the more formal interviews.

Maintaining Friendly Relations. Finally, one should never quarrel or argue with the child, and one should always try to part from him as a friend. If one has failed with him, one can usually understand the failure by looking at the world through the child's eyes. A good understanding of a child with whom one has failed destroys, fortunately, the desire to give the child a final "piece of one's mind" and prevents the disastrous effects of such finales. Sharpness on parting with the psychiatrist not only nullifies any good that may have been accomplished, but also interferes with the possibility of anyone else's giving the child help.

When the therapeutic contact is finally closed, the child should always be made to feel that the psychiatrist is still his friend, and that he is eager to help with any problem that may arise later. Very frequently children with whom a good rapport has been established will wish to return to the psychiatrist for help at a much later date.

PART II

THE BOYS

The reader of these case histories is asked to remember that they are reported primarily for the purpose of illustrating and explaining the two ideas advanced in the earlier chapters: the first is that of so organizing one's mental approach as to make one's treatment more effective and of less potential danger; the second that of differentiating and therapeutically utilizing degrees in psychiatric rapport.

Most of them are not cases that illustrate definite problems in uncomplicated form. Many of them, as would be true in any chronological series, are so complicated that they do not lend themselves well to group classification.

To make the material more interesting and readable, especially from a social view-point, they are grouped in chapters by placing together those that show some general similarity in their psychiatric or social problem. Some do not fit well into any of these groups, and others could well be put in any one of several.

The writer has found in so grouping the cases for report and discussion that, while the method has disadvantages, it also has one great advantage. No one will feel, while reading the cases, that they have been selected to fit or to lend credence and support to any theory of causative mechanism. It is important to remember that these particular cases were selected from a chronological series. They were chosen from the larger group which came to the clinic for study during the same period because they, in the seriousness and complexity of their problems, suggested a distinct need for intensive treatment.

CHAPTER IV

MISUNDERSTANDINGS

The Child who is a Stranger

NEARLY all problem children have as a part of their total situation the fact that they are not fully understood by those whom they wish or need to have know them best.

A psychiatrist sees some children who have this as the most important part of their problem. These are more fortunate than many. Their problems can nearly always be solved if their parents are co-operative and understanding or if the child may be socially controlled. Besides this, nearly all adults can sympathize with them, for most people feel at times that they, too, are misunderstood.

The second and the fourth case of this group are representative of children who needed no other adjustment than to have those in their dynamic environment realize how they felt. The third case needed but little else. The first case had many other and more serious aspects to his problem; in fact, he would fit into nearly any group, so complicated was his situation. He is grouped here because good results were obtained largely through one person's understanding his emotional life.

Case No. 1
SANDOR ROMANO

Sandor is a bright, active, pleasant eleven-year-old boy, well nourished and fairly well developed. He is dark-complexioned and has curly hair and expressive eyes. He showed average general ability on age-level tests; I. Q., 104. His father is Spanish, his mother is of Canadian French ancestry.

The situation: Sandor lives in a small industrial town in Rhode Island. The family situation has always been upset. There has been some economic stress, many neighbourhood quarrels, and dissatisfactions. Before I saw Sandor, he had been having much difficulty in school. His teachers reported him as not working and as failing on this account. They said that he was the leader in mischief, and that he quarrelled and fought a great deal with the other boys. At school the boys insisted on treating him as a Negro, although he had no Negro blood. The boy resented this and fought and quarrelled about it. His mother reported him as being disobedient about playing on the streets; and she said that in coming home from school he got into scrapes that worried her. He quarrelled with his brother and sisters and was dishonest in the home. He occasionally stole small articles elsewhere. She said he was uncommunicative and hard to understand. She complained especially about long-standing and frequent enuresis.

The mother herself is an extremely unusual person. When I first saw her, she looked the picture of health, but reported herself dangerously ill and said that she must always have arrangements made for her death. She told us about the many trips she made to the school and about the long arguments and discussions she had with the teachers in regard to Sandor's conduct and management. Many letters that she had written to the school authorities were available. These were a strange mixture of praise and condemnation of the boy and criticisms of the teachers for punishing Sandor for things of which he was unquestionably guilty. His mother said she "worked her life out for the boy and worried about him," and that she did as much as any mother could do. To show how much she tried to help him, she said that after discovering, by spying on him, that he was indulging in masturbation, she watched him very closely and wrote a letter to the teacher and one to the janitor of the school, telling them what a bad boy Sandor was in this respect and asking that they watch him and see if he continued this habit. She asked the janitor to notice him when he went to the toilet, and if he remained more than two minutes, to open the door suddenly. The mother was asked if she talked to the boy about these habits, other than to scold him, and she said: "Certainly, I told him it would kill him, and that he would go crazy before he died."

The family situation was even more peculiar than the mother. There was an older half-sister, feeble-minded, whose father was an Italian. When this sister was five years old, the mother married Sandor's father, who had been a soldier in the Spanish Army. There was a younger brother, who was probably a full sibling. About the time of this younger brother's birth the father and mother were divorced. At that time the present stepfather was showing the mother attention, and the father disclaimed parentage of this younger child. The present stepfather then married the mother and believed the child to be his own. The mother was much interested in religion and took very unusual attitudes regarding the children's attending all the services of her Church. She talked to the children much about heaven and hell.

Sandor had been excessively punished, by both the mother and the stepfather. One form of punishment was to make the boy strip and kneel on the floor, on which rice had been spread. He must then hold his arms out, and if he allowed them to sag or allowed any part of his body other than his knees and feet to touch the floor, he was beaten severely. In this way confessions of misconduct were obtained from the boy.

Thinking about the boy: The mother was seen several times. Her personality and conduct had to be considered. In talking with the boy it was evident from the first that he had been told what to say and what attitudes to assume, and that he was not telling me much about himself when he was talking. It was useless to *think about* this boy unless a deep rapport could be established with him so that he would talk freely of his real experiences and of his emotional life. Theoretical thinking carried one too far afield in Sandor's case.

Thinking for the boy: Any plan to help this lad should certainly have included a change in his environment. But since his family situation was peculiarly upsetting and his experiences had been unusual, it was thought in conference that an attempt thoroughly to understand the boy's mental life was justified, and it was felt that this should be done before any social adjustments were made.

Thinking with the boy: The boy was seen many times. He soon became interested and glad to come to the interviews. At first this was because I took him for automobile rides and on a picnic or two. He did not readily get the desire that I should understand him, but finally this was accomplished, and then the boy was willing and glad to tell me how he felt about life and to tell me all about his troubles. He asked, and was assured, that the things he told would not be reported to his family.

This very interesting lad had many things to *think* about *with* me. He said that he thought a great deal about his own father, and that he hated his stepfather because he had taken his father's place and because his mother liked his stepfather and let him punish Sandor excessively. He had no picture of his father. He believed that his mother had one, but would not show it to him.

He had frequently searched among his mother's things when she was away, hoping to find his father's picture. He said he had a good remembrance of his father's appearance. He cried when he went to bed, often for a long time, when he was thinking of his father. His mother had told him many bad things about his father, and these had nearly broken his heart. He tried hard not to believe them and not to remember them. He could not understand how his mother could have quarrelled with his father and married the man he hated. His mother had always told him that his father was dead. A year or so earlier he had found out that this was probably not true. He wanted very much to see his father.

Sandor did not tell me freely of his troubles until after he was accepting my ideas, even though they were not backed by reasons that he accepted as valid. His problems were discussed slowly and carefully. I *thought with* him about foster-homes. He knew about boys' being allowed to go to good foster-homes and he wished to go. He said he wanted to do anything to get away from his unhappiness, but he felt he should not go until after his mother's death. We talked seriously and frankly about his mother's health. She had told him that she would not live long; she talked about dying and described imaginary death-bed scenes and told him what she was going to ask him to promise her while she was dying, and she described her probable sufferings at that time.

In this period of treatment it was evident that he was accepting what I said as true. He could and did change his emotional responses about many things. He was told that because his mother worried and was nervous and did sometimes have pain, she really believed she was going to die. He was told that many other mothers felt the same way, and that he must not blame her or think that she was trying to frighten him by this talk. He was told that, while he must feel sorry for his mother, he must realize she was not in a serious condition and that he was no more likely to lose his mother than many other boys he knew. He had been told these things before, but he had failed to believe them. When he did so, it was a big help to him.

Each time when Sandor would come to see me, he would have new things to tell and to talk about. Lack of space forbids even mentioning all these things. The excessive punishments which Sandor had been enduring needed much thought. Sandor told me of his day-dreams. He said he day-dreamed that his father and mother were living together and that they were the king and queen and he the honoured prince. He imagined what his home would be if there were no quarrelling there. Sometimes he day-dreamed that the family were dead and that he was all alone and that everybody liked him and he could have his pick of many good homes. He said: "It's terrible to think of your mother as dead, but if she can't live long and is sick and unhappy, maybe it isn't so bad." I *thought with* this boy about his bad sex habits. He was frank about these things and told me how he had worried about them. He believed that masturbation (which he practised but slightly) caused his enuresis; he believed he was very likely to go crazy because of it. He had often been tempted to enter group sex activity with other children, both boys and girls, but had not done so. He said that this was a big temptation sometimes. He was ashamed and distressed because the janitor and teacher knew about his bad habits and was bitter because they were spying on him. He accepted my way of looking at these problems and he believed and understood what I told him about them.

There was another thing that entered largely into his behaviour and emotional life. Sandor was very fond of music. His feeble-minded older half-sister had purchased a violin for him and had arranged for lessons. He spent much of his time playing the violin at home, but he would not practise regularly, especially when he was told to do so, and he occasionally ran away instead of going to take his lessons. His stepfather frequently threatened to destroy the violin and was jealous because the younger half-brother was not the one to have the privilege of violin lessons. This was, of all, the hardest thing for Sandor to talk about. Sandor's best friend was a little boy of his own age who also played the violin. Sandor went to his home sometimes to play and to practise. This little boy had a fine father who loved him and who sat beside the boy while he was practising—encouraging and praising him. To see this made Sandor very unhappy because it made him think about his own father. When the other little boy was praised for his playing, Sandor thought that if he, too, had a father to help and praise him, he could do better. These thoughts came to him at night, but more especially at the time he was taking his lesson. They made him want to cry, and so he did not like to go for his lesson. He did not want his mother or stepfather to know how he felt about this. He told me the reason he liked me was because I could understand how he felt about his violin. All these and many other things were discussed with this boy.

Sandor had many mental conflicts and distortions of reality. There was the fact that the boys thought he was a Negro. This was a natural mistake. Sandor insisted when first seen that it was because they hated him. He said that he did not look like a Negro.

The Church to which his mother and the children belonged taught that movies were sinful. He was never allowed to attend. At first he said that boys who went to movies would go to hell, and that he did not wish to go to the movies. The facts were, however, that he occasionally had been going without his mother's knowledge and he was quite undecided as to whether to change his mind about the punishment he would suffer for it or to stop attending. He both loved and hated his younger brother. He would play with him and feel that he loved him, and very shortly would be fighting with him and hating him. This brother taunted him before the other boys about his enuresis. The mother had threatened to report the enuresis to the neighbours and others as punishment for disobedience. His mother accused him of many things he did not do, constantly nagged him, and threatened to punish him by keeping him home from summer camp, where he had spent two happy weeks each summer for several years. To hear this boy talk about his camping experience one would believe that he had spent most of his life in camp.

The *thinking with* this boy was particularly interesting and instructive because as I considered each one of these problems and decided upon some solution, he would take some new emotional attitude towards it and these attitudes in turn would help in the handling of other problems.

It required but little effort on my part to prevent the boy from adopting any feeling of dependence or of attachment for me, although he was in deep personality contact for a period of three or four months.

It seemed at the beginning that Sandor's problem was largely an environmental one, but after the boy was known better through the establishment of psychiatric rapport, it was very evident that personality responses based on a concealed mental life were even more the problem, for they were unusually unhealthy and profound.

There was little reason to believe that this boy could be permanently helped if he were left in his environment. A change was strongly advised, but for various social reasons it could not be carried out. When it became evident that this could not be done, the next best things were done as a compromise. It was arranged that he stay in summer camp six weeks instead of two. His punishments were controlled to some extent; re-education of the members of the family was undertaken; considerable co-operation was obtained from the younger brother, but little from the other members of the family. At the end of the period of four months' contact, during which time Sandor was seen about twenty-five times, it was felt that the results probably would be poor, even though at that time the boy was assuming a much more normal attitude towards many things. This prediction of failure was based largely on the fact that I had seemingly failed to find something or someone in his life to take my place. After contact was broken, I wrote a letter to him about once a month, and he wrote to me frequently. When he wrote to me, he always said or implied that he believed I understood his feelings.

Results: I have occasionally seen this boy for three years after the case was closed. He is a very different boy from what I had feared he would become. The environmental situation is essentially unchanged, but his behaviour has improved steadily during the intervening years. He is getting much better grades in school and has been promoted regularly; his school behaviour is much improved; he is doing very well with his violin and he is seldom seriously disobedient. He is open and frank with me, but shows no particular desire to "lean on me," though he is anxious to have my opinion about things. The enuresis stopped about one year after the period of treatment. His sex habits have been stopped, and almost no temptation remains. He still fights considerably, but I believe it is better for him to do so. This boy has apparently become loyal to life itself as he finds it now.

He is by no means a complete success. He is not considered an "angel" in the neighbourhood or in the school. But he is a psychiatric success. New problems and new emotional burdens have arisen during the past years, and he has met them in a frank and open fashion. The father, who had early been so large a factor in the boy's emotional life, suddenly appeared about one and a half years after the period of intensive treatment closed. The father proved to be an undesirable, unadjusted man. He wanted Sandor to go away with him. But the boy faced the problem and thought it out and decided that he did not wish to go. In a large measure he has overcome the bad habit of feeling sorry for himself and of day-dreaming on the basis of this self-pity. What is more important, he has found that his new emotional attitudes and his improved behaviour are bringing him more satisfaction and happiness in life than did his old ones. This boy, even should he become delinquent, is a psychiatric success, in that psychotherapy has helped him to make a mental and emotional adjustment that will be of lifelong benefit to him.

Occasionally I see a child that I feel I understand so well that I can predict the child's behaviour and responses in any new situation by thinking how I myself would act and feel under similar circumstances. The ability to do this increases the child's confidence in me. Perhaps this was the reason Sandor responded so well to my attempt to help him. Cases like this are encouraging, for they show that a child may be changed even though it is impossible to change an environment that seems largely responsible for his troubles.

*   *

The next boy's situation and problems were very different, but he, too, needed to be understood.

Case No. 2

RALPH STAPLES

Ralph was an unusually attractive eight-year-old lad when I

first knew him, three years ago; good-looking, healthy, dynamic, friendly, and frank. Mentally he is superior; I. Q., 126. Formerly he was left-handed, but was "broken" of this when he was six years old.

The situation: Ralph was brought to the clinic by his father through the advice of social workers. He was considered a personality and psychiatric problem. The parents reported some disturbing behaviour in the home, mostly in the form of mood reactions towards the other members of his household. There had been some boyish disobedience and peevishness at home which worried the parents particularly. The fact that the lad refused to speak to one or the other of his parents for a day or more at a time upset them greatly and made them feel that he was becoming a serious problem. The parents were very anxious that the boy should learn to speak German, the family being of German descent, and for some time before Ralph was known to me, he had been required to take private lessons in German every day. He had been doing only fairly well in school. His mother had read of school difficulties and behaviour problems being caused sometimes by "breaking" a child of left-handedness, and she was concerned about this. The parents were both away from home every day, the father in business, the mother in agency work. His only companion in the home was a French nurse who very closely supervised him. The family, believing that the neighbourhood boys were unsuitable for companions and not his social equal, did not allow them to come into the home to play and seldom allowed Ralph to visit their homes or be with them on the playground or on the street.

Thinking about the boy: The story of the situation as given by the parents was interesting. The boy's version, given in a frank, somewhat critical, but not self-pitying way, was even more so.

This friendly little chap was pleased that he could come to the clinic and he came to see the "boy-doctor" in a friendly attitude. Of all the men he had ever met, except his relatives, he liked best his family doctor. Ralph said the doctor had talked to him "like he was a man," so he believed that any doctor who was just for boys would be a very interesting person. He came to the first interview ready for the rapport of personal trust. He told about his father and mother and his home life in open, boyish fashion, occasionally saying that he would not want to make his parents feel badly. (They would have, had they known some of the things he said.) However, they had instructed him to tell the doctor everything and he was glad to do so. He did not feel that he was breaking confidence with them.

Ralph wanted to be allowed to play with the other boys. These boys did some things which he would not do, but Ralph believed that he could play with them without getting into trouble or learning to be bad. He had on one occasion stolen an apple. His parents had never learned of this. His conscience had bothered him and he was relieved to make the confession. He was sure that he would never do it again because he didn't enjoy worrying about it.

The thing Ralph wished the most was for his parents to be with him more. But when they were with him, he said they treated him as a baby and he did not like this. His father never seemed to have the time to answer questions. He always told Ralph that he was too small to understand when he asked about things. He said the reason for his refusal to speak to the father for two days a short time before was that his father spoke very sharply to him, reprimanded him, and told him it was none of his business when he asked questions about the mechanism of gear-shifting while they were out driving. Ralph had decided to treat his father as he felt he was being treated. When I asked him if he thought that was very manly behaviour for a boy, he said: "Well, it got me a chance to come here, anyway."

He did not like the way the maid treated him. He said that the parents would give the maid a long list of things he was to do and not to do, often written on a piece of paper, when they left in the morning, before he was up. He said he would be willing to mind his parents themselves, but "When I have to do it because she says to, it makes me mad."

The other boys knew a lot of things he did not know. Once he had been ridiculed by a group of schoolmates for saying that the doctor brought babies. He had asked his doctor friend about this and had been told to ask his father. He did not do so because he believed he would only be scolded and was sure his father would say he was too small to be told. He knew that most other boys as large as he dressed and undressed themselves and took their own baths. Occasionally his mother helped him; he liked that, but he did not like to have the maid help him as she always insisted on doing. This particular routine and the taking of the German lessons were the things that he had most acutely resented.

Ralph wished very much that he had a brother and he sometimes pretended that he had one and was playing with him. He liked this kind of day-dreaming play, but his numerous duties and close supervision usually prevented him from indulging in it. He did, however, enjoy it after he went to bed at night, and sometimes day-dreams went over into real dreams. They often were the kind that frightened him. He told of these dreams freely and I, from their content, believed that there was a good deal of sex curiosity in the boy's mind.

He never cried because he could not do the things he wanted to do, except when he believed it might help him to gain his ends. He had no bad habits. His doctor friend had warned him against masturbation and he was interested in being big and strong, especially so because his father and mother were always saying that he was too small for such things as scooters and bicycles which he very much desired to have.

Thinking for the boy: In Ralph's case the problem was largely the parents. They were well-meaning and were taking a serious, but not very understanding, attitude towards the boy. It did not seem to be necessary to search for mental conflicts or dynamisms to explain this boy's behaviour, although he was brought to the clinic for that express purpose by parents who had been reading much semi-scientific literature on the subject. Some of this the boy himself had been able to read. I believed that it would be unwise either to establish a deep rapport or to make an attempt at mental exploration until social adjustments had first been tried. This boy had made an adjustment between himself and his parents that, under the circumstances, was fairly good. One could not be sure that it would be so well handled if the problem were frankly discussed with him. But a psychiatrist in whom the boy thoroughly trusted and believed could plan to give this boy good advice and counsel and could expect him to understand its reasonableness and to realize what he might gain by following it. The psychiatrist's real duty of course was to re-educate the parents and show them where they were making mistakes in their son's home life and education.

Thinking with the boy: At the end of the first interview Ralph asked: "Have you any little boy of your own? A kid would sure be lucky who had you for a dad." He was in personality contact with me. This was a deeper rapport than was really needed and deeper than was utilized in *thinking with* him. It came without any effort on my part. It would have occurred with any adult who listened to the lad without patronizing him and who intelligently answered his questions. He asked many questions of all sorts. To me the embarrassing ones were those concerning my possible attitude towards my parents if I were in his situation. He said he had never before talked with a man who knew so well how a boy felt. I had three interviews with Ralph. It was necessary to adopt a rather reserved and serious attitude with him lest he become too much attached to me. He would have very willingly gone deeply into his mental life and probably would have been able to revive and tell many forgotten experiences which had been disturbing to him, but I felt that this was not wise, and so I did not encourage him to do so.

I *thought with* Ralph about various things, mostly under his direction. I encouraged and advised him. His boyish questions about sex I dealt with frankly, and when his curiosity was satisfied, he did not again refer to them.

Results: A good foster-home in a fine group of boys was obtained. The lad is now an outstanding boy in an outstanding group. He is happy, well-behaved, and contented. His school-work is excellent. I saw him a year later. He was friendly and pleased to renew acquaintance. Almost at once he asked if he might talk with me alone; he said he had some questions to ask. It developed that some of his friends had been indulging in crude and childish sex play and he wanted to know what it all meant and to receive my approbation for his keeping out of it.

Ralph's case is a success, largely, of course, as a result of social efforts. Good social treatment alone would probably have succeeded, but the psychiatric treatment helped make this more sure and hastened the results.

Parental re-education would have been much the best way for Ralph to have been helped, and this was attempted, but since the parents did not feel that it was possible to arrange their lives so that they could be with the lad in the home, the next best thing was to change the environment. He went from a high-class home to a much simpler and far less comfortable one physically, but he was happier from the first day of the change.

This case is interesting in that it well illustrates the fact that understanding people in a child's dynamic environment are much more important than are the physical conveniences or luxuries of life.

*   *

"Each case is a law unto itself." Had the next boy been removed from his environment, the happiness of three people would have been destroyed.

Case No. 3
RICHARD ELWOOD

Richard has been known to the clinic since he was eleven. He is now fourteen and one-half years of age. When first seen, he was a small, well-developed, good-looking, friendly, but very sad and serious little boy. His health was good, but he was tall and slender-bodied. His very childish face accentuated his height and the fact that he was underweight. Mentally he was of superior ability by age-level tests.

The situation: The foster-mother told Dick's story. She had adopted him when he was six. She had believed until recently that it would be possible to make this boy feel he was her own child and she had tried to do so. She had reluctantly realized that this would be impossible and had told the boy all she knew of his early life, which was very little. Before coming to her, he had lived, she believed, nearly all his life in an institution. She and her husband had taken the boy because they wanted a child.

They had intended to keep him and send him through college if he proved worthy. She believed that children should be trained very rigidly and had always felt that under no circumstance could they keep this boy if he ever showed tendencies towards dishonesty. The institution had reported that he had earlier been guilty of stealing food and small change.

The foster-mother was active in Church and in society. She was in good health. The foster-father is an architect.

Both she and her husband feared at the time the boy was first seen that they had made a mistake in taking this boy. They felt that were he to become a bad boy, it would break their hearts. They were very fond of him and thought that the longer they kept him, the harder it would be to give him up, and believed it better to do so then than to wait longer. The boy was brought to the clinic as a last resort to see if I could help him overcome his delinquencies. These delinquencies seemed serious only when viewed in the light of the parents' attitude. The boy had stolen small amounts of money from his foster-home on several occasions, but had readily confessed these faults to his foster-mother. He had stolen food from the ice-box and had told several lies to his foster-mother to defend himself. His foster-mother had all these things written on a paper. She told us that she had a large scrap-book in which she collected clippings from the papers that reported instances where boys who had been good boys in good homes had later become criminals. She read from this book daily to the boy. The foster-mother, aside from this very rigid moral attitude, made a most excellent impression and in most ways seemed to be understanding this boy very well. It was evident that both she and her husband had genuine affection for him.

The foster-mother was much concerned because she believed Richard had been masturbating recently. She had noticed that he occasionally touched himself, which she believed meant that he masturbated. She reported him as being independent and disobedient. When asked for examples, she told of times when he had forgotten to say "sir" and "ma'am" when addressing his parents and she believed that at times, when he had been denied some privilege or pleasure, he deliberately neglected to say "Thank you" at the table. The instances she gave of disobedience were all failures to perform small tasks that were his regular work when he came from school.

Thinking about the boy: Dick was an unusually attractive and well-behaved boy. He was full of life and spirits. As he grew older, he was doubtless finding it hard to understand and to accept the strict responsibilities and behaviour standards demanded by his foster-parents. There was the early, largely unknown, period of Dick's life, which might easily have left its mark on his character and conditioned his present responses. These things one might think about theoretically. There was nothing in the foster-mother's story to warrant a belief that this was true, except that his present delinquency was taking the same form as that reported when a small child. The parents were at an age when it would have been impossible for them successfully to have taken another small child into their lives. They believed that if they gave up Dick, they would be lonesome. They wanted to try to keep him. The boy was sad, depressed, and discouraged because he believed that he was certain to lose his home and the love of these two people who meant all the world to him.

Thinking for the boy: As far as one could tell, without deep exploration of the boy's mind, the problem was not one of personality or even of serious behaviour. The big situational need was for these three people to be helped to understand one another and thus to avoid a tragedy which would affect the lives of all of them.

The question is to be answered was: "Is this possible?" It was important to know all that could be found out about this boy's behaviour and responses to his environment so that through this understanding one might interpret him more intelligently to his parents and incidentally give him help with any real problems in his mental life. Since the parents must be interpreted to the boy, he must be made to understand that in return for all the wonderful things they were doing for him, he must live up to their ideals. This could much better be accomplished by someone whom the boy had learned thoroughly to trust. It was both unnecessary and undesirable for this boy, who had such very fine loyalties to such fine people, to reach a deep stage of rapport.

Thinking with him: This boy was seen at regular intervals for several weeks. The first thing that happened was that the lad upset my plan to have him stay in a superficial stage of rapport. Ten minutes after he was first alone with me, this unhappy and thoroughly frightened and discouraged boy had reached the rapport of personality contact, and throughout our acquaintance I had to make a distinct effort to prevent him from becoming dependently attached to me.

It was now possible to get from the boy a very frank and analytical story of his life as he remembered and understood it. He remembered a good deal about his early life. From the first he understood that his foster-mother wished him to feel he was her boy, and he pretended he believed it to please her. When told the truth by her, he was not disturbed, but he would have been willing to continue the pretence. He said that all the children he had known when he was young were orphans, and that he had never felt sorry for himself because he was one. When he thought about it at all, he thought that if his parents were the kind of people who would desert him when he was a baby, they probably were not such good people as his foster-parents. He was glad he did not remember them, because he thought that if he did, he might feel differently about the situation.

He said that when he was in the institution, the boys he liked best were those who, with him, were successful in stealing food and other small articles. They got a lot of fun from it, as well as the food they wanted, and they were not punished much for it. Though he had forgotten their names, he still thought of them as his friends. He remembered, also, several fights he had had with the enemies of this group.

He said he had more toys and playthings than most of the boys he knew and that he hated to give them up, but he felt he would have to because his foster-parents told him so and because he did not see how any boy could be so good as they wanted him to be. He felt badly about it, more on account of being separated from his foster-mother than from losing his good home. The boy very frankly discussed his sex problems, and it was found that he had not been masturbating; his simply mild sex handling was largely on a curiosity basis. He had been led to believe that this is very sinful and was wondering why.

We talked about the fact that he was an adopted boy and did not know who his parents were. Dick had done one of the best jobs of *"thinking about"* this himself that I have ever seen a child of his age and circumstances do, so that I did not *"think with"* him about it. I *thought with* this boy for a little while on the occasion of our second or third interview about the fact that his foster-mother had believed and reported him to have bad sex habits. It was explained to him that she was mistaken in what she thought he was doing and he was told, in response to questions, what these things were of which she was accusing him. He asked normal and frank boyish questions. He was told he had done nothing wrong and that this attitude of his mother's only went to show how interested and anxious to help him she was. He was told also that many mothers made the same mistake. Judging from his frank reactions, I believe it will be a long time before anyone will need to *think with* him again about these things, and I believe that this experience will probably cause him to seek some adult's advice when it is necessary.

Dick said that the first time he was accused of dishonesty, he did not feel that what he had done was really dishonest. He was angry because his foster-parents thought of his behaviour in this way. He felt aggrieved and defiant, and these attitudes evidently led to more serious offences. Soon he was short-changing his foster-mother when he did errands. When these more serious things happened and his parents told him they would no longer own him as their boy, he became much discouraged, and instead of facing the situation and trying to behave in better fashion, he thought he might as well live up to his bad reputation.

I *thought with* this boy concerning some of the things I had *thought about* the most. In simple words I told him that some boys, when they are unhappy as he was when a little boy, found friends who did bad things, and themselves learned to do these things in order to be one of the gang. They would then be doing the wrong things, not because they were bad boys, but because they were lonesome and wished friendship. It was explained to him that it was very easy, if this happened, for a boy to do these things years later if he again became discouraged and unhappy, and that it was also easy for the boy wrongly to believe that a repetition of the bad things he had done before would bring him relief from his lonesomeness and unhappiness.

We talked about what fine people his foster-parents were and how much they loved him, and how hard it would be at his age to find another home where he would be cared for. He was told that a boy as big as he would be expected to work hard in a new home and earn his way, and that he would not really be an adoptive son, as he was in his present home.

This boy was seen a number of times, and despite the fact that he was in excellent rapport, he was still discouraged about making good, and insisted on adopting the attitude that we might as well give it up and get it over with. (This, I feel, was partially due to the failure of the parents to help me encourage the lad while I was seeing him.) Failure seemed inevitable despite the good rapport. He was showing some mild dishonesty during the period of treatment.

Then one day something happened. One can seldom point to one particular thing he has done or said as the crucial factor in accomplishing the effect one has strived for, but in Dick's case this was apparently possible. I was talking with Dick about football. I was *thinking about* why I was failing in such a hopeful situation with such a hopeful boy of very active loyalties, a fact he was demonstrating at the moment by telling me about the boys on his football team. I happened to say something to the boy the general idea of which I had said to him many times before. Because of the remarkable response, immediately after the boy had left, I tried to remember what had been said and wrote it down as follows:

I said: "See here, Dick, I'll tell you what you're like. You're like a good football-player who is on a team that has better uniforms and a better field to play on than almost any of the other teams in the neighbourhood. You are a good player, and it is very likely that some day, if you stick by the team, you will be captain, but because you are not now the one to decide just what plays are to be made, you are thinking of turning in your fine uniform and

all the good things that go with it. If you do that, you may never
get on any other team at all. If you do, it will be on a scrub team.
Just now your team is in the most important part of the whole
game. The first half is almost up. You have the ball on your op-
ponents' three-yard line, and it is the fourth down. The captain
of your team is asking you to carry the ball through the centre
of the line, and you think you ought to make a drop kick instead.
If you make the touchdown the captain's way, you will be just
that much nearer being captain yourself some day. If you refuse to make the play, you will be put out and the game will probably be lost. Now, how about it, boy? Can't you make a touchdown
through the line?"

Before this analogy was half finished, Dick was sitting up in his
chair, and his eyes were sparkling. When I finished, his eyes were
still brighter, because there were tears in them. It was the first
time I had seen him cry. He said: "Can I go home now? I'm going
to make that touchdown."

Results: And he did. I had a few more short interviews with him.
These were concerned mainly with listening to his description and
reports of progress in the game he was playing at home. The
foster-mother came in several times to ask me what had been done
for Dick that made him such a different boy, and incidentally to
assure me that she was sure it could not last. I utilized these interviews by giving suggestions to her.

This case is a complete success. The three people involved are
happy and well adjusted and will probably remain so. I have
recently seen the boy after a lapse of more than a year. He is one
of the finest, happiest, and most unselfish boys I have ever known.
The foster-mother has nothing but good reports of him and feels
now that even if he were to become a bad boy, she could not give
him up. Dick was very much pleased to see me. He greeted me

in a manly open fashion and immediately commenced to talk about the old football game.

This case is interesting in that, though it included many situations and experiences that often cause mental and personality difficulties, they were not operative. It was not the understanding or meeting of such things as these that helped the lad to take better attitudes and to be willing to face the situation which he had before refused to do; but rather, I feel, it should be explained thus: In some way not understood and possibly not understandable my personality reacted on his. I had been trying very hard to reach the boy and he had taken me very definitely into his environmental values. Had he read the same analogy to which he responded in this dramatic way from a book or had some stranger told it to him, it would not have been given any more affective value than were the numerous other stories and preachings with which his mother's scrap-book was filled.

* * * *

The next boy to be discussed has everything in his environment that any boy can need. He has all the physical and mental equipment he can ever use. But he was misinterpreted and was beginning to misinterpret himself.

Case No. 4
SAM ALBERTSON

Sam was, when first known to the clinic one and one-half years ago, a roguish, attractive, good-looking, and well-developed American boy of eight years. He had superior intelligence by age-level tests. Very careful physical examination revealed nothing abnormal except that he had lost the second toe of his right foot.

The situation: Sam was at that time the most doctored boy

in the small city in New York State in which he lives. The toe had recently been amputated to correct a deformity from an early accident. Before it had been finally removed, he had undergone five operations in an attempt to correct the existing contracture and he had had it baked, X-rayed, encased, and massaged, times without number. Sam had been examined by many specialists of all sorts. These examinations had been made on the slightest symptoms of illness or any indication of "nervousness." He could talk quite glibly of his experiences with doctors and made many interesting comments on them. He tried hard to believe himself to be sick and delicate because his mother wanted him to, though when in school or at play with his comrades, he often had trouble in remembering that he was. However, he really was at that time considerably concerned about his health.

He was brought to the clinic because the specialists had failed to find out what the trouble was. His mother had been reading popular magazines and attending lectures and had decided that what he needed was psychiatric help. At first she had been puzzled as to what particular kind of psychiatric help he should have or for what particular thing he might be examined. A short time before, the boy himself had made the diagnosis when he rushed into the home, having escaped from several boys who wanted to fight him because of some success he had made in the schoolroom, and said: "Mother, I know what is the matter with me. It is fear, that's what it is, it's fear." So he was brought to me to be treated for a fear complex.

Sam has two sisters, two and three years younger than he, who have I. Q.'s of about 130, while Sam's was only 123. This also had worried their mother and she had reproved Sam for it. She wished us to look into this matter also and see if his I. Q. could not be improved.

His mother reported him as having shown many signs of personality trouble. He objected strenuously to going to bed at half past six, when his sisters did. He became angry and even bit his teeth together and clinched his fist when made to stay in the house and play with dolls instead of going out to play football with the boys. Once he said he believed he could kill the girls to get them out of the way so he wouldn't have to play with them all the time. His mother said that recently something had happened in school that was important. Sam was the chief performer in a school play that was being rehearsed. He was taking music lessons. He was being tutored in arithmetic because he did not get an A. He was the class president, which office consumed considerable of his time. The teacher wished him to be president of a program committee and he refused, giving as his reason that he had too much to do. Following this the teacher and the mother in conference decided that Sam must have an inferiority complex. Sam's mother had talked to him about this, and while he at first insisted that it was a desire to play football and to go to gym that made him not want to assume these new duties, by the time he came to the clinic, he had been thoroughly convinced that his mother and teacher were right.

Thinking about the boy: From the reports of several physical examinations showing excellent physical condition I could be sure that Sam was not ill. From the story told by the mother and from my interview with her, it was quite easy to believe without even seeing the boy that probably if he really needed a doctor at all, he needed a psychiatrist. The lad told the same story as the mother and showed that he was believing it as best he could and was really commencing to respond emotionally to this belief. He told me of his feeling of inferiority quite glibly. He told of sleeplessness; sometimes he lay awake half an hour after being put to bed at half-past six.

However, very near the surface was a fine, active, healthy boy with normal interests, and one could see that the whole thing was half a game and half real with him. One felt that it was almost a waste of time to think about the lad when the mother was in the waiting-room with no one thinking about her.

Thinking for him: Here was a fine boy without any real problems and without any genuine personality troubles. He was soon going to have some very definite ones if nothing was done for him. He could be seen only a few times and his mother herself had not come as a patient. Part of the limited time available was spent in an attempt to re-educate her, but it was easily evident that this would not be highly successful. So it was decided to do some serious thinking with Sam and to put his situation frankly before him. The mother had told me that she wanted to put the boy completely in my hands, and that she wished me to do anything I could to help him.

Thinking with him: He was friendly, frank, happy, and talkative. It was very easy to establish a feeling of personal trust towards me in this boy's mind and to have him hold the belief that I was seriously interested in him. Because the period of treatment was to be brief (it consisted in three interviews at that time and one a year later), care was taken to see that he did not assume a deeper rapport than that of a feeling of personal trust.

Most of the time was spent in talking about mothers. We thought up all sorts of excuses for mothers who loved their boys very much and worried too much about them. He had been doing some of this kind of thinking before, whenever he was allowed to think by himself, which was very seldom. Ideas did not really have to be given to this boy. He simply needed help with formulating them, and courage to respond to those he already had.

After every possible precaution had been taken to prevent any loss of loyalty to this very loyal mother, this boy was carefully but firmly told that he was not sick and never had been, that it was perfectly natural for a boy to want to play with other boys, and that he was not a bad boy. He was told that many chronic invalids among adults were "sickly" simply because people had so considered them for such a long time that they finally came to consider themselves so. He was made to understand that his mother probably would never be able to stop worrying about him, but that she did it because she loved him. He was told that it was most important for him to stick by his mother and to be frank with her as far as he could, especially about any misbehaviour or about his desire to be like other boys. He was told also to remember always that she was mistaken when she thought he was sick, and that it was best for him not to complain about his health or tell her of any little symptoms he might have unless they were very disturbing.

These were not entirely new ideas to him, but it was new to hear anyone whom he believed and trusted say them. Doctors had often told the mother the same thing in the boy's presence, but he had rejected them without second thought because his mother had. His personal trust was well shown by the fact that while not one word was said to him about not telling his mother what he was told in interviews, he did not report it to her and never has. When she tried to have him do so, he told her that ladies could not understand such things. (When he reached home, he did take his father into his confidence, as we afterwards learned, and gave his father a very comprehensive idea of what he had been told.)

Sam asked many questions and demanded proof of his good health. It was a genuine delight to talk and think with this intelligent boy.

Results: The doctors have lost a patient. Sam became so free from symptoms that there could no longer be any excuse for treating him as a sick baby, and gradually he has been given more privileges. Fortunately (for him) his sisters, soon after the time he was seen, needed, their mother believed, treatment for overweight and for having too red cheeks and too much blood. They were also given serum to prevent them from catching cold.

When seen a year later, he was as fine and happy and healthy a boy as one could wish to see. He had looked forward to the interview and had especially asked that his father instead of his mother bring him to the city for it. We three had a very interesting hour together and all agreed that there are some problems that men-folks understand best. The father reports him as being kind and genuinely loyal to his mother and sorry for her when she worries. He tells me that the mother treats the boy less as a baby since she has come to believe that he is not sick. The father has come to see how important it is that the boy should have normal activities and interests, and he says that it was the things this eight-year-old boy told him following his treatment that helped him to understand this.

Had this type of treatment been carried out without the element of trust entering into the relation between the lad and the psychiatrist, he would not have been helped. While deeper rapport would have been extremely easy to establish, it was not wise to seek for this response without first seeing if results could not be obtained without it.

This bright boy probably would have solved his own problems sooner or later, but the treatment given him was a definite help and, while he was still young, removed things that might have been of serious consequence to him later.

CHAPTER V

PLEASURES FROM DELINQUENCY

The Child who Believes he is Making himself Happy

T should be emphasized that for clarity these cases are grouped roughly under problem and situation headings, but they are not selected for the purpose of illustrating particular dynamisms. It is well to select for one problem-group heading a classification freely used by many who deal with problem children. Much too freely doubtless; but there are some children who consistently get more pleasure than unhappiness from misbehaviour.

Of my entire group of cases there are only five that can in any way be classified thus. In none of these cases was the pleasure received from delinquency the chief factor, and in only two of them was it a large one.

Long-continued delinquency does not usually bring to children even the small amount of pleasure that it sometimes does to adults. But unless one knows a delinquent child very well, it is often easy to believe that he is finding delinquency pleasurable. Many children will persist in this explanation for their bad behaviour, some of them use it for an excuse, and some actually believe it to be true, when it is not.

The first case in this group is illustrative of those children who so insist and who, through failure to be understood, must be dealt with socially on this basis.

Case No. 5
BURT SMITH

Burt was almost fifteen when first seen in the clinic. He was a
well-developed, round-faced, healthy boy. He was boisterous, noisy,
forward, and at times rude in his behaviour. Despite this he was a
likable chap. He had very good mental ability. Tests, showing irregular performance, gave him an I. Q. of 116.

The situation: Burt's family history was negative. He lived in
a well-kept, middle-class home and was the second of four siblings. His younger brother had been killed in a hunting-accident
one year before I knew Burt.

His personality traits, which his parents believed were the real
cause of his trouble, were reported as selfishness, hatefulness, disobedience, dishonesty, and distrustfulness. At times he was affectionate, and always industrious. The parents were discouraged
and worried by Burt's behaviour and by his antagonistic and disobedient attitude. He had been stealing for three years, recently
rather large sums of money from lodgers and parents. He had
frequently truanted from school and was defiant when reproved
for it. On one occasion he had remained away from home all night.
He lied about these things. The parents felt they did not understand him and they believed that he would soon spoil his thirteen-
year-old brother or get into some serious trouble himself.

Thinking about the boy: Everyone who knew Burt, his teachers,
parents, friends, and the psychologist who tested him, said they
could not understand him. They could not understand why he was
a "bad" boy. An excellent history given by his parents failed to
help much towards understanding him. This boy told his story
willingly and glibly, as though he had rehearsed it, but he told it
only in so far as it concerned his behaviour and environment. He

was not frank about his emotional life. He exaggerated his delinquencies. He tried to impress others with his manliness and daring. He criticized rather than justified himself, but he did it in an impersonal way.

He said he had only been caught a few times in his stealing, that more often he had enjoyed the results of his dishonesty. He said he had many friends whom he never could have met had he not used the stolen money to gain their attention.

He said he did not love his parents. They were too strict and they thought more of the other children than they did of him. He believed that it would "teach them something" to have him show them how modern boys lived. Often he stayed out late at night, and he enjoyed shocking his parents by this behaviour more than he did the actual staying out itself. He said his parents did not understand him and never should have had children. He seemed to look at life in a superficial and selfish way and to be loyal to nothing except to having a good time.

Burt wanted to quit school. He wanted to show his parents that he could take care of himself. Every day he had a new idea as to what he was going to be, and at the particular time that he had each idea, he would be very sure about it. At different times he was going to be a sailor, a ranchman, a hermit, an automobile-racer, or a horseman.

If one wished to understand this boy, one must think about whether the boy consciously recognized the mental equivalent behind his behaviour. He believed that he did the things others thought he should not do because they brought him pleasure. One could not tell whether he really was getting pleasure from his misdeeds unless one knew more of the boy's mental life. Burt was very verbose and talked freely of all sorts of things. He glibly told of his developing sex emotions. He said he had a vantage-place in the woods where he watched young couples in sex affairs and he reported himself to have unusual dreams following these experiences. He said he had been approached sexually by many girls, but that he had always refused them.

In the absence of a good rapport one could not be sure whether these things were true or not. If they were true, they might easily be making mental conflicts. If they came from his imagination, they might be taken as evidence that conflicts already existed. If he was only repeating as his own experience things that he had heard or read, one could reasonably feel that the boy's behaviour was indeed motivated by the emotional returns he received from shocking people and from having a good time.

Thinking for the boy: His parents and social workers had tried many plans for Burt before he was seen in the clinic. It seemed that nothing could be done for him without altering his personality responses, or at least understanding them—and, on this understanding, attempting to give constructive social advice.

Thinking with the boy: He was seen for six rather long interviews, and a sustained effort was made to establish rapport with him. Burt did not want help. He was proud of the fact that no one understood him. He believed himself perfectly competent to solve his own problems. His ideas and his attitudes could not be altered. No loyalties could be found and none were developed. He was convinced that *I* knew much about boys' problems, but he was telling me about himself to convince me that *he* knew more. He finally did tell some facts of his intimate life and some of his emotional responses, but only to show that he was wise enough to know that doctors were used to such things, and that he was not afraid to tell them.

Burt had a friendly belief in me from the first, but earnest effort failed to have him reach any deeper rapport than this. At the end of the treatment I felt that it was easy to predict how this boy would behave in response to any given situation, but why he would do so was as much a mystery as ever. One could not be sure of the truth of anything Burt said. Late in the period of treatment he told of having had a vision the night before. He attempted to describe it so that it would seem to resemble a symptom of mental disease. It was very difficult for even a credulous psychiatrist to believe that this decidedly extroverted lad was having hallucinations.

Results: The boy was seen a year after he was studied in the clinic, for follow-up interview. His behaviour is the same. He is critical of his parents, wants to be independent, resents any authority. He has been in several minor delinquencies with a group of boys, has been accused of stealing on a number of occasions. He was entirely friendly, but lied in a boastful way. He said he was glad to be asked to come back and renew acquaintance and said some of the advice given him before had been useful to him.

The social outlook for this boy is not good. He certainly needs psychiatric help, but a good rapport could not be established and I could not understand or help him. Even now, if someone could reach this boy and make him want to be understood, he could be helped. Everyone who knows him thinks he has many good characteristics which, if developed, would make him a fine man. He needs to be convinced of the necessity of understanding himself so that he may reach his goal in a better way. And he is in dire need of loyalties in his life.

Burt was probably not a bad boy because of the pleasure he received from being bad, but since he could not be thoroughly understood, it was thought necessary to deal with him as though this were so. But working with him and doing things for him on the basis of this assumption have proved a failure. The failure was psychiatric rather than social.

*   *

The next two cases are brothers. Their delinquency probably brought as large a measure of happiness and pleasure as delinquency ever does for children. There was little pleasure in their life other than this. The pleasure obtained was contributory to the continuation of their problems. It is interesting that neither boy emphasized the fact that they enjoyed their misbehaviour.

Case No. 6
FRANK JACOBI

Frank was first seen at the clinic five years ago, when he was ten and a half years old. At that time he had diseased tonsils, a nasal obstruction, and very bad teeth, all of which contributed to his under-developed and generally poor physical condition. His large expressive eyes drew attention from his grimy and rather narrow face. Mentally he was of good average general ability.

The situation: A typical tenement home of the poor class gave Frank what little shelter he had from his life on the streets. The mother had died several years before. A paternal aunt whose health was bad kept house for them.

Frank was first referred to the clinic with a group of boys by the juvenile court for stealing small articles from parked cars. He was seen but once at that time. Further interviews were advised because he at first confessed to some extensive sex habits and sex activities of a very disturbing nature with boys and men in the neighbourhood. Later he grew frightened and denied these experiences. Two years later, after another court appearance on some minor charge (this was his seventh appearance within two years), he was once more referred to us for study.

Thinking about the boy: It seemed probable that the mild but long-continued delinquency was of environmental origin. Frank lived in the very worst part of the city and certainly seemed to need social attention rather than psychiatric. There were two things, however, to *think about* that were of interest from the standpoint of the boy's mental life. One was the fact that the lad seemed glad to come back and frankly said he was. The other was the story of many sex experiences he had told two years earlier. From the fact that he had told those things at that time, one could infer that they had had much emotional value for him. At that time nothing had been done to help him understand his situation, to correct his bad habits, or even to help him understand why he had been asked to tell about them. Something would have been done, of course, had the clinic been able to arrange for his revisiting for treatments.

Thinking for the boy: His bashful eagerness to tell of himself and to ask questions of a general nature made us believe that he desired a chance to ask other, more intimate questions; and it suggested that probably here was a psychiatric situation after all.

Thinking with the boy: His earlier interview at the clinic had been with a woman psychiatrist. This time he said, immediately upon entering the interviewing-room, that he was glad to see that it was a man doctor this time. He said he had liked the lady, but that it had been hard to talk with her even when he was a "kid," and now that he was bigger, he would be ashamed to talk to her. He had thought it over before coming. By this statement it was easy to see that he either wished or expected to discuss his sex problems. The rapport of personal trust was almost immediately reached with the boy and he needed no deeper rapport.

He again told of his early "bad" experiences and said that they had been continued ever since. Sometimes he had tried to stop them. He said that when he had been in the clinic before, he did not understand some of the things that were said because he "didn't know what all the big words meant," but he had understood that his habits were considered unhealthful and wrong. He knew that the "cops got after" boys for having them and he had often wondered why this was. When he was told that he might be free to ask me questions and use the words he knew, he said that he would have liked to ask questions before, but he was afraid. He asked many questions. In fact the entire *thinking about* these things was really done by answering the things the boy asked. Some of his questions were very disturbing and made one wonder if permanent harm might have been done to him by his experiences. For instance, he asked: "Why do boys want to do it to girls when it is just as much fun or more with other boys and it ain't so apt to get the cops after you?"

Very simple Anglo-Saxon words were used to express our thoughts, and our thoughts were all practical, common-sense ones. This lad had already rejected as untrue some of the things he had heard from his elders. The fact that they had said them made him wonder all the more. He did not believe that bad sex habits would "make you go crazy" or that the "cops would kill you if they caught you" (both of which statements had been used as a warning to him and to other boys), because he knew boys who were very strong and not at all crazy who had them, and he had concrete evidence of what the "cops" did when they caught boys and girls and even men in bad practices. When he was told that if a boy kept on doing such things, he might become like some of the depraved men whose money he had taken, but whom he really loathed, it seemed reasonable and undesirable to him. He asked whether or not he would be like those men when he grew up if he stopped now, or if he injured his health. He wanted to know about boys who did not do these things at all. He believed that every boy has as strong temptation as he had to do "bad" in this way. Frank did not know the connexion between sex and birth, and when this was explained to him in a way that he could understand, he asked whether or not a man's children would be weak or more apt to be like him if the man had had bad habits when he was a boy. Frank and I thought over the answers to these questions very carefully, and the answers all had what seemed to the lad logical reasons to back them.

I asked Frank's opinion of the causative connexion between sex and other delinquencies. He strongly believed that they went together. He did not know about the genesis of the connexion, but he was sure that if a boy "ran" with another boy or with a gang who practised these things together, he was apt to stick in everything the gang did. His personal testimony was that often he would have kept out of trouble on the street were it not that some pal with whom he was indulging in sex play encouraged him to take part.

Two interviews were held with Frank at that time, and later he came back three times to talk things over and to report his progress. Then still later came the very interesting instance reported in connexion with his brother's case.

Results: Frank stopped his mutual sex practices at once. He said after talking them all over that he saw their bad side. Most of the temptations towards them disappeared and he had little struggle with himself to overcome them. However, he had not done so without gaining the contempt of his friends. His masturbation was not so easily discontinued, but he had been told that this would probably be so and he was not discouraged or disappointed. In a few weeks he succeeded in stopping this, too, and he did it with very little help of substitutive interests. In fact, losing his friends more than offset the few substitutive activities that were provided for him. He accomplished his fine changes in behaviour by making for himself concrete decisions based on practical advice given him by a friend whom he could trust. He quickly realized that he felt stronger and better after his behaviour improved and this, of course, furnished a good incentive to proceed along this new path. When a boy meets his sex problem frankly and overcomes sex habits in this way, results are more sure of being permanent than when he does so because someone else wants him to, or because he is afraid.

I have recently seen him again. His sex problems are solved. His delinquencies are becoming fewer. He was in court once on a rather serious gang charge. He came to me at once to tell me about it and to ask for advice. He said he was innocent, and later his innocence was established. This case was a psychiatric success in that it helped the boy to meet and to solve his serious problem. If he later becomes delinquent or a social failure, it will still be a psychiatric success, for his sex life will be more normal throughout his life because of the treatment. As you will see in reading of his brother, Frank and his family are social failures in a large measure, and without social help the boy may easily become seriously delinquent.

Case No. 7
FREDERICK JACOBI

Frederick was seen in the clinic when he was ten years old. He was a dirty, grimy little street urchin of only fair development, handicapped by badly neglected teeth and diseased tonsils. He was subdued and shy. His features were regular and rather sensitive.

He was normal, but of poor general ability.

The situation: Frederick is a brother of Case No. 6. He was brought to the clinic by his brother without suggestion from anyone. Several months earlier, as reported in the preceding case, his brother had been seen and had been helped to straighten out in his own life a serious sex situation. The brother said: "This kid is getting into the same bad things that I used to do. I am no angel yet, I admit [he himself had been recently in court again for street delinquency], but I got away from those things and I don't want to see him get mixed in them. I wish you would talk to him. He won't talk to me."

Thinking about the boy: Simply stated, the problem was to give instructions to an unco-operative boy with whom his brother had failed to establish a positive rapport. All we knew about him was from the brother's meagre report. All the brother could say was that, from things he had seen and from the type of children with whom the small boy was playing, he knew Frederick must need these instructions.

Thinking for the boy: It was important to decide, in *thinking for* Frederick, what degree of rapport it was best to establish. Certainly this rapport must be positive, for undoubtedly this little boy would give a good deal of emotional value to the interview. The response to me, then, should include a belief that I was informed on such matters. It should also include confidence that the things I said would be for his own real interest and good.

Thinking with him: More than an hour had to be spent in talking with this lad about all sorts of boyish things and in proving to him that I remembered how I felt when I was a boy. This hour was an essential entrée to the stage of personal trust. After that was reached, it was a simple matter. He believed the things he had been doing were wrong and harmful, but all the boys he knew did them, and it was lots of fun. At first he told the story of the bad sex practices and activities of his group very objectively—as though he himself did not take part. In time he said he took part in them too. Most of the sex information was given him in response to questions which he was glad to ask very freely after he had made his confession. At the close of the interview he said he did not know that boys ever talked about such things with men. He thought they just had to find out for themselves. At my suggestion he agreed to talk it over with his brother when he got home. I did not let him promise me better behaviour, but I told him I should like to have him come back within a few weeks and tell me about himself.

Results: He did come back a month later and again several months later. The second appearance was because he had been involved with a large group in his neighbourhood in some street delinquency. He reported at both of these interviews that he had stopped all masturbation and mutual sex play with the other boys, and that he had told them the things I told him. In fact, he acquired among his playmates the reputation of being very well informed on such matters. He reported that two other little boys had quit these things, or said they had, because of what he told them. Nothing was found that would tend to link his sex experiences with his delinquencies. Discontinuing his sex habits had no apparent effect on them. Only one small part of this boy's problems was touched, but undoubtedly he was helped. In this case the psychotherapy must be given all the small credit for such success as was obtained. The inadequacy was in the lack of social help, for this was badly needed and never given.

* *

The next case is an example of those children who accept the "fun of the thing" as an excuse for their delinquency, but not as a reason for it. This particular boy may have been trying to deceive himself in the matter. If so, he was failing to do so.

Case No. 8
HENRY EVANS

Henry Evans, a New Hampshire boy, twelve years old, of German ancestry, was an attractive-looking, active lad, well developed and healthy. He was highly supernormal on the age-level tests; I. Q., 139. He was in the first year of high school despite the fact that he had changed schools frequently. He made an unusually favourable impression by his conversational powers, his excellent general information, and his reasoning ability.

Henry was under suspended sentence from the juvenile court because of a number of serious charges of dishonesty. He had taken two automobiles, and with companions he had been guilty of breaking and entering three times, although he had been apprehended in this only once. The calibre of the father is shown by the fact that he boasted that he "pulled wires" and hinted that he bribed someone to have the boy put on probation rather than committed.

The situation: Henry's home had been broken up about two years before. His father and mother lived separately. The father continued to love the mother, who cared nothing for him. Each was trying to possess the boy, their only child, but the mother paid little attention to him when she had him. The father tried to supervise the boy by having him constantly at his place of business when he was not in school. When he was with his father, they kept a bachelor apartment. The father was excessively proud of his boy and had his business stationery printed "Henry Evans, Sr., and Henry Evans, Jr." The father criticized the mother and told Henry that she was seriously delinquent, while the mother retaliated in a similar fashion.

Though the father reported that five members of his immediate family had been in jail or in the penitentiary, earlier generations had excellent reputations. The father had taken the attitude towards the boy's dishonesty that it was "something born in him" that he must overcome and stamp out.

Thinking about the boy: I *thought about* his unusual environmental situation and about the peculiarities of his father and mother, whom I interviewed. I *thought about* the fact that none of the stealing was for personal gain; the boy did not keep the loot. It seemed that this boy must be unhappy, but it was impossible to tell how he was facing his situation emotionally until I *thought with* him. It was evident that his companions had been most undesirable and that serious social consequences might be in store for this boy unless his environmental situation was changed and he was helped to correct some of his behaviour tendencies. *Thinking about* this boy in terms of his long years of experience with his father and mother suggested that a change of environment alone would not be likely to effect desirable alterations of behaviour.

Thinking for the boy: In conference I thought first of a change in his environment by placing him in a foster-home, but his parents were unwilling to do this. The father and mother each considered themselves entirely capable of handling the problem if the other would keep out of the situation. Because I believed the father would co-operate, as he said, in making possible my regular psychiatric contacts with the boy, I decided to attempt to help him through psychotherapy. I saw the boy but twice at this time. The father then sent word that the boy was all right and needed no more help.

Thinking with the boy: In the two interviews the boy was obviously reaching out for help; he clearly appreciated and admired
the psychiatrist's ability to understand his problems and to think
about them in the same way as he did, but this was as far as the
matter went. While considering with him his many conflicts over
the father-mother situation, I discovered that he was trying to deny
the real significance of his mother's behaviour, that he was trying
to make himself feel that his father did not really care for him.
He definitely said that his father did not understand him. I did
not let the boy sense my attitude towards the parental relationships, because I felt we had not yet reached the place where he
would accept ideas simply because they came from me. Had I
been able to reach this deeper stage of rapport with him, it would
have been effective as a step towards better development of his
own emotional attitudes, and necessary as the first step towards
better behaviour. He reached only the rapport of *friendly belief*
in me.

Results: Very shortly the boy committed more offences and was
sent by the court to a private correctional school. Eleven months
later I happened to visit this school and by chance learned that
the boy was there.

It was very interesting that, while the boy did not recognize me
at first, as soon as he found out who I was, he talked spontaneously
of the things we had discussed earlier, and went on with them from
the place where we had left off. The boy had made a good record
in this school. Probably no harm was done by suddenly breaking
off the superficial rapport eleven months earlier, but we cannot
be sure of this. Perhaps a little good resulted, for during the interview at the school the boy voluntarily brought up his sex problems. They had not, however, been serious at any time.

This case was a failure in so far as we did not give the boy enough help to keep him out of a correctional school. Certainly he might have been benefited by further treatment. The failure could be traced back to my misplaced confidence in the father's promises of co-operation; I might have judged from the man's character that he would not carry the plan through. It should have been insisted that the boy be placed by a social agency in a foster-home at once. Then a psychiatric treatment could have been undertaken with almost certain success.

Although this lad had been given but little help to face reality and to understand himself, he said at that time that he knew his source of danger would not be the temptations that would come when he again met his old comrades. He said the danger would lie in the discouragement and in the unhappiness that would come when he again tried to live with one of his quarrelling and separated parents. This proved to be true, and very soon after his first discharge from the school he was returned because of more of the same type of delinquency. Soon after this his mother died suddenly, and now, several months after his second discharge, he is enough better behaved so that he is still living in the community.

The case is a psychiatric failure as far as one may know. This very intelligent boy, however, remembered well things that had been said to him and he earlier very definitely desired help and understanding friendship. And perhaps the brief attempts at psychotherapy at first and the occasional brief interviews I had with him in the school may, now that some of the stress of his environmental situation is relieved, be of help to him.

*   *

The last boy in this group really believed that his delinquency was continued because of, if not caused by, the profit and pleasures the delinquency brought to him and those he loved. When he was helped to understand himself, he no longer enjoyed being a bad boy.

Case No. 9
JAMES GALLIO

James Gallio was eleven years old and very small for his age when I first knew him, two years ago. He was a shrewd, self-reliant street urchin, equipped with a healthy, active body and a mentality shown by tests to be considerably above normal. He was an excessive smoker.

The situation: Jim was referred to me because of gang stealing of a rather serious nature. He was a member of older gangs and a leader of small boys in some successful breakings and enterings. His father was dead, his mother worked out, and he, being among the middle members of a large group of siblings, was neither small enough to need care in the home nor large enough to be expected to stay at home and care for the others. There was an intense family loyalty in this entire group, and the chief reason that Jim was referred for study and treatment was to try to get his co-operation and consent to being placed away from his home. This placing-out procedure had already been decided on. It was believed that were he to be placed without altering his emotional attitude towards the placing, it would take a long time for him to make adjustments that might result in character-building.

His personality traits were reported as good by all who knew him. He was friendly and happy, helpful and loyal in the family. He always tried to have his family benefit by his successful stealing, and to take things home he would take chances of being detected. His school behaviour was good. He made friends easily and was a leader.

Thinking about the boy: As for his physical environment, that part of the city in which he lived was known to be very bad. Experience has taught that a family situation such as his often leads to trouble. These things in themselves furnish many good reasons for his type of misbehaviour, and a psychiatrist is very apt to do little *thinking about* such problems. This is especially true when the situation is not complicated by bad personality traits or unhappiness in the child who is being studied.

Thinking for him: The *social thinking for him* had already been done by an agency. This included the plan to change one normal emotional response by psychiatric study and treatment. It was quite natural that this boy, who was happy and successful in his environment and loyal to it, should want to remain in it.

The problem of how deep a rapport would be necessary to accomplish the change, if it could be accomplished at all, could only be determined by experiment, but one might expect it to require a rather deep response.

Thinking with him: This lad conformed strictly to the psychiatric responses as they are interpreted in this book. He first came to believe that I knew something about his problems. This was accomplished by *thinking with* him; that is, by letting him express his ideas and listening to them first, and not arguing or scolding him about them. He then came to trust me as his friend and to be willing to listen to my advice and response. After the second interview he believed that I was not only his real friend, but he came to want me to like him and to overlook his faults, and he began to admire my ideas and to wish that he might meet my ideals. He was anxious to have me interested in him and to understand how he felt.

From this point on I could see the real boy and I found some unexpected and interesting things in him. He was essentially unhappy, but he had learned many ways to forget his unhappiness. He was worried for fear that he would be seriously punished by the law, but besides this he sincerely wished that his family were in better circumstances and had better ways of living so that he could be a good boy.

For example, while he was in the early superficial rapports he told about and defended the fact that all the children in his family drank wine. I did not argue with him about this or even tell him how I felt about it. Had I done so, or, at least, had I adopted this attitude towards many of the things discussed, no further rapport would have resulted. After he reached the stage of personality contact, I simply let him know what my ideas were about children's drinking wine, particularly undersized ones like him. Very shortly after this Jim and I discussed plans to convince his mother that she should not serve wine to the children. Jim had suggested it!

The boy had now gone far enough in his emotional responses to warrant my belief that I might accomplish a change in his attitude towards being placed. He and I thought about his mother's future situation, and how she would need him badly when he was older and was able to earn money. The same thing had been discussed with him before by others, but he had not listened to them. He was interested now because that was the way I looked at it. Because he wished to please me he tried to feel about it as I did. In this way, and in others, the boy was finally convinced that it was best, and he was willing to go to the foster-home.

The good rapport which had been established was useful in that it permitted us to think about some of his other problems. His sex situation was quite like that of many street urchins. He had a good deal of sex knowledge he had gained from observation and from sex play with little girls. He was an excessive masturbator. To these things he had not given much emotional value. No one had ever told him they were bad or harmful. Most of the children he knew did them, and he was too busy with his gang life to pay much attention to such things or worry much about them. (He did, however, tell me of a neighbourhood situation and another little boy's experience which made me feel that this other boy probably needed help. Good social work enabled this other lad to be seen. He proved to have conflicts over sex matters as was suspected and it was possible to help him.)

Jim and I thought a good deal about a boy's remaining loyal to his mother while he lived away from her, and about mothers who were proud of their boys when they grew up to be young men.

Jim was seen seven or eight time in the course of his first treatment. Only towards the latter part of this treatment was my contact with him so good that I could get him to feel he was leaving home willingly and to think of this as an opportunity to be a good boy.

Results: The year following these interviews was spent in a very good country home with a most understanding and patient foster-mother. Jim was a happy boy from the first. Twice during the year he ran away from the foster-home to come and see his mother. Each time it was when he was not allowed to make visits that had been partially promised him. Aside from this there was practically no delinquency. Although he was constantly with other boys who smoked, he stopped the habit entirely.

Since good rapport was established, Jim has never told me a lie. Whatever he said about himself could always be relied upon. Once he stole a small amount of money, which he considered he was borrowing, for his expenses in running away to go home. He did much better in school than before. His sex habits ceased entirely. Jim made a very interesting comment regarding this when he was telling about his school companions in his foster-home. He believed they knew nothing about masturbation. He said he thought it must have been some Boston boy who started "the whole business." He thought that probably Boston boys were the only ones in the world who had ever masturbated. James is one of the boys whom I am still following. He is using his intellectual equipment very well. He is making a fine school record. His agency visitor feels that he is too good material to trust in his home environment yet. When small problems develop, usually in the nature of feeling he should go home to live, I see him for an hour and help him face his problems a little more squarely and he again becomes a happy, well-behaved boy.

Jim's case is a success, perhaps with the laurels to be meted equally to psychiatric and to social efforts. Neither set of efforts would have been as completely successful operating alone as they were operating in combination.

It is interesting that this little thirteen-year-old boy is having a very definite influence for good on the entire family. They sometimes see him in his foster-home and are proud of his success and of his good standards. When he visits his home, they do not let him see them drink wine, and in other ways they try to measure up to his ideal. He has been giving his brother, one year younger, very good advice and instruction and he is trying to set a good example that the younger boy can follow.

CHAPTER VI

PREVENTIVE PSYCHOTHERAPY

The Boy who should be Prepared

PSYCHIATRY, as it deals with the problems of childhood, has preventive as well as therapeutic duties. In any group of cases appearing in a clinic operating in a socially enlightened community, there are always some to be studied with the definite purpose of anticipating and preparing for serious life situations before these situations have actually created problems or before the existent problems have increased.

Children who need sex instruction, but who have no disturbing sex problems, make up a large part of this general group. Such cases are not included in this series.

Sometimes, however, more complicated problems present themselves. There are seven cases in this series that seem best grouped together under the general heading:—"Preventive Psychotherapy."

*   *

To one who knew the first lad in this group and saw him meet a hard situation in so fine and healthy a way he is a most interesting case. He is one of those who give the psychiatrist and social worker encouragement and enthusiasm for their work.

Case No. 10

BENJAMIN ARTHUR

Benjamin was fourteen year old when I first knew him, two

22637   99

years ago. He was a strong, well-developed, robust lad, an active, sensitive boy with good ambitions and alert responses. On mental tests he rated as having average general ability.

The situation: Benjamin was first brought to the clinic for advice about arrangements for a foster-home and some very mild delinquency there. His unusual social history, coupled with the knowledge gained from an acquaintance with him in superficial rapport, seemed to point to a future crisis in his life that might easily overwhelm him.

His father, who had been a man of excellent character and reputation and a prominent member of church circles, had fallen in love with a young woman of excellent family, four years before his death. She bore him two children, of whom Benjamin was the elder. Shortly before the birth of the second child his wife had learned of the affair. The father, already repentant, obtained the wife's forgiveness. They were a childless couple, and the wife took Benjamin into the home as her own child. They moved into a new community, reared the lad in entire ignorance of the true facts of his birth, and kept from him the fact that he had a brother.

Financial reverses came. The father died. His wife continued to support both boys and to love and care for Benjamin, but she would never see the other child. The mother of the children never claimed them and passed entirely out of the situation long before I knew Benjamin. After the father's death the supposed mother took a position away from home, that she might be able to give the boy a good education. This made it imperative that he live in a foster-home. She saw him very frequently, however, and Benjamin was very loyal and affectionate towards her.

The supposed mother, whose health was very poor, had some property that she wished Benjamin and his brother (of whose existence Benjamin was ignorant) to share jointly at her death. She had relatives whom she believed would try to prevent this. She believed that Benjamin could not be legally adopted without being told of the true situation. She wished to be sure that he would have the property, but her whole life happiness was tied up in the boy and she felt that she would certainly lose him were he to be told the true facts.

Benjamin's case, then, was found to be a much more complicated psychiatric problem than that for which he was brought to the clinic. He had been very mildly delinquent in his foster-home.

Thinking about the boy: The more one *thought about* this fine, happy, but sensitive boy, the more one realized that he was soon to be facing a serious crisis in his life. It was felt that his mother could live but a short time.

Strangely enough, his greatest unhappiness was that he had no brother. He said that as he was now older, he did not mind not having one so much as he used to, but he believed that every boy was better and happier if he had a brother near his own age.

Complicating the problem, also, was the fact that, although Benjamin was as loyal as one could wish to his supposed mother, his greatest loyalty was to the memory of his father. He could not distinctly recall him, but he had been taught to respect his character and attainments and he was very proud of them.

Thinking for the boy: The problems for which he was originally seen were easily solved, but one could not stop there. He was seen several times and *thought about* very seriously, and a psychiatric plan was decided upon.

The mother came to consider the situation more seriously and said that if the clinic thought it best that she tell him the facts, she was willing to make the necessary sacrifices this would involve. It was established that the question of property could be handled safely without the lad's being told of his true parentage. Consultation with the mother's physician revealed that she had but a short time to live. The plan decided upon was for me to establish a deep rapport with this boy, to maintain it if possible until the time of his mother's death, and to be the boy's trusted friend—to be, in fact, the one to whom he would naturally turn in a crisis, the one who might influence his emotional responses.

Thinking with the boy: The earlier interviews made the establishment of a rapport of *personality contact* easily possible, and this was maintained through regular but not frequent interviews until the time of his mother's death, several months later. There was no man in the foster-home or in the boy's immediate environment whom he had learned to trust or to admire, which fact made the maintaining of the rapport easy and justifiable.

During the months before his mother's death adolescent sex problems came suddenly upon him through a group of supposedly excellent young people. He came to me with these problems early, and his emotional responses to them, and his sex feelings and his handling of temptations, were patterned after my attitudes and influenced by my instructions.

If, in a situation like this, one wishes to think of a child's responses in terms of mental mechanism, it is most easily thought of thus: the boy identified me with his father ideal and through this received pleasure in feeling about things in the same way that I did. He was in no way dependent upon me, but was made happy by the belief that I was proud of him, which was actually true.

He came to me often during his mother's last illness. A few days after her funeral, together we faced the fact that he must now be told.

It is impossible to describe the technique, if the word may be used, of such an interview. The technique, if one thinks of this as what is said, is not the important thing. It is *the rapport* existing between the psychiatrist and the patient that is the essential thing. Had a stranger or one with a negative or neutral rapport told the lad the unhappy truth he would have heard only this: "She whom I loved was not my mother. My own mother was bad. My father was not what I thought him, and they have cheated me out of my brother, who really is the one I wish I had loved." That was not what he heard from me, and it was not so much that *I pointed out* the love and sacrifices of those now dead as it was that *I, myself, saw it* in that way. He saw it in that way, too, because between him and me there existed that elusive but vital personality association that is so meaningful in human relationships. When we try to understand it and planfully to establish and to use it, we may call it psychiatric rapport.

Results: Benjamin came from that critical interview with a greater admiration for his father and a greater love and loyalty for his supposed mother than he had before. He came with forgiveness for his real mother, and an intense desire to see and to know his brother and to "make up for lost time" in his associations with him.

Nearly two years have passed since his mother's death. Benjamin and his brother are happy normal boys who mean a great deal to each other. Benjamin is making an excellent school record and is preparing himself for a useful life.

The boys come to see me informally occasionally and consider me their friend and adviser.

How is one to measure psychiatric success in such a case? It is hard to state that definite things have been accomplished or to prove that anything has been accomplished, for we cannot point back to an apparently wrecked personality and show how we reconstructed it. The boy says that had it not been for me, he believes he would never have understood and would never have been happy again after he had learned the things I told him. His friends who know him think that he has handled the hard situation well. They believe that this fine boy would be unlikely to have handled it in any other way. I, knowing the boy very well, as sensitive, intelligent, but immature, feel that preventive work was essential and outstandingly successful. Didactically described in a case report and statistically recorded, it might be classified differently.

*   *

The next two boys were brothers who were facing a most profound inalterable experience over which they had no control. The first one already had many mental problems of the greatest significance; the second had few. They make a very interesting contrast when considered therapeutically in the light of this difference between them.

It was so important to solve their one major problem that their delinquencies were not seriously discussed. In addition to the constructive help given them regarding their one problem, something else was accomplished. These boys found by experience that accepting a friendly and understanding person in their dynamic environment is a pleasant and helpful experience. It will be easier for others to help them from time to time, throughout their lives.

Case No. 11
JOSEPH LAKE

I have known Joseph Lake and his brother, Henry, for three years. When he was first seen, he was just thirteen. He was normally developed, though when first seen he gave the impression of being small for his age and older than he really was. He had the typical features of the Negro race; his skin was brown, but his hair was straight and the shape of his head in no way suggestive of his racial origin. He had good physical health, and his mentality was slightly above normal on age-level tests.

The situation: Joseph was first seen at the time of a tremendous crisis in his life, and his emotional responses to the crisis were even more profound than the situation was disturbing. We can describe only the high lights of this remarkable situation here. Joseph was the elder of two children of what was thought a legal marriage by everyone except the father. Recently it had come to light that the marriage was not legal. The father was an Algerian Negro of wonderful physique. He had a fair education and was an extensive reader. He was a leader among a considerable group, many of whom were not Negroes. Speaking Italian well and being a convincing talker, he was able to persuade many people that he was of Italian descent. He claimed to have been married four times and to be the father of twenty-seven children. Checking up on these statements showed that they were approximately true. The boy's mother, whom the father had always treated with excessive cruelty in every way, gave up a fine Italian home and severed all her racial connexions to run away with and, as she supposed, to marry this man, whom she continued to worship as much as she feared him. The family not only had been abused and poorly provided for by the father, but had been forced for many months to accept as a member another white woman who was this man's mistress. This unusual father had many unusual and cruel ways of inflicting punishment on his children. He was intelligent enough to know that for Joe mental suffering was the most torturing form of punishment, and this sensitive and intelligent lad had been made to suffer both physically and mentally beyond description. When I first knew Joseph, the law and society had taken active cognizance of the situation. The home was to be broken up and the children placed out in foster-homes. The problem we faced in the clinic was to help Joseph and his brother face the situation of leaving home. Both were refusing to do so. Joseph was literally willing to lay down his life rather than be separated from his father, his mother, and his home. He had been refusing to go to bed at night and would sit by the fire with his hat on nearly all night, deep in thought. When asked why he did so, he said he thought somebody ought to do some thinking. He was bitter and defiant in his attitude towards the social workers who were sincerely trying to help him. He was disagreeable and arrogant to the other members of his family. He would defend his father to others, but in his presence he would refuse, absolutely, to speak to him or to take off his hat.

Thinking about the boy: At first Joseph was unwilling to reveal anything of himself, his life, or his situation. He was decidedly on the defensive, suspicious, angry, depressed, and contemptuous. Three long interviews were held before any degree of rapport could be established. Resentful and bitter statements he made during this time made it perfectly clear that there was much for us to know about this boy's mental life if we were to help him. There were many theories of the causation of his present mental responses that could easily be elaborated from what was known of the boy and from what little he was saying.

Thinking for the boy: Excellently planned constructive *thinking for* Joseph had been done before I saw him. If a psychiatrist were to add anything to this planful thinking, he must *think with* him. How easy it is to find plausible theories of mechanisms when *thinking about* a child with such a situation and with similarly peculiar behaviour! And if one *thinks for* such a child on the basis of his theories only, how far from right one might be!

And so the first *thinking for* him, as far as my part of the plan was concerned, was the decision to establish, if possible, a deep enough rapport to enable me to understand the all-important "way he was feeling" about his life situation. I could not intelligently advise the type of foster-home or settle the question of whether or not the brothers should be placed together unless I were successful in this understanding of his mental life.

Thinking with the boy: The responses of this lad during his first two interviews with me were most unusual. He remained inaccessible in a manner that was distinctly suggestive of an early dementia præcox case. Finally, during the third interview, in some way, possibly because I was neither criticizing nor scolding the boy, the element of trust seemed to enter his feeling towards me. He began to ask questions and to tell me of his mental responses and to give me the superficial reasons for his behaviour. And at last Joseph came to believe that I understood in a way how he felt and how much his ideas meant to him. When this happened and he found that he had a friend who understood and did not condemn, a new kind of satisfaction came to him. Joseph then was in complete personality contact with me. He would easily have assumed the attitude of dependent attachment. Had the situation been such that I could have maintained the prolonged acquaintance necessary when a child is to be treated in this deep stage of rapport, I should have allowed this to occur, for it was justified in view of his great unhappiness and emotional upset.

There were many reasons why Joseph did not want his home broken up. Necessarily, in the complicated and unhappy situation he had handled his father-mother response in a very unhealthy way. He had early identified himself with his cruel and unusual father, but at the same time he had built up his loyalties entirely around his mother and her race. He seemed to have split his mental life in such a way as to give all his affection to his father and all his loyalties to his mother.

He hated and was jealous of his father. He had even thought of killing him because of his treatment of the mother. Nevertheless, he had invariably defended his father before others. He told me he would rather die than know he would never see his father again. He detested strangers and did not want to be among them. He said strangers had now entered his life and were disrupting it.

He told me finally, when he did not think I would be surprised or laugh at him and hoped that I would understand and give him encouragement, that he did not think himself a Negro. He considered himself Italian and wished—oh, so much!—that others would do so too. He did not want to be considered a Negro, partly because he liked Italian boys better, but much more because he wished to be a great musician and he wanted to be an Italian musician! He knew that if he were to be taken from his present situation, he must live among Negroes.

Despite the fact that from his earliest remembrance he had been denied in every way any responses from his environment to help him maintain this belief and desire, he had so distorted reality that he really believed himself to be an Italian and believed that some day he would be so accepted. He had shut himself away from his environment because of its unfriendliness all his life. After he had confessed these feelings and discovered that he was being neither laughed at nor discouraged in this hidden ambition, he became anxious to confide the remainder of his emotional life. Among other things, he said he had wondered if something might not be done to his skin so that he would not be so dark. He believed that if he were rich, this would be possible.

He thought he had known of his father's unfaithfulness to his mother long before his mother or the other members of the family knew it. He had lain awake at night and worried about it. He had tried to excuse his father's behaviour to himself. He had done all he could to conceal the facts from the rest of the family. He had reached the conclusion that he must assume the duties of the head of the family. Much of his misbehaviour in the family could be understood when this was known. He had hated his father's mistress, and, for fear that her true position in the family would be discovered, he had felt himself obligated not to let it be known. He liked Italian boys and wanted to be like them, but he hated them for refusing to accept him. He told of early sex traumas and of his present loathing for all sex things. He told of his desire for good clothes, which, since he could not have them, he attempted to deny by assuming an indifference to his appearance. He told of his hatred for his brother because the brother was willing to pass as a Negro and to play with Negro boys. He told of his resentment towards his brother for refusing to accept his authority. He told me of many other things, both in his environmental and in his mental life, that had always made him unhappy.

For most of Joseph's problems I had no solution. But I did not deny the validity of them nor did I make light of his impossible ideas about meeting and solving them. Sometimes I could tell him how I believed I should feel were I in his circumstances, in a way that would make him consider my statements; and because he had become loyal to me I could and did change his attitudes regarding some things.

I finally convinced him that first of all he must become a more happy boy, with more understanding friends, if ever he was to reach any of his goals or if ever he was in any way to help either his father, whom he loved, or his mother, to whom he was loyal. And I convinced him, not by arguments, but by making him believe that I myself believed that these things could be accomplished only by his accepting the sort of environment (living with his brother in a fine Negro family in a home some distance from Boston) that had towards the last of my treatment been selected for him.

I believe that that was all I accomplished except to make him know, when the treatment had to be broken, that he had a friend who partially understood how he felt about all his problems and sympathized with him.

The prognosis seemed bad; in fact, the case seemed so hopeless from a psychiatric standpoint that I was willing for the social adjustments to be made even though they removed the possibility of my seeing him further.

Results: A year later he was seen again. He was glad to renew old acquaintance. It was almost impossible to believe he was the same boy. He was happy! After the first few weeks in the new home there was no further misbehaviour. Last spring he won the marble championship of his city. He proudly displayed his medal. His school report was good. He was accepted as a leader by both the Negro and the white boys of his acquaintance. He and his brother got to be chums.

Who is to be given the credit? Probably the foster-parents first and his agency and visitor next. But when this lad was seen again, it was interesting to note the many things he remembered that were discussed with him during his short period of treatment and to see how thoroughly he accepted them as a part of his beliefs and of his mental life. He quietly told me that while he no longer considered it necessary to try to make others think he was Italian (he says he is happy and having a good time the way it is now), he still thought that some day he might become a great musician. When he does, he will be thought of as an Italian. One cannot be sure that this boy's problems are so well solved that he will adjust well to later life, but possibly they are. If psychotherapy afforded him anything beyond the therapeutic value of the actual confession, the bringing of his concealed emotions to the surface, and the consciousness of a friend who could understand him, it was this: it redirected his loyalties into more normal channels. As yet they are far from being of the sort that will carry him through to adult adjustments in the best way, but something has been accomplished. Joseph is still a very interesting boy to *think about*.

Joseph is still indulging in many mental suppressions, and he is avoiding many of his mental problems, such as his love for the undeserving father and loyalty to the mother, whom he now does not see and is in no way helping.

But if this lad goes on to a normal and well-adjusted life, how instructive it would be to know and understand the mental responses and adjustments that must, in a large measure, be responsible for his success!

It has not been possible for me to see this boy during the past year. His agency gives good reports of him. He is doing well in school, seems happy, and is well-behaved. This is very interesting when one considers the last developments in his brother's case, which is given next.

Case No. 12
Henry Lake

Henry is a brother of Case No. 11. The fact that Henry was five inches short for his twelve years was not so noticeable because of his good posture and good nutrition. His hair is fine and his features and the shape of his cranium are not Negroid, although he is of a typical quadroon colour. Mentally he is of about average general ability.

The situation: The physical situation is the same as his brother's. They have always lived together in the same home and under the same conditions. The critical situation in his brother's life had to be faced by this boy as well.

Thinking about the boy: The two boys presented a very interesting contrast. Henry was equally serious and sad over his family situation, but he was doing all he could, in every way he could, about it. He had thought it over and talked it over with others. He was co-operative towards the social worker who was trying to help the family. He, too, did not wish to lose his father and said that, as far as he was concerned, he would rather the old situation would continue, but he knew that it was not best for the others. He had been treated even more cruelly than the brother, but was willing to suffer this treatment if he could still have his father, of whom he was very proud. Henry, too, wished to be considered an Italian rather than a Negro, but at the same time he laughingly said that he "has found out that this does not work," and that there was no use trying to make his boy friends believe that he was anything but a Negro boy. He said that being part Negro helps in some ways. He was a good ball-player and believes that comes from the Negro part of him.

Altogether one was justified in calling Henry an "extrovert." He had normal interests in boys' activities. He was glad things were not worse than they were. He was planning on what he would do for his mother when he was old enough to work.

Comparing Henry with his brother and considering their entirely different responses to the same environment stimulate many theoretical questions.

How far back in the boys' life-histories would one need to go to find the determining factors that account for their difference in personality responses? Was there something innate in the boys which made the environment impress them in such different ways, or were these differences determined by differences in very early problems of life?

Thinking for the boy: The only constructive thing I believe could be done for Henry was negative. It was the decision to resist the temptation to explore this friendly, frank, co-operative, and unhappy boy's mind in search of dynamisms. A deep rapport could have been easily established. The boy was making a very good adjustment to a very bad situation. To require him to make a re-adjustment, which would probably be necessary if all the old mental struggles and unhappy situations were reopened, would be unnecessary and very likely harmful at this critical time.

Thinking with him: Henry's brother had told him about "the doctor who talked to you" and he trusted me before he had even come to the clinic. He was unhappy. Had I told him that I believed I could help him or even that I was very sorry for him, he would immediately have adopted a deep personality contact with me. The things we thought about were considered objectively and we talked little about how Henry felt about things. It seemed to me that he felt much better about them than I should have done under the circumstances, and so any idea or suggestion I might have given him about his emotional responses would have been of negative value.

Instead we thought much about things he might do now and in the future. I pointed out as many of his good characteristics as I could see and praised him for his successes. We discussed his personal habits and I answered his questions about them. We thought about his brother and some of his problems and planned some things that he might do to help Joseph.

Results: A year later the lad was seen again. He was doing very well in school and was a star on the baseball field. He is a happy little Negro boy who is proud that he is part Italian instead of a sad, little Italian boy, sorry that he is part Negro.

At this time Henry seemed to be successfully adjusted. This success was largely social of course. The psychiatrist aided only by giving advice and encouragement to the boy and to his social agency. It seems now that I should have gone deeper into the lad's problems. I have not seen the boy in the last year. I wish I might now have the opportunity to see and attempt to help him. His agency reports him at present to be rather seriously misbehaved sexually. However, he is of good material, considering his entire background, and some understanding person should, I believe, be able to help him.

While these two boys are now seemingly unequally adjusted and Henry is now the misbehaving boy, one feels strongly that Joseph's old problems are not so entirely liquidated as his brother's and that the final outcome, as far as a normal mental life is concerned, is much more precarious in Joseph's case than in his brother's.

*   *

The next lad's problems were simple and were met immediately after the situation developed. It is typical of what comes into nearly every tenement boy's life. If these problems are not understood at the time, they often make trouble later.

Case No. 13
BOBBIE THADDEUSKI

Bobbie Thaddeuski was a short, sturdy, healthy Polish boy of thirteen. He had a rather dull, downcast, apathetic expression, slouchy attitude, and hanging head. Mentally he was normal, but of poor general ability.

The situation: The lad lived in a tenement home with his uncle and aunt, who were in moderate but comfortable circumstances. He had been an orphan for seven years. He was reported as a good, usually happy boy who worked well. He obtained nearly all the fuel-supply for the family by collecting wood. The schools reported him well-behaved except on one occasion. Shortly before he was seen in the clinic, he had been caught exposing himself to the other boys in the schoolroom and had been expelled for this. There were no girls in the room, and the teacher was a man. He was referred to the clinic because his principal felt that he had perverted tendencies or that he was mentally ill.

Thinking about the boy: Bobbie was perfectly willing to tell his story, and this rather dull boy had no trouble in convincing me that he was telling the truth. He said he had borne the brunt of a good deal of rough, vulgar play and talk among the boys. He never liked the boys who did or talked about these things and never understood why they wanted to behave in this way. Recently there had been some quarrels and fights with these boys, arising over their attempts to expose Bobbie while playing on the school grounds. The other boys frequently exposed themselves in the schoolroom when the teacher was not looking, and they thought it was very smart and laughed at Bobbie for not doing it, also. On the day of the occurrence they had dared him to do it and threatened that if he did not, they would "beat him up" after school. He believed the easiest way out was to do it, and he was caught. Bobbie is slow, awkward, clumsy, and easily embarrassed, and it is easy to see why he was discovered. He was much upset about it, disgusted with the experience, and much ashamed that he had been dismissed from school.

Nothing in his history or in our interview led to the belief that he had mental problems or pervert tendencies, although he had been referred to the clinic as a probable mental case. *Thinking about* him led to the conclusion that *thinking for* him would solve his problems. Probably little *thinking with* him would be necessary or desirable. The plan of help included, of course, an interview with the school principal about such problems in general and about this boy in particular. This principal was shown how errors might easily be made in evaluating such behaviour in a thirteen-year-old rather dull boy. He was convinced that a thorough investigation of the situation should be made, and as a result of this, Bobbie was entirely exonerated from blame, reinstated in school, and put in a different group. He was happier in this new group, and some extra social and play activities were provided.

Thinking with the boy: During the time when his situation was being remedied, he was seen twice, and the rapport was one of *friendly belief.* At that time he was told that he would be welcome to return if he wished.

He voluntarily came back to the clinic on two or three occasions, and he came to have a feeling of personal trust in me. He lived in a neighbourhood with a rather depraved group of boys who had given him much sex teaching and had developed in him rather unfortunate emotional attitudes towards such subjects. These attitudes were discussed frankly with him. He had erroneous ideas of why his former behaviour was considered so seriously.

There was one other thing regarding which I *thought with* this boy. He had been told and had hoped that he might go through high school and thereby be able to earn more money when he grew up than he otherwise would. It was evident from our psychological study that this would not be possible, and I attempted to prepare him for the new plans he must make when he would later come to realize this. I told him how much people admired boys who were loyal to their homes and to their foster-parents, and praised him for his good habits of industry.

Results: The result has been all that could be hoped for. The boy had been in no more trouble when seen a year later. He liked his school, but is having hard work to keep up with his class. He said that he had been wanting to come to get advice about continuation school and work. He asked other questions of a personal nature in a way that made one feel that he would remember what he was told.

I have seen him again recently. He is a well-adjusted working boy, who feels that those in the clinic have been and still are his good friends.

Bobbie is a boy who had experienced few emotional crises in his life. The time of his life at which he was studied was therefore of great importance in patterning his emotional responses. The one who helped him to understand and meet it meant much to him. Help given to such a boy at such a time by an understanding friend is almost sure to be of constructive and permanent value.

*   *

The next boy is one of the most interesting children I have ever known. To understand how a lad has learned as well as Ned has to meet hard situations would be invaluable to those seeking to give personality help to children.

Case No. 14
NED WILLARD

Ned was fourteen years old. He was a tall, good-looking lad whose dark eyes always had a pleasant, sincere, and thoughtful greeting for everyone. He would be instantly noticed in a group. He was pre-adolescent in looks and physique, but adult in many of his responses. He was healthy, although somewhat underweight for his height. Mentally he was of average general ability.

The situation: Ned is the illegitimate son of a professional man who occupied a prominent place in his group. A complicated and unhappy family and social situation makes it impossible for this man to see the boy or even to support him. His mother is dead. She died from want and neglect when the boy was six years old. He was living with her until that time and nearly suffered the same fate.

Since that time Ned has been in four different foster-homes. To all of these he had made excellent adjustment except to the first, where he had been for several months before the agency took him. This was an unsupervised home, and he was abused, neglected, and allowed to be on the streets much of the time while he lived in it. Since this period of his life he had been a happy, helpful, and beloved child. He was never delinquent. His school record was excellent. Ned was seen because the clinic was asked for advice as how best to meet the particularly disturbing situation that had been discovered in his foster-home. This home had previously been thought to be ideal. (See Cases No. 15, 34, 46.) A homosexual man had lived in very intimate association with Ned's foster-family during the entire four years of his stay. It was not known how much Ned was involved in the affairs of this man, but it was known that the man had been very kind and helpful in many ways to the boy during all this time. It was feared by his visitor that homosexual acts had occurred and that the boy would be greatly disturbed by being separated from the man and from his home and by being told of the entire situation, all of which was socially necessary.

Thinking about the boy: The reading of the very excellent agency case record of this boy raised two very interesting questions to think about.

Early in life he had been deceived about his true situation, and he had not been told the truth about many things. There were social aspects that had seemed to make this necessary. One could be very sure that this sensitive and intelligent boy had been thinking of these things. He certainly remembered the disturbing circumstance of his mother's death. His treatment in the first home and his street life during this time could not have failed to leave some impression on him. Before coming to his present home, four years before, Ned had been in a fine foster-home, with a wonderful foster-mother. He had learned to love her dearly, and she had returned his affection. The foster-mother's health became very bad, and they had to be separated for this reason. Shortly before the time when the unfortunate occurrences in his last foster-home had been discovered, Ned had been assigned to a new visitor because of the agency's policy of assigning boys of Ned's age to the custody of a man. His visitor previously had been a woman who had known Ned for many years. He had felt bad about the change.

When thinking about all these things, I wondered how he had adjusted himself so well to them all and how he had developed into so fine a boy, despite his experiences with many things that so often spoil children's happiness and unfortunately condition personality traits. I wondered also whether he would continue to be normal and happy after this new tragedy in his life, and, if so, how he would do it.

Thinking for the boy: Everything considered, it seemed best for a psychiatrist to establish a rapport with him and be the one to tell him of the situation. This was important because of the necessity of obtaining a frank and truthful statement of the facts from the boy. The social and legal problems were not yet solved, and it was felt that, of all the boys involved in the home, Ned would be the most truthful and reliable. Also it was felt that possibly a psychiatric understanding of the lad would be of help to avoid any unfortunate mental reactions to the whole homosexual affair.

I went with the officers of the society, who, of course, were very much concerned about the situation, to the rather distant town where he lived. Fortunately I had met the boy on one former occasion when calling on another lad in the same foster-home. So it was easily arranged that Ned should accompany me on a little excursion and picnic lunch to the mountain while the agency officers spent the time studying other aspects of the situation.

Thinking with the boy: The time spent with Ned that day and on later occasions was very interesting. Within an hour he was in excellent personality contact with me and was seriously discussing his life and asking many questions about his future plans.

He was then told frankly the reason for my visit. He listened through it all with a serious but unafraid expression. His responses, after a moment of silence, were typical of the boy: "Gosh, I suppose that means I have got to move again and lose my home, and it means trouble for Mr. — too. He ought not to do those things. I thought he didn't so much any more, and I didn't know it was against the law." When it was explained to him that he owed it to himself and to the other boys to tell what he knew about the affair, he did so quietly and without much display of emotion. The way he had handled the homosexual situation was interesting, typical of all his behaviour and of his personality.

When he had first come to the home, the man, who certainly had felt a sincere friendship for this boy, aside from his abnormal sex attraction for him, had taken occasion to sleep with Ned and had tried to have him respond to his advances. The boy's earlier experiences in the slums of the city had taught him in a general way of such things, and he had been neither shocked by the man nor responsive to him. He had told the man that he did not like such things, that they hurt him and made him feel bad afterwards; and he had asked him not to do them. This request had been granted, but the friendship and helpfulness of the man for Ned had been continued. This man had taught Ned the use of tools, had encouraged him to save money, and had frequently assisted him with his school-work.

Ned said he had thought about these things from a standpoint of health always. He believed them to be common. At different times he had warned the various boys who had been in the home against them because he thought they were unhealthy, for he knew from his earlier experiences and from things that he saw that they must have happened with other boys. Ned said that had he known that they had been considered criminal, he would have warned the man.

At the close of this trying day of our acquaintance Ned made a statement that I shall never forget. I congratulated him on behaving in so manly a way and told him he was worthy of the best traditions of the Boy Scouts, in which organization he was an active member. He said: "Well, I guess I just always am lucky, after all. Here I've lost the best man friend I ever had, but at the same time I've got two new ones now, for I have both you and Mr. H. [the new visitor]."

The question of whether or not he would continue to be normal and happy was very easily answered, even before this first interview was over, and some light was also thrown on the question of how he did it. Ned meets his problems exactly as he finds them, and as soon as he has met them, he commences to lay plans as to what he will do to solve them. And he searches for new loyalties when he needs them.

Later this boy was frankly told that he might help other boys and girls by trying to help me understand how he had always been a well-behaved and happy boy and how he had learned to make so many friends. I still see him occasionally and he says he remembers that statement. I thought with him about a number of things, at his request, not, however, as a psychiatrist usually must think with a boy, but rather as a normal father should think with a normal child.

That a true personality contact was established between us is shown by the fact that a few months later he told his visitor that he wanted to know all the facts of his parentage and early life. He asked to be allowed to come to see me, that I might be the one to tell him what he wanted to know. When this had been done, Ned said that it was much the hardest experience of his life. He had known for a long time that he must go through it, but earlier when he wished to know about his parentage, he had decided that probably it was better to wait until he was older before asking to be told the truth.

Results: The results are, of course, excellent in this case. To describe his adjustment and happiness in his new home would sound too much like the last chapter of an old-fashioned novel. The psychiatrist and social worker did the work they were supposed to do, at the time when it was necessary, but in this simple case they deserve no special credit for results obtained. The credit all goes to Ned and to those who early in his life helped him meet and understand his environment.

It was largely through Ned's story and because of his attitudes and wishes that it was possible to deal psychiatrically rather than legally with the homosexual man in the situation.

(Because of the absence of any serious psychotherapeutic problem, this case is reported very briefly. This boy is still being observed and studied very intensively, not because he needs any help, but because I feel that much may be learned from the understanding of the normal as well as the abnormal mental responses. It happens that three other serious environmental and emotional episodes have occurred in this boy's life during the year that has elapsed since the case report given above was closed. All of these crises have been of the sort that often spoil a child's adjustment to life. But they have not spoiled Ned. I wish to know, as well as I may, why they have not done so.)

Case No. 15
BERNARDO POLUSO

Bernardo Poluso was thirteen years old when I first knew him in the clinic, almost four years ago. He was first seen, not as a problem boy, but in connexion with his brothers, Cases No. 34 and 46.

He was an unusually attractive, alert, serious boy of superior mentality. He was taking the responsibility of a man. Physically he was below normal generally, because of poor nourishment and excessively long hours of work before and after school.

The situation: The family situation, one almost as bad in every way as can be imagined, is described under his brothers' cases. Bernardo was not delinquent and was in no way a social problem, but, in a sense, he was a problem from a psychiatric standpoint; for it would certainly add to the psychiatrist's useful knowledge to know why and how this boy was handling his situation so well when his brothers were responding to exactly the same environment with serious social and psychiatric problems.

Of the three lads Bernardo was the most thoughtful and sensitive. One would expect him to feel the disgrace of the family's behaviour and economic situation more acutely than the others. He had the best ambitions, worked hardest, and was kind to and thoughtful of others. He was most often unjustly punished; yet he was in no way poorly adjusted, whereas his brothers were.

Thinking about the boy: Bernardo was seen frequently, as his co-operation was needed for the social and psychiatric treatment of his brothers over a period of several months. I *thought about* him as well as I could, knowing him only as a friend and acquaintance, and tried to understand why he was neither bad nor seemingly unhappy. From theoretical thinking alone one was almost forced to the conclusion that the lad must be ignoring the emotional side of the family's problems and that he must be really indifferent to the many unhappy situations.

Thinking for the boy: The agency that was interested in his brothers knew him also, and they planned for him to spend a few weeks as visitor in the home of his brother, Case No. 34, who was living under supposedly ideal conditions in the country. Here Bernardo was exposed to the same unfortunate situation as his brother and another lad. (See Cases No. 14 and 34.) The boys had been for a considerable period in close association with a homosexual man who had in many ways befriended them. The agency visitor felt that Bernardo should be taken as a psychiatric case with the idea of helping him to liquidate that experience.

Thinking with the boy: It was easy enough for me to establish a personality contact with Bernardo. I felt justified in doing this under the circumstances, for here was a lad with many environmental difficulties to face, who might be developing unknown harmful responses to the unfortunate experience to which he had been subjected.

When Bernardo reached with me the rapport where he wanted me to understand him and to know all his feelings and secrets, I was able better to understand his mental life and his usual way of meeting his problems. I found that he was in no way ignoring or failing to appreciate his unhappiness and the things to which he must adjust his life and responses. He told me of many more which I did not know.

He constantly had to realize how his brothers, who were making so much trouble and unhappiness for others, were being, in a way, rewarded for this by good foster-homes, good food, and a quiet life, while he, who was doing so well, must be in the unhappy home situation, with all its hard work and discomforts. In fact, he was working many more hours than anyone supposed and giving all the money to the family. He would not do otherwise because he felt it was dishonest. He was refused any money to buy clothes and the needed things for school because the father insisted on believing that Bernardo was "holding out" ample amounts from the money he earned to supply himself with these things.

In the family he was ridiculed for his ambition to go through the Mechanics Arts High School and was constantly told that he must go to work as a day-labourer as soon as he was old enough. He had been frequently punished for complaining that his younger brothers told lies to protect themselves. There were many similar things like this in his life.

How had he survived all these things without either becoming delinquent or developing mental conflicts?

Early in my acquaintance with him, when I needed co-operation in helping his brothers overcome excessive sex habits, I had talked with Bernardo as his friend and adviser about his own sex habits. He remembered these things and developed new loyalties to ideals of good health and a normal life. He said that when he experienced homosexual advances in his brother's foster-home, he remembered what he had learned and what he had decided at the time about taking care of himself. He tried not to respond emotionally to the advances of the homosexual man, but to a certain extent he had done so at first. He did not report them and he blamed himself for this. He knew he should have done so to protect his brother, but this vacation was the first one he had ever had and he was afraid to risk spoiling his outing and returning home so soon.

The experience through which he had passed had been a rather serious one. It was necessary to talk the whole thing out very freely with the boy. It was essential that he really understand his own emotional response, and he must be told facts about such abnormalities in a way that he could understand. The person who helps a boy to do these things must be, if they are to be done wisely, in good rapport with him, the same rapport, in fact, that wise and understanding parents have with their children in the serious hours of their associations.

This lad was not harmed because he was loyal to his ideals. This capacity for loyalty explains all his behaviour. He was very loyal to his undeserving father and to his vacillating mother, to his disloyal brothers, and even to his unhappy environment, and he received his satisfaction in life from these loyalties themselves.

He became, of course, loyal to me after the personality contact was established, and later, through this loyalty, I was able to help him handle what came very nearly being an impossible situation for him. This situation was brought about when his parents severed connexions with the agency that had done so much for them. It was hard for Bernardo to maintain his loyalties both to the agency and to his parents, but he managed to do it for a considerable period of time under very trying circumstances.

Still later (I have been his friend and adviser ever since I first knew him), new and harder problems came. He was finally taken out of the most unhappy situation at a time when it became impossible for him to hold his loyalties to his undeserving father any longer. These had meant too much in his first good adjustments for him to discard them in a healthy way. He developed many undesirable personality traits. He enjoyed making his brothers unhappy by asserting his superiority, in looks, athletic ability, and past record, and thus created the hardest problem one of his brothers has had to solve. He seemed to be lazy. He seemed to reject his religious beliefs and his standards of morality. Many hours have been spent with Bernardo, more than with any other boy in the series.

Results: But it has all been worth while. He is now sixteen years old and one of the finest boys I have ever known. He will be an outstanding man who will do much to add to the happiness of others as well as make a success of life in the broadest meaning of the words. He is loyal, kind, industrious, and happy. It is well that these things are true, for his younger brothers and sisters are going to need just that kind of an older brother.

What does a psychiatrist do for a boy with such problems that a parent cannot do? Nothing, provided the parent has as much patient understanding as the psychiatrist's training and experience give him. Nothing, provided the parent can disassociate his own problems from those of the boy and look at the world and its experiences through the boy's eyes. But what more important task can the parent or the psychiatrist have?

Case No. 16
CARL EDRO

Carl was first known to the clinic about two years ago. He was a healthy, well-developed, mature boy of almost sixteen. He had fair average mental ability on age-level tests.

Throughout the two rather long interviews that we held with this boy, he was worried and unhappy. He was friendly and frank, but he was never quite sure that he was right to be trusting us.

The situation: The boy was complained of for indecent exposure. Carl was an accomplished musician. He played the violin very well, taught privately, and was the youngest member of a very good orchestra. He was reported to be pleasant and friendly, but fairly solitary. He had few friends and no close ones. He took little exercise, and next to his music his greatest diversion was cheap detective and adventure stories of the Dick Merriwell and Nick Carter type. He had never been encouraged to help in the home or to take much interest in the family affairs because the family wanted him to concentrate on his musical education, which had been started early. He saved his money and already had several hundred dollars towards advanced musical study.

His friends and family thought him a boy of most excellent habits until he was arrested for indecent exposure.

Thinking about the boy: The boy's situation in the light of his mode of living and personality traits was easy to understand. He told his story freely. To be helped out of his difficulties he would have been willing to tell it in the same straightforward way to anyone who would listen without being shocked or disgusted. His behaviour seemed less serious when reported in this frank manner than in vague and ambiguous terms, as it had been in the reports we received in the clinic.

This large, well-developed boy had only recently learned the most elementary sex facts and had only recently learned of solitary sex habits. He had reached adolescence before having any conscious sex drive. He had reacted by much ideation in regard to these things. About three months before the interview, he had one day discovered that a number of older girls who ate their lunch in a room across the court from his room were surreptitiously watching him as he changed his clothes. His curtains were so arranged that they could not see his face, though he could observe them. Carl was much excited by their giggling and apparent pleasure while they were observing him. This incident had started a series of similar ones every few days, over a period of two or three months. Carl became more bold in exposing and exhibiting his body, and he showed signs of sex excitement when the girls were watching him. He had never spoken to any one of the girls.

Charges were preferred by the girls only when they were discovered by their superintendent while enjoying watching the boy. It was evident that the charges had then been made to prevent the revelation of their part of the drama.

Thinking for the boy: This boy needed intelligent instruction to help him to understand himself and to meet his situation. The most important question to be decided in thinking for Carl was whether or not there were real indications of perverse tendencies. This conclusion had evidently been drawn by others. Careful investigation of the incidents showed that there was no reason to think he had any abnormal sex tendencies.

Thinking with the boy: This boy quickly came to believe that I was his friend and that I could explain a lot of things he needed to know. Among these was the reason for everyone's making such a fuss about what had happened. He had at no time considered it anything but crude play and was distressed to find that the family considered themselves very seriously disgraced by his behaviour. But, as previously stated, throughout the interviews he never came to trust me fully and one could easily tell that he was labouring under some doubt as to whether or not he was acting wisely in so frankly discussing his behaviour and emotional life.

It did not seem necessary to establish a deeper rapport with Carl than that of friendly belief, for even though this lad had suddenly been made to feel himself almost a social outcast and was very unhappy about it, there had as yet been little alteration in his personality in an attempt to adjust himself to these new experiences.

Together we discussed adolescent sex problems very freely. We decided that, while he was not altogether to blame for his foolish behaviour, it was best for him to accept the blame and not try to make others look at it differently. We decided that he should face the whole matter squarely and accept probation as a good if not a necessary thing and to co-operate with the probation officer. We discussed how necessary it is for boys and men who are following artistic careers to have other interests to make them well balanced, healthy, and happy. Especially we talked about the desirability of physical exercise and a healthy rugged body and about the foolishness of too much day-dreaming. These were reported as rather crude and childlike thoughts about robbery, Indian fighting, and the like. We talked of directing his imagination and reading habits into other channels that might be creative and of their nature, such as composing music or helping others to artistic attainments who were less favoured than he.

We finally decided that it would be best for him to be entirely frank with his probation officer, who was a man of good understanding and socially minded. The probation officer proved to be very helpful and he continued this understanding relationship with Carl for the several months covered by his probation.

Results: Carl has been helped much by his friendships thus established. There has been no more misbehaviour of this or any other type. Probably the original experience would have been enough to have prevented this. His interests are more normal; he has become quite loyal to some athletic interests that were established through his friendship with the probation officer.

The important thing is that this sensitive and high-strung boy could very easily have repressed his emotions at the time of his crisis, and consequently have withdrawn more into himself by denying the reality of other people's beliefs. Thereby he might have laid the foundation for abnormal mental life. Frank facing of the situation and the much needed instructions prevented this.

Three years have elapsed. He is making excellent progress in his musical education, has good friends, both boys and girls, and is still saving his money and will soon be able to go to Europe for musical study.

This case illustrates the fact that sometimes important psychotherapy may be given in a state of superficial rapport. It is probable that had this particular boy been seen at a later period, a very much deeper rapport would have been necessary to accomplish the same results. Psychotherapy without doubt did much for this boy. Most of the treatment was given by the intelligent probation officer, who occasionally consulted with the psychiatrist. It is not a case that one can say for sure would not have solved itself without expert help, but if the initial attitude—namely, that the boy was a "sex pervert"—had been maintained by those seeking to help him, it is very likely that much damage might have occurred to his mental life and emotional responses.

CHAPTER VII

LACK OF LOYALTIES

The Child with No Hero and No Good Ideals

OYS or girls are more often bad, unhappy, or unsocial because they have no reason to be otherwise than because they have a positive reason to be as they are.

How important it is for every child to have friends and loved ones to whom he is loyal! There are few who ever learn the most necessary lessons of life without loved and responsive individuals to help them, or who continue to put in practice these lessons after they have been learned if they lose or throw away the places they hold in the hearts of their friends. And how many of the hard adjustments of life can be made, and life still remain worth while, if good loyalties to other people exist! Loyalties to ambitions and ideals are for many adults enough to maintain socially good behaviour and some degree of happiness. This is not often true of children.

Many of the boys discussed in this book have needed loyalties badly. Many more than the five cases reported in this chapter would never have been "problem" boys had they had these loyalties. The cases grouped together here represent the five boys who of the entire group were most seriously handicapped in this way, and quite naturally one might expect to find a large percentage of failures.

Three of the five boys in this group, the first, third, and fourth, failed to receive constructive help in the treatment. With the other two, excellent results were obtained. If loyalties can be developed, success results. If they cannot, nothing is accomplished.

* *

The first boy is typical of a considerable group of older children seen in any child-guidance clinic. They are difficult to help and very hard for a psychiatrist to understand or treat because their habits of shutting others out of their lives make the establishment of rapport a very difficult matter.

Case No. 17
GODFRIED JOB

Godfried Job was first known in the clinic three years ago. He was a short, stocky boy of fifteen. He was healthy, robust, and freckled. His expression was depressed and serious. Intelligence tests rated him as having fair average ability.

The situation: Godfried was a neglected child. For years he had been such literally, although it was only two years before the time he was seen in the clinic that he became one officially. His mother was a drug addict. His father was dead. Other members of the family, all of whom are in poor circumstances, had tried to keep Godfried and had failed. Later, after he was taken by an agency, several good supervised homes were also unsuccessful in helping the boy.

Although the report of Godfried's characteristics seemed unusual and mixed, all the reports from various homes and at various periods were quite similar. Godfried was affectionate, fond of little children, generous, and very faithful in keeping promises. He was honest in money matters. He would lie to get out of trouble, and he was quick-tempered. He was indolent, lazy, and shrewd in avoiding work. He was sly, though he seemed frank. He was fearless, quarrelsome, and grouchy. He was a day-dreamer, did not forget grudges, and was apt to take revenge long after a supposed injury. He had received very little good training, lived much on the streets, and was reported to have bad companions. When I first knew him, he had not been seriously delinquent in any way except that frequently he had run away from foster-homes. From these runaways he would often return voluntarily.

Thinking about the boy: Godfried was a boy with unusually disturbing and peculiarly grouped ambivalent personality traits. He had made a poor adjustment everywhere he had been, although some of the places had been very good. In each of his foster-homes it was the *kind* of boy Godfried was, not what he did, that caused the trouble. No one understood him, and very few liked him who knew him well.

Theoretical *thinking about* him was not fruitful even of theories. One might say in general terms that lack of training and his early environment probably accounted for his unfortunate responses, but his peculiar personality possibly pointed to something in his mental life which it would be constructively helpful to understand. To be superficially acquainted with him was to like him, and everyone who knew him felt he would be a fine lad if it were not for his antagonistic and disagreeable attitudes.

Thinking for the boy: Largely because intelligent superficial psychiatric study and faithful social work had failed to help Godfried, it was thought justifiable to attempt to establish a rapport deep enough to explore his mental life. Even if nothing were found that seemed to be upsetting or that could be helped by psychiatric efforts, that exploration would doubtless aid in his social adjustments.

Thinking with the boy: Two psychiatrists had seen him in the clinic before I knew him. Both felt that the interviews with him were unsatisfactory and unproductive.

He came to the clinic five times for treatment. On one of these occasions he hid in the hall until the time of his appointment had passed. He had promised to come, and he did so, but took this way of avoiding the interview.

During the first interview he was talkative and boastful, but he became rather serious, and it seemed that he was going to become friendly. He was frank at this time, though he was not questioned about his deeper problems. He said enough, however, to make me feel that there probably were conflicts in his mind that he half wished and half dreaded to talk about. I believed that a good rapport would develop and made an appointment for the next day.

It is not possible to say what happened. I do not believe it was due to personal dislike, but probably more to a fear or a distrust reaction. In the first interview he had gone far enough to know what would happen if he allowed himself to trust me and talk frankly with me. He decided not to do it.

Though I tried hard, I did not again come so near to establishing a positive rapport with Godfried as I had done on the first day. As further efforts were failures, I felt there was danger of his becoming antagonistic, and so the attempt to understand and to help him was abandoned.

Results: A year and a half later the agency's reports still show that the boy's responses to his environment are gradually becoming worse. He has been in some trouble with the police over minor affairs. He changes jobs and homes often and is never satisfied.

The case is a complete psychiatric failure, probably because the attempt to establish rapport was not successful. We can guess that he would have been a difficult boy to help had this rapport been established, but we cannot be sure of this. This boy, with his excellent abilities, will be a distinct loss and probably a liability to society unless he is helped.

Godfried had never learned how to give himself, or how to take others into his life. This was probably the reason he did not respond to efforts to establish rapport. The art of making friends and trusting them should be learned early in life. When one remembers how necessary are one's own loyalties towards other people and ideals, it is easy to see how any child, and especially one without a real home, may fail to respond to life in a normal way if he does not have them. Many of the failures of life, both in children and in adults, failures so complicated with peculiar or delinquent behaviour that they may seem to be based on a much more complicated mental response, are the direct result of the failure to become loyal to any person, ambition, or ideal.

*   *

The next lad and his problems are not easily described. He is one of the boys whose failure to have loyalties has not been due to failure to do his part, but because in his environment and in his mental life there have been no people and ideals to which good loyalties might be attached.

Case No. 18
Herbert Eilers

Herbert, a healthy, active, erect, and alert little boy of ten was first known to the clinic three years ago. He was considerably over-active, and sometimes his over-activity seemed unmotivated. Mentally, on age-level tests, he was given a superior rating.

The situation: Herbert was an unloved child. His father and

mother had quarrelled when he was three, over the parentage of
his little sister. Earlier, before the parents separated permanently,
there had been a temporary separation, with much strife as to
who should have custody of the boy. Both the mother, who was
supposed to have the custody of Herbert, and the father, who was
supposed to support him, had failed in their duties. His mother
had died a few months before I knew Herbert, and he lived with
his invalid maternal grandfather, whose income was very meagre.
Earlier Herbert's older sister had been a member of the family.
She committed suicide shortly after she was sent to a school for
delinquents. The true facts of her death had been kept from Herbert
and he believed her to have been accidentally killed. Herbert's
life had been spent mostly on the street. He had learned to steal
and to dispose of stolen property for others. He was very skilfully
truant. A few months before I knew him, he had been placed in
a truant school while on probation to the juvenile court. Here
his behaviour had for a time been better, but later, through a series
of unfortunate temptations and opportunities, the bad behaviour
had recurred. He had not only stolen, but destroyed property,
truanted, and run away from his foster-home. His habits were
known to be bad. He slept and ate irregularly, smoked excessively,
and practised masturbation.

Thinking about the boy: Despite all these things Herbert said
he was happy and he really seemed to be. His only interests were
in his delinquency and he knew no others. He said that as soon
as he had been restrained from delinquency in the truant-school,
he had become much more unhappy than he ever had been in
his former neglected situation.

He had never had anyone who really loved him and he loved no
one, nor was he loyal to anyone. He thought his parents had never
really cared for him, and his grandfather was old and feeble and

paid him but little attention. Many people he knew *liked* him and he *liked* them. This boy was entirely frank with anyone who talked to him. He seldom lied even to the policemen who apprehended him in his delinquencies. He told his story and reported his emotional experiences in the first interview exactly as he did later when a deep rapport had been established. One came easily to believe that Herbert was probably leading a very normal mental life despite the difficult things that had happened to him, but his behaviour was very far from normal.

Thinking for the boy: Herbert was an interesting lad, who would, without doubt, always live an active, dynamic life. The problem was to direct this activity along more normal channels. There was little reason to believe that mental conflicts played any large part in his problem. It was easy to understand why he behaved as he did, when I put myself in the boy's place and looked at life through his eyes. To explore his mental life merely for the purpose of searching dynamisms would be feeble justification for establishing a deep rapport; but there was another and much better reason for doing this. As a result of his unhappy early experiences, Herbert had formed the habit of shutting people out of his deeper environmental values, although he had accepted them superficially into his life.

He really had no knowledge of the good things of life, either by precept or by experience, no good ideals of his environment to which he might become loyal. What Herbert most needed was someone towards whom he could develop a genuine loyalty and trust. That person could transfer these loyalties to others and thereby lay the foundation for a much more normal life. When I considered Herbert's history and his story, the problem seemed serious enough to justify the attempt to establish a deep rapport for therapeutic reasons. Herbert was a frank, talkative, dynamic lad, selfishly in search of new experience. He had met few people who did not withdraw from him when he offered himself in his search for new emotions. He could make friends easily, but because he was selfish, he could never keep them. His habits of begging, his entirely insincere promises, and his inconsiderateness soon lost him any friendships he established.

As soon as he found that our new acquaintance was proving a new experience, he became interested. He had found someone who was interested, not in his misbehaviour, but in how he felt about it and in what prompted it. In his harum-scarum way he had been thinking about this himself, and he had some questions to ask. When he came to trust me to the point where he dared discuss it freely, to his surprise and pleasure he was neither scolded nor rejected. When he did talk freely, he gave me his philosophy of life and his reaction to his experiences in a way that convinced me that he had no conflicts in his mental life. He was doing something to meet his situation as he saw it, and he knew why he was doing it. He did not *have* the good things of life, so he was going to *get* them if possible. Pretending that he liked people brought him pleasure and obtained for him things that he wanted. Hating his father, whom he had not seen for four years, made him unhappy, so he only pretended to do that when in his family. He had been taught to hate his father by his grandfather, and by his mother, too, before she died. It was easier to pretend that he was still doing it. But he was thinking of running away, of finding his father, and of asking his permission to live with him. He said that he wanted to do this because his father had a lot of money and would buy him things.

The psychiatric problem with Herbert was not to make him understand how he felt about things, but to make him actually feel differently about them. Scoldings had failed, punishments had failed, and attempts at control had failed. The boy came to believe that I liked him none the less for his misdeeds or for the selfish reasons behind them, though he knew very well my opinions of these things. He believed that I was loyal to him and he soon became as loyal to me as any normal child should be to his parents. This loyalty brought him a new kind of happiness.

He would ask many questions about how I felt when I was a boy and what I thought a boy ought to do. He said: "Does that boy who was just here steal?" It happened that the boy did not. "Do you like him better than you do me?" I explained to him that the boy's good behaviour was certainly a factor in his favour; that though I did not like him any better than I did Herbert, I did not think the other boy was tempted to steal, because he had a mother whom he loved and who would be made very unhappy if he did such things. Herbert thought about that and brought up the subject the next day.

After we had been friends for two weeks, it was learned from social reports that Herbert was staying home evenings and reading to his grandfather. I asked him where he had been the evening before. He said: "Grandpa was alone and I stayed with him." He was reminded that he had earlier said that this was not his job and that he was not going to do it. He said: "I thought maybe you would like me better if I did."

This part of the treatment was comparatively easy. Any man who has thought about children and who has not forgotten how life looked to him when he was a child could have accomplished the same temporary results. The real psychiatric task was to find some understanding person in the boy's environment and to help the boy transfer his newly developed loyalties to that person.

Social investigation of his father was made. The reports were very good and the father was asked to come for an interview. He had many difficult emotional problems of his own. Earlier in his life, in order to solve these, he had deliberately avoided this lad and had tried emotionally to deny his existence. He had remarried. He was a lonesome man, and he finally became interested in the boy and anxious to help him. After seeing him twice I was sure enough of my ground to be able to do some very serious *thinking with* Herbert about fathers and what they meant to boys, in the way of real happiness. We talked about fathers who sometimes had very good reasons for seemingly neglecting their children. And he was made really to understand his father's situation. The most touching incident I have seen in connexion with any of this series of cases happened in my office when these two first met.

The boy, not recognizing his father, was allowed to become acquainted and to visit with him in his friendly way for a little while. Something made him suspect that it was his father, and he came to me and whispered: "Is that my dad?" When he was told that it was, he rushed to his father with inexpressible sincere joy and happiness in his face. Very conveniently another little boy arrived for an interview at this time, and as the two left to walk in the park, it was significant that Herbert did not inquire how long the other boy would occupy my time, as he usually did under similar circumstances. The next day the father again met him at the office at the time I ordinarily gave to Herbert and I did not see the boy.

Only two or three other interviews were necessary in this boy's treatment. There seemed to be no tendency for him to hold to his old feeling of dependence and attachment towards me, and his visits soon ceased altogether.

Results: Herbert was seen recently for the first time in more than a year. He was very glad to renew the acquaintance, but showed very little tendency to display affection. The year had been a happy one. He had not been dishonest. He had done well in school. He was enthusiastic and happy about many normal and boyish things.

He had lived for a month with his father, but the social situation would not permit this permanently. A very fine foster-home was obtained for the boy, and the boy's loyalties seemed shared between his father and his foster-mother. Now Herbert makes friends who remain his friends. He seems to have learned that to be loyal to others brings the best returns in happiness.

Herbert's case is a success, from both a psychiatric and a social standpoint. Neither psychiatry nor social study could have succeeded independently. Without the personality help social efforts would have been of no avail. Personality changes would have accomplished *something*, even though his environment had remained the same, but the final success in its present form could have evolved only from the combined efforts of social and psychiatric help.

It seems to me that a psychotherapeutic technique such as was used for Herbert is a major procedure. As in any other major procedure in medicine or in surgery, the results, if they are obtained, may be expected to be definite and far-reaching. In my opinion, had this boy met his father without first learning through his experience with me that real loyalties and genuine affection brought happiness, his father would have meant only another person to do things for him.

*　　　*

The next boy is one on whom a very great deal of social and psychiatric treatment has been done. Why such boys have failed to develop a trust in and a loyalty to anyone is very difficult to determine. They must take at least one person into their lives if they are going to want, or ever to be able, to tell of their emotional life.

Case No. 19
CHARLES JONES

The Judge Baker Foundation has few older, better-known patients than Charles. In the clinic he has been known from the time
he was a healthy little boy of seven and a half years, weighing
fifty-two pounds, until the present, when he is a young man of
eighteen, well-developed, healthy, and of good appearance. The
mental tests given at various times during these nine years have
always been consistent and have shown him to be somewhat supernormal in general ability.

The situation: Charles's father and mother died when he was two
years old. Until the age of seven he lived in various unsupervised,
usually undesirable homes; part of this time he spent with relatives. When he was seven, he was taken by a child-placing agency,
and he has been with them ever since. During the subsequent years
he has been in fifteen different foster-homes. At present he is in a
private school for "behaviour problem" children. His personality
has always been an important part of the agency's problems. He
has never been confiding or affectionate towards anyone in his
environment. He has been bold and forward, always seeking to
assert himself and to attract attention. He quarrels readily and has
no close friends; his ambitions are never high, and until two
years ago they had been very changeable. Since that time he has
insisted that he wants to join the Army.

Because of these personality traits he has, of course, adjusted
very poorly to all of the many schools he has attended. He frequently
gets into minor delinquencies in these schools and in his foster-
homes. Occasionally he has stolen small sums of money and quite
frequently has been in trouble for petty stealing from shops and
stores.

Thinking about the boy: When I first saw Charles, two years and a half ago, very extensive social, mental, and psychological studies were available. Four different psychiatrists had seen the boy and given opinions as to his problems and emotional life. Psychiatrists and agency visitors had made various attempts to study his emotional and mental reactions and to influence his personality traits. All the reports stressed the fact that Charles was cross and self-pitying. All of these contacts temporarily improved the boy's *behaviour*, but none of them succeeded in effecting a change in his unfortunate personality traits.

At three different times in his life he had had unfortunate sex experiences. The first had been with an older boy who had taught him masturbation. The next had been in the nature of a homosexual attack by a young man, which the boy probably had experienced quite willingly. The third came soon after this in the form of another homosexual experience with another older man. Following these affairs he had expressed much bitterness about them to other psychiatrists; he had told of them frankly, and he had been quite willing that the young men involved should be punished. One of the men was actually committed for the offence.

After the last experience his sex habits had been overcome, but he frequently took refuge in these as explanations for his misbehaviour and for his poor adjustment in his foster-homes. No change in his personality traits resulted from his improvement in habit behaviour.

When Charles was about nine, in one of his first supervised foster-homes, he made the only genuine attachment he had known in his life's experience. This attachment was for his foster-mother, who was kind and good to him. It was largely through her influence that he overcame many of his sex habits, and she handled the situation during the most serious one of his sex affairs. Later he was accused by this same foster-mother of wanton destruction of property in the house, and although he denied this most earnestly to the psychiatrist in the clinic and to others, the foster-mother refused to believe that he was innocent, and he lost her affection and finally his home. Later it was learned definitely that the boy did not do the things of which he had been accused. A reconciliation was never effected. The boy insisted that she had mistreated him and should apologize. Following this occurrence Charles's troubles and disagreeable character traits all became worse and he added to them laziness and a very definite tendency to brag. He also developed a dislike for school and a contemptuous attitude towards all who tried to help him. He allowed others to believe him guilty of sex activities with girls and of other delinquencies of which he was actually innocent. He took pleasure in telling his best friends about his wicked behaviour, most of which was conveniently fabricated.

Before losing his best foster-home he had expressed a distaste for being aided by charity organizations and had some desire to earn part of his own way. Since then he has been a chronic and successful applicant for various forms of charitable help.

These are only some of the high lights on the unhappy life of a high-strung, sensitive, spoiled, but withal likable boy.

The multiplicity of his problems, and the infinite variety in the detail of his emotional responses, made definite *thinking about* him impossible.

Thinking for him: When I first knew this boy, he had been refused further shelter in a foster-home which he had liked as well as he had ever liked a home, excepting the one he had lived in when he was nine, and he had recently been expelled from a school that he liked as well as he liked any school. This had not been because of any definite act of delinquency, but because of his upsetting behaviour and his irritating responses to every situation.

He was thoroughly unhappy, discouraged, and sorry for himself; but through the influence of a patient and loyal agency visitor, and of Dr. Healy, who had long taken an interest in him, this boy had now reached the place where he said he was willing to co-operate in anything that would change his situation for the better. His desire was based largely on a selfish feeling of wanting to get happiness and other more concrete things.

Charles was now nearly sixteen. An attempt to explain to him the general idea of psychotherapeutics was made. He said he was willing to come for regular interviews, and that he would do anything he was told if it would help him at all. There could be no objection to making another attempt, for even if nothing was accomplished with him, there might be something gained by being able to furnish the agency with a prognosis on which they might base further social plans.

Thinking for him: For a period of nearly a month this boy was seen every other day. Most of these interviews were rather long. He came regularly, was entirely co-operative, even felt aggrieved if the interview had to be shorter than usual, but nevertheless his co-operation was of a most peculiar type. He seemed to expect some definite thing to happen that would suddenly change him, make him feel differently, and solve all his problems. Formerly he had been rather antagonistic and contemptuous of any attempts to understand or to analyse his mental life. His present attitude might be compared to that of a person who, having always objected to surgical procedure, suddenly develops an acute appendix and insists frantically that he wants an operation immediately.

Charles came to me in the rapport of friendly belief. I thought that if I could establish a personality contact with him, I might help him, and I still believe that was true. At the end of this treatment I did not have quite so good a rapport as in the beginning. While the friendly element still remained, a good deal of his belief that I could help him had quite naturally disappeared, for I had certainly failed to do so. Although I tried very hard to make this boy want me to understand him and to know his very personal problems, no feeling of personal trust could be reached. Charles tried at times (he had insisted from the first on knowing details of how I was to help him) to do what he believed I wanted him to do. At times he gave me the impression of a person trying to co-operate with someone who was attempting unsuccessfully to produce hypnotic sleep.

Towards the latter part of the treatment he was told that perhaps if he would simply decide to become entirely frank in regard to all his emotional experiences and tell me about misdeeds that were not known, this might in some way aid me in what I was trying to do for him. He did this and told some of his behaviour delinquencies not known before and seemed to give as true an account as possible of his conscious mental life.

Here is one of the interesting things that came out at this time: He was asked carefully to consider his past life and to tell me which things in it had made it hard for him to be well-behaved and happy. He replied: "The biggest thing is that when I can't have my own way, it is my nature to do something to make trouble. I want to run wild and I've got to. Sometimes I do this when I want to get moved from my home or to get out of the school, and sometimes I do it when I like the place where I am. Lots of times, especially when I was a kid at Redwood [where he had lived with his loved foster-mother], I was blamed and punished for things I did not do. I never forgive people when they treat me that way. I think I should not be so ugly and disagreeable if they had not said the things they did. I just don't like to go to school; I have tried to like it, but somehow I just don't."

Since he failed to mention the two things which, when he was studied before, were considered the basis of his difficult behaviour, I urged him to go further, to think carefully about all of his past and to tell me other important things which had brought him unhappiness. He seemed to try to do this, but he said that he could think of nothing else. He was then asked about the early sex experiences and troubles. When they were mentioned, he smiled and said that he used to talk about them a lot, but that he guessed that they did not amount to much and he supposed he was as much to blame as anybody else. He also mentioned the fact that he seldom masturbated now, and, while he liked girls and they liked him, he had never been immoral. He thought that his early sex experiences had done him no harm.

He was then asked about the way his family treated him. He said: "Well, I forgot them. That was a long time ago and they treat me all right now." (The truth was that they had been particularly disagreeable and antagonistic; in fact, at this very time he was being refused a home in the family of distant relatives.)

At the end of the treatment my opinion was that possibly this lad was doing some fairly good thinking himself and that he might be in a certain way improving his life's condition and even personality reactions by his own thinking, but I could not *think with* him because I could not enter his environmental values. Whatever I said to Charles he considered as "preaching" or "lecturing." For years he had been thus treated, and he had learned to resent it. As a result, the things I said, even if they *did* comprise good advice, added to his problems rather than helped him.

When the treatments were discontinued, I felt that I could think about him more clearly and intelligently than before. I feel now that I have a fair idea of the emotional experiences which may have conditioned the undesirable personality traits. I have some moderate comprehension of his mental life. To explain this to the boy would do no good unless in some way he accepted it emotionally. Such an acceptance on his part could come only through the influence of my personality on his.

Results: Ultimately all we succeeded in doing was to give some social advice which was apparently fruitless in accomplishing results. The social agency has always done much for this boy and is still trying to tide him over and help him. They hope through social treatment to lead Charles away from a life of delinquency, and there is some slight evidence of their success in this. It is very questionable whether they can lead him to a life of happiness. If happiness ever comes, it will be because some person, perhaps his future wife, will enter the boy's life in such a way that he will develop loyalties to that person and find that a different and more satisfying form of happiness comes through this than through selfish responses. He is now an inmate of a private disciplinary school. He plans to enter the Navy.

Charles was a fine boy who only needed some reason to be good. He had no good reason to be bad. If any desirable person could ever reach the place in Charles's environment where the boy would wish to copy and to please him, that person could easily mould this boy's responses and behaviour. And this is true even though he is a large, overgrown, "know-it-all" boy.

*   *

More different psychiatrists have *"thought about"* this next boy than about almost any boy that has ever come to the clinic. But they have done an almost incredible minimum of *"thinking with"* him, considering the fact that they have spent a total of two hundred hours with this boy of superior intelligence. The failure has occurred because the lad could not be induced to do his part of the

the thinking. There were probably many active dynamisms in his mental life that acted as handicaps, but some good loyalties would have overcome these.

Case No. 20
HERBERT RUGGLES

Herbert had been a friend of the clinic since he was eleven. He was fifteen when I met him. He was a well-developed, healthy, erect, active boy, alert and intelligent-looking. He was always friendly, but always reserved.

The situation: Early in Herbert's life his parents had separated. Until the time the clinic first knew him, he had lived with his father and stepmother. He was an unhappy boy in an unhappy home. Three younger half-brothers added much to his problems. Two years before I knew him, he had been first placed in a foster-home, and it had been necessary to change him twice since that time.

When I first knew him, his behaviour and personality traits were about to cause the loss of the third foster-home. This was a good home physically, but the foster-parents could not understand the boy. He was reported to be talkative, boastful, deceitful, untruthful, uncommunicative, ego-centric, disobedient, and lazy. Enuresis was a constant and an unusually disturbing problem. On the credit side he was reported as loyal, generous, even-tempered, and not grudgeful.

Thinking about the boy: In the clinic records the many pages of his case report were covered with the opinions of several other psychiatrists who had seen him before I knew him. Altogether I spent about fifty hours talking with this boy, but I did not succeed in *thinking with* him. All my ideas are merely ideas *about* him.

I think this boy had early mental conflicts about his parental situation. I think he had early sex traumas and teachings. I think his enuresis was an unconscious protest reaction. I think much of his undesirable behaviour was on this basis also. I think that never, except possibly when he was a very small child, has he taken any person so deeply into his life that he consciously accepted or copied this person's ideas and opinions. I am certain of none of these things. Others who have seen him differ from my opinion in many respects. But since none of us have succeeded in *thinking with* this boy, each is fully entitled to his own belief.

Thinking for the boy: This had been done very well by an excellent agency visitor who worked with him for years. She arranged for a hundred interviews in the clinic, in the hope that we could help her better to understand the boy. What little help we were able to give does not contribute substantially to her understanding of him.

Thinking with the boy: Very shortly after I met Herbert, he told me, in his friendly, half-frank way, that he never had and never was going to tell anyone "all he knew." He always insisted that there was nothing very important to tell, and he declared that he never worried much about anything.

The descriptive phrase "friendly belief" describes this lad's response to me. After a year's acquaintance, and after the physical problem of his enuresis had disappeared, he became apparently frank about his emotional attitude towards it. His peculiar responses at that time furnished some proof that there must be conflicts in his mental life.

I tried very hard to establish a deep rapport with Herbert. He never objected to interviews. In a way, he looked forward to them. And he wrote interesting letters to me at times. He seemed interested in my efforts to understand him, but often he seemed more amused than interested.

Results: The period of my active treatment lasted only a few weeks, though I saw him occasionally over a period of two years. Later another psychiatrist attempted to make a contact with him. I feel that my efforts to give him any personality help have been unsuccessful. I have not changed any of his peculiar responses or altered his outlook on life. I have developed no loyalties in him. I do not feel that I may be credited with any of his improved behaviour. (He is a somewhat better-behaved lad than he was.) He has never been delinquent. His visitor believes that I have had a "good influence" on him and she likes me to see him occasionally. The boy says that he likes to come and see me, and when his visitor asks him, he says I have helped him a great deal. However, one has to take what Herbert says with a grain of salt.

If the psychotherapy effected any helpful results, I do not understand why or how, and I do not know actually what I did for him.

One should never give up with this sort of boy as long as opportunity to help him presents itself. He is fine material and needs help badly. The outcome of his life depends largely on whether or not he gets it.

*   *

The last boy to be described in this group is so placed because of the final outcome rather than because of the theoretical diagnosis. The rather unusual and unexpected results seem more logical if one thinks of Charles in terms of loyalties.

Case No. 21
CHARLES ROBERTS

Two and one-half years ago Charles was brought to the clinic. He was then twelve years old. He was a tall, dark-complexioned boy with a pleasant, polite, and friendly manner. His clear-cut, regular features, his deep-set eyes, and his intelligent and interested expression made him a decidedly attractive boy. His health was excellent. He was normally developed. He was supernormal by mental tests; his I. Q. rating was 120.

The situation: He was the third member of a large family, all of whom except himself were well-behaved and happy, and doing excellent work in school. His father was the minister in a large and active church. The home was physically excellent. The intelligent and sensible parents had always tried very hard to understand and to help Charles. His special form of bad behaviour was "running away." During the preceding two and one-half years he had run away from home more than forty times, if you counted only those occasions on which he was away at least one or more nights. In addition there were many short runaways. Careful observation and thought by the parents had never been able to reveal to their own satisfaction any drive or reason behind the boy's behaviour. He usually had some superficial excuse for his runaways, such as a slight quarrel with his siblings or a desire to avoid some hard job. The reasons were never the same. Sometimes he had no reason.

He usually ran away alone. He would go to some suburban or more distant town, where he would make the acquaintance of a policeman or an officer, or possibly some private citizen. Frequently he would ask to be allowed to sleep in the police or fire station. He could always tell some story so plausible that even those who were in frequent contact with runaway boys were satisfied that he was not one. Sometimes he would frankly say he was on a little runaway trip of adventure and tell who he was. He could do this often in so frank and engaging a way as to enlist the co-operation rather than to raise the objection of the officers.

The parents had tried in many sensible ways to stop this behaviour, without success. On one of the rare occasions when he had run away with another boy, he had connived at the other boy's stealing money for the trip. Outside of this he had never stolen anything in connexion with the runaways or at any other time.

The father reported his personality and behaviour as determined, stubborn, affectionate to younger siblings, but not to the parents or to the older children. "He is a distractible boy and does not finish what he starts in either work or play. He 'whoops it up' much around the home and in the neighbourhood, makes more noise than all the rest of the eight children put together. He talks very much. He is proud and boastful in his activities, uncommunicative with parents and others. He is sensitive, but never repentant. He could be made to cry by being criticized, but never by being whipped. He is unusually fearless and willing to take dangerous chances." His father says, too, that Charles is afraid of absolutely nothing; on his runaways he sleeps out in the woods alone.

Thinking about the boy: The story as given by the parents threw little light on the reason for the boy's behaviour. These intelligent parents had thought about Charles much and realized in advance that anything he or they could tell would probably not answer the why of his behaviour. The parents believed that these questions must be answered if their boy was to be helped. In other words, all the *thinking about* him possible without a deep rapport had been done before he ever came to the clinic. The glib, interesting stories he told in the first interview revealed nothing new that I could in any way interpret as causative.

Thinking for the boy: In Charles's case there could be no question about the necessity of establishing personality contact. The challenge lay in whether or not I could. The *thinking for* him had also been well done by the parents. They knew that because of their social situation, and for the sake of the other children, Charles must lose his good home and be placed in some disciplinary school unless he could be helped to change his behaviour. They realized, wisely, that Charles was a boy who would be unlikely to adjust well to such a situation, or to receive help from it.

Thinking with the boy: Charles was friendly and believed that I knew a great deal about boys and their problems from the first. He said that, while he got all the fun he had in life from his runaways, he was willing to give them up if someone could keep him from wanting to run away.

He was interviewed regularly every day over a short period of time. The most interesting evident fact was that he had no loyalties in life deep enough to influence his behaviour, no loyalties so strong as the loyalty to his own selfish pleasure. There was no one whose ideas he was willing to accept and to try out or whose emotional responses he wished to copy simply because they came from that person. A deep rapport would be absolutely necessary if we were to know this boy's emotional life and to help him.

After two or three interviews Charles began to trust me entirely and to believe that I was really trying to help him. He was frank, but not enthusiastically so. He did not exhibit the earnest desire to be honest with me, to be understood, which is usually an encouraging sign one wishes to see in difficult cases. He would listen carefully to everything I talked about, but, despite every effort on my part and no antagonism on his, I could not come to mean enough to him for him to accept my ideas without my presenting an array of reasons to support them. For a reason to be valid with Charles it usually had to carry with it some promise of immediate pleasurable returns. At the time of the treatment I did not reach a deeper rapport than that of personal trust.

The boy's complete frankness made it necessary for me to think with him about many things which are really best approached only with a child in deep rapport. It was very difficult, as it is always under these circumstances, to substantiate my advice by supporting it with reasons that he would accept, or to impress upon him my ideas of his behaviour and mental life. The superficial rapport gave a fairly good opportunity for understanding Charles's mental life, but this process did not put me sufficiently in his dynamic environment to make me hopeful that the treatment would be successful.

The various things we thought about together might be briefly summarized as follows:

Charles had felt he was not so smart as the other children. He believed that his father was ashamed of him and therefore did not like him so well as the others. He did not blame his father for this, feeling that it was his own fault and that perhaps he was born "that way."

He did not like athletics, his only reason being that the other boys did not like him. He knew that he was successful when he took part, but he dreaded taking the initiative and making new contacts.

He told me of the pleasure he received from day-dreams and described them rather bashfully, but in detail. All his runaways were preceded by an elaborate day-dream of what he would do on the trip. Sometimes he actually put off his departure for a day or so to complete a day-dream. In the day-dream he thought of long, eventful excursions in which he often played the part of the hero. These day-dreams frequently involved the use of firearms, but he was always on the side of the law, not against it.

The most important thing he told me about himself was that he has always felt in some way different from others, and he remembered that he used to feel bad about this. He had ceased to do so now. He believed he would always be different. This feeling was closely akin to what is ordinarily thought of as a feeling of inferiority. Charles was too successful in anything he undertook to have any conscious feeling of inferiority, except possibly in regard to his place in his father's affections.

In regard to sex problems he showed quite the same response. He felt that he was different from other boys because, although he had tried to enter into the sex habits of the boys he knew and to copy their behaviour, he received little pleasure from it. This added to his feeling that he was not like the others. He did not like erotic stories, while the other boys all seemed to enjoy them. He said he sometimes wondered if he would be like other men in this respect when he grew up, but he did not much care if he wasn't. He'd rather not care about such things at all than to think about them as much as some boys and men he knew, who had got themselves into serious difficulties.

He was never home-sick on his runaways. He said his mother never had much time for him, with so many others in the home, and his father was too busy to spend his time with the children. He believed that this was the reason that he did not feel lonesome when he went away. He believed himself very fortunate in being able to get so much fun out of adventures. He was somewhat self-critical regarding his failure to be concerned about the worry and disturbance he made in the family, but he dismissed this with the thought that "it wasn't his fault" if he didn't worry like other people. While Charles would talk about all these things, he was not anxious to do so, and he did not ask questions.

At the end of this period of treatment I felt that probably this boy had been really frank. I seriously discussed all these various things with him and tried to show him logical and sensible reasons why he should change his behaviour. To some extent I explained to him the mental mechanisms that I guessed might be in his life. I had very definite theories while thinking about him, many of which I dared not touch upon when thinking with the boy, and yet the problem was so acute that one felt that shooting in the dark would be better than not shooting at all. It is probable that if I had been able to establish a deeper rapport with this boy, I could have understood him much better.

At the end of his treatment I made this report at the clinic: "Possibly some concrete advice has been given this boy that will be of use to him. The bottom of the problem has not been reached and the probability of any great improvement in his behaviour is not to be expected."

Results: After the interview the boy had one more runaway episode and one more rather serious family upset in the home, when he borrowed his father's shot-gun and went hunting without permission and against regulations. Both these things happened soon after he was treated.

A year later the boy was seen for a check-up interview in the home. The parents reported that he had gradually improved since he had been first seen in the clinic. During the last few months his behaviour and co-operation in the home had been much better and he had shown no tendency to run away. His father reported that Charles was gradually becoming more confidential with him, and that he felt better able to understand and to help the boy. Both father and mother were pleased and gave the entire credit to the psychiatric treatments. They said Charles was much more interested in normal boyish things, was making many friends, and was doing better school-work. No follow-up report had been received from this boy for several months, so that these reports came as a complete surprise.

When the boy was given the opportunity to talk with me, he

was more than pleased to do so. He greeted me in a much more boyish, lively way than he had ever done before. He at once began to talk confidentially about some of his old problems and brought up adolescent sex questions in a way that suggested he had been waiting for the opportunity to talk with me. When he was complimented on the change, he said it was all because he had come to the clinic. I frankly told him I did not believe that I could be given the credit. He said: "You sure can. I never felt the same way about running away and hating my brothers afterwards. I just thought about the things you said, and found out they were true."

Charles is an unexpected psychiatric success. The intelligent parents made the psychiatric approach possible and undoubtedly helped the boy hold what he gained from the psychiatric study.

The mental dynamisms in Charles's case are not yet understood and his success therefore cannot be thoroughly comprehended. The boy is the most successful case I have ever known with whom only a superficial degree of rapport was obtained. Possibly he took me more deeply into his environment than I realized. One would suppose his intelligent parents must have often reasoned with him and explained life to him, as well as or better than I was able to do. While thinking was "mixed" and unorganized in this case, "something" happened, and, according to the boy himself, it was the thing he needed, as a goad to better behaviour. The environmental situation did not change, but the boy did. His personality traits are being directed towards more normal and healthy ends. The case is not understood, but in some way the psychiatric contact was the entering wedge that enabled the parents to continue the personality influence that the boy needed.

It seems to me that from a practical therapeutic standpoint the following might be considered a good rule: When one is not reasonably sure of the causative dynamisms in puzzling cases, a very safe and often efficient thing to do is to attempt to develop loyalties towards whatever good people and things the child has in his environment, or to add someone to his environment to whom he may become loyal. One is unlikely to do harm by this procedure.

CHAPTER VIII

INFERIORITY

The Child who is Not Equal to his Environment

LL psychiatrists and others who are thinking about the mental life of children recognize the fact that, no matter by what term it is called, a feeling of being inferior to or of being less successful than others in some way is a common experience in childhood. They recognize, too, that the changes in the mental life and behaviour of children that occur in response to this feeling may be and often are of serious consequences.

Perhaps some over-emphasize the importance of these consequences, but, on the other hand, perhaps it is so vital that it cannot possibly be over-emphasized. Many of the boys reported in this book feel themselves inferior. The following five cases have been selected because this problem seemed to be present in a rather uncomplicated form.

It seems to me that children having this problem are more easy to understand than many others. It also seems to me that, while the child who feels inferior does certainly have mental conflicts and develops "inferiority complexes," these conflicts are not so deeply hidden in the child's mental life as many others. These two facts render these young patients more easy to help than many others. A large group of psychiatrists dealing with children wish to place all their patients in this group. Possibly a very natural

161

and laudable desire to help them all may influence their opinions.

*   *

The first boy is a very good example of one whose delinquency is directly based on the feeling of being inferior, whose lack of success fostered the belief that he was being mistreated.

Case No. 22
GRANT DEAN

When I first knew Grant, he was fourteen. He had been known to the clinic for five years. He was usually subdued and reserved, though at times he was friendly and even vivacious. He had been studied in the clinic at rather frequent intervals. His pubescence had been precocious. He was well-developed and healthy.

Though retarded in school and even considered "backward" by his teacher, thorough mental testing revealed an intelligence quotient of 119.

The situation: A full description of the home situation and the boy's responses to it would be rich material for a modern "psychological" novel. For many years the family was one of "God's poor." Proud of their respectability and of their church connexions, they were constantly soliciting help in genteel but persistent ways. When it was given to them, they felt they had given their donors an opportunity to perform a religious duty, for which opportunity the latter should be grateful. The long-standing poor health of both parents made the agency's assistance very necessary. There were several children, both older and younger than Grant. Two years after he was first known in the clinic, his mother was killed in a street accident, and his father was invalided for life.

Since that time the father has taken the attitude that he is a long-suffering saint. Indeed, to the casual observer he appears to be. But to those who know him well he is a shrewd, persistent, and deceitful beggar, constantly capitalizing his unfortunate condition, pitying himself, and making the life of his children miserable by his demands and nagging criticism.

Grant had probably suffered the most. He was the "bad boy" of the family, and he was never allowed to forget it. Early in his life he joined other boys in stealing small articles from shops and from pedlars' carts. He also stole small amounts of money at home. This behaviour has reappeared at intervals, though there have been long periods of time when he has not been guilty of dishonesty. The family has always considered him a thief, watched him closely, and denied him many privileges because of this. When they were very young, he and a brother were involved with other children in unfortunate sex activities. These were only vaguely understood and probably over-emphasized. The father would not let him forget this episode; he constantly accused him of sex misbehaviour, though he had been guilty of none for a number of years.

Thinking about the boy: His personality characteristics when he was first known were reported as follows: He was unhappy, dissatisfied, and deceitful. He was a liar, both offensively and defensively. He was uninterested in school, and he was doing poor work there. He complained much about being mistreated and not enjoying the privileges other children had. When I first knew him, three years later, the report was much the same, with the additional facts of much quarrelling and fighting with his younger sister and his older brother.

For years the father had threatened to report his misdeeds to the police. But when questioned by social workers, he would cover up the boy's delinquencies. He punished and scolded the boy excessively in attempts to correct his behaviour. During the first three years of his acquaintance in the clinic, no deep psychiatric rapport was established with this lad. The changing but constantly unhappy environmental situation, the boy's constant lying and well-thought-out excuses, his lack of emotional response to trying situations, and his early history of bad companions and tragic happenings, all furnished material for theoretical *thinking about* possible causative dynamisms. In staff conference the possibility of a dynamic association between the early stealing and the early sex experiences was suggested as a possible mechanism to be explored.

When I saw the boy three years ago, there were new phases of the situation and new complaints of his behaviour. He had recently begun to avoid even *talking* about his misbehaviour, and he was playing by himself more and more.

Thinking for the boy: A previous placement in a foster-home effected no improvement in his behaviour, though it seemed to make him happier. Social plans for the family, including an ineffectual attempt at re-educating the father and older brother in their attitudes towards this boy, had been tried. At this time I tried to establish a good rapport with him. I saw him several times. I failed to reach him. As far as I could judge, I did not help him at all. He did not trust me enough to tell me the truth about himself, and he did not reach the place where he wanted to be understood. He denied to me, and probably to himself, that he was unhappy. Nearly a year later I saw him again and tried to give him personality help.

Thinking with him: At this time Grant was in more trouble, and he was willing to admit that he was unhappy and frightened. His father was threatening quite realistically to ask help from the police. The boy remembered some of the things we had talked about before, and he came to see me willingly, for he wanted help. He suggested that he would not have been in this trouble had he followed my advice from the start. For a long time the former interviews seemed to have accomplished nothing; now they fostered the ready establishment of a good personality contact.

During the months that followed, Grant was interviewed only occasionally. His treatment was not so regular nor so thorough as it should have been. However, he was very frank and he was sincere in his desire to be understood. He came to consider me a friend who could help him if anyone could. He was accepting my ideas and trying them out. At least he was meeting his situation more frankly.

As Grant's frankness increased, it became evident that his father treated him with even less understanding than we formerly supposed. The father would take from the boy things he had stolen, ostensibly to return them. Actually he would not do so, but he would conceal this dishonesty from Grant. When he was confronted with it, he would explain that it was to protect the boy from the juvenile court.

Morning, noon, and night the father pointed out to Grant the dozens of ways in which he was less successful and less likable than his younger brother. This boy was in Grant's class at school and received better grades. He had never stolen. He helped the father more with home duties.

The father accused Grant of doing many things that he did not do, and scolded him as much for these as for his real delinquencies.

Grant had definite and deeply concealed worries and conflicts in his mental life, as well as those represented by these very obvious problems. These conflicts came to light through the questions he asked after he had entered a good rapport.

These questions concerned moral and religious matters. He did not understand others' beliefs and was confused by the various things he had been told. Some of the religious beliefs were associated in his mind with his mother's death. Many of the questions were about sex and his developing sex feelings, his old experiences, and the physical effect they would have on him. He had developed a rather fatalistic attitude towards sex, with much erotic daydreaming, but no masturbation.

In some way he had developed the belief that stealing was a disease. He had tried unsuccessfully to deny this belief, and on the basis of it he took a pessimistic attitude towards the possibility of his overcoming his tendency to steal. These things were thought out very thoroughly with the boy, and during the discussion of them he became entirely frank. He could not recall instances or events that seemed to associate the early sex experiences with the beginning of his stealing.

There were many other things to be considered. He expressed very freely complaints against society and his family. Earlier these complaints had been adjudged as one of his bad personality traits, but inspection of the situation revealed that he was justified in many of them. His loneliness, his father's attitude, and his difficulties of adjustment in school to a different racial group were instances in point.

Grant believed himself to be a bad boy and hopelessly inferior to the other members of his family. Because of the difficulty of the social situation, which made it impossible to see the boy regularly, I did not for a long time allow a deep rapport, but I finally did establish a personality contact with him. Because of the difficulty of making very necessary social and environmental adjustments and the unavoidable delay in making those that could be made, my treatment of this lad was not so successful as I feel it might have been.

I did help him, however. He developed a good loyalty to me and a confidence in my opinions so strong that when I saw his few successes and admired them, he came to have a much greater confidence in himself. I helped him understand his developing sex feelings and by encouragement and explanations made him wish to overcome his fantastic and unhealthy sex ideation and to a large extent to succeed in doing so.

By explanation and by making him feel unafraid to be very frank, I was able to help Grant take a much more understanding and healthy attitude towards religion. And I did this without, I believe, in any way disturbing the religious beliefs that he and his family held. His faith in God was of great help to him; it had tided him over many hard places despite the fact that much of fear entered into it.

But in so far as I utilized my rapport to help him understand and face his home situation and his family's attitudes towards him and his towards them, I increased the seriousness of the total situation. So this, the most necessary thing to be accomplished, had to be avoided.

Results: During his irregular treatment and for several months afterwards Grant remained in his impossible environment. For several months he stole nothing, and he felt that he had overcome his temptations to be dishonest. He was more helpful and co-operative in the family. His school-work improved distinctly. He said that learning correctly the facts of sex and freely discussing his religious problems had made him feel much better. He frequently expressed his thanks to me for what I had done for him. He continued to have new questions to ask, but they were never irrelevant ones.

Treatment was discontinued before it should have been. I failed to transfer the loyalties he had for me to any other person and I failed largely to convince others of the good points I thought I saw in the boy. He later went to an institution for homeless children, where he is adjusting rather poorly.

With Grant, as with all children who wish to be appreciated, establishing rapport was comparatively easy. A child of this type reaches out quickly for anyone who can see and appreciate his good traits and his abilities. He is a boy who was helped by treatment, but who needs more help. I think, however, that his adult adjustments will be fairly good.

*   *

The next boy had known what it was to be successful and to have others like and appreciate him. Then, later, he began to believe that this could never be his lot again.

Case No. 23
BERT ROOK

At the time of his treatment Bert Rook was eight years old. He was a normally developed, healthy boy with refined features and an intelligent but serious expression. Mentally he was of good average general ability.

The situation: Bert was brought to the clinic by his mother, who said he was entirely out of her control and that he must be placed away from home. During the past few months he had developed many bad personality traits, and with them the habit of soiling himself in the day-time. He had no trouble of this sort at night, nor was there enuresis. His mother reported that at school he fought with the other children and broke windows, that he would not study, and that the teachers were unwilling to put up with him longer. At home he quarrelled violently with his twin sister and was disobedient and unhappy at times. The mother said that formerly he had been well-behaved, happy, affectionate, and obedient. His home was a good middle-class one. The parents were in comfortable circumstances. His father, a successful travelling man, was away from home much. His mother reported no bad sex habits, nor had she ever suspected any.

Thinking about the boy: There was little to account for this boy's behaviour in the history his mother gave. There had been no sudden change in the home or school situation preceding the sudden change in his behaviour.

This little eight-year-old chap, intelligent and responsive, told a straightforward story which in itself did not seem to furnish many suggestions. Still one could be certain that something definite and concrete had occurred to affect his behaviour. Physical disease, such as encephalitis, was ruled out by both the history and by the physical examination. But the physical examination furnished a clue to the solution. The anal region and the sex organs revealed local irritation, and the boy displayed an unusual modesty and an unwillingness to be examined.

Thinking about the boy: By a process of elimination of other causes and through the suggestions given by the physical examination the most logical assumption was that excessive sex habits were the cause of both the physical difficulties and the personality and behaviour problems.

Thinking with the boy: This friendly lad very quickly passed from the rapport of friendly belief to that of personal trust. He gave his own reasons for breaking windows and behaving so badly in his home. He became frank about his emotional reaction to his lack of sphincter-control. When he reached the stage of personal trust, instead of talking quickly and loudly, as he had done at the beginning of the interview, he showed a tendency to whisper and to be less voluble. The names of two other little boys appeared frequently in his talk and seemed closely linked with the emotional responses he was giving to his present situation. Bert and I thought about these boys for a little while, and he finally told me they were "dirty" boys. I was willing to talk about other things after he told me that, but Bert did not want to. He began to cry. He said he was afraid. Of what? That he would be sent away from home. Why? This had happened to an older boy he knew. What for? Bert did not know. He was now crying very hard. "I think you do know, Bert, only you're just a little afraid to tell. Remember, I was a boy once." Then Bert asked me through his tears if I would promise not to tell. "I won't tell anything you tell me if you don't want me to." Then he climbed into my lap, hid his head, and told me that he, too, had been very bad and "dirty." He told about perverse sex acts that another little boy had learned from the older boy who had been sent away from home. He told about the little boy's teaching them to Bert and to another little boy in his group. Bert had practised these acts frequently. These perversions, together with much masturbation, which developed simultaneously, were so interesting and pleasurable that they had been continued for several months, although Bert had lived in the greatest fear that they would be discovered. Bert believed that his lack of sphincter-control was entirely due to this; in fact, it seemed to be almost a part of the sexual emotions.

This confidential confession occurred when the boy was in the state of personal trust. With this rapport we could have helped this little conscience-stricken, frightened boy solve his problems, by giving him the needed sex information, adequate encouragement, and assistance in overcoming his sex habits, for to know the problem was to solve it in this case. The difficulty was that he and I alone knew it, and I had promised not to tell anyone without his consent.

We went to lunch together. During lunch he asked me if big folks did not always hate boys when they found out such things about them; he told me he had supposed that anyone who found out about it would immediately punish and hate him. In another

they did not seem to be offences at all; they were then simply terrible things that had happened to him. He was a thief. Earlier he had stolen a great deal from foster-homes. Recently he had been stealing in the school and from stores. He was a skilful liar. An instance of this is that for a long time he made his father and new stepmother, who had taken the boy when his mother finally completely deserted him, believe that his mother had boarded him in a coloured woman's home. When he was taken to this place to prove his statements, and the people were found to be white, though of a very low type, he insisted that they had changed colour, and would not admit that he had been lying. He was disobedient at home and in school. He would not work in school and was a disturbing factor in many ways. He smoked. He masturbated excessively. He was a sex teacher of normal and perverse acts to both boys and girls. He had been dismissed from school irrevocably. A sentence quoted from the report of the superintendent of his school follows: "He will not be allowed under any circumstances to come to school again. He could ruin at least twenty little girls a day."

Franklin's stepmother had proved to be as real a friend as this boy had ever had, but she now considered him impossible and had come to loathe and hate him because of peculiar and disgusting perverse excretory habits in which he had been indulging for some time. Frank was literally friendless until taken over by the agency.

Thinking about the boy: The reports from the court, agency, and school furnished abundant material to think about, and it was well they did, for the usual method of talking with him for a while before commencing to think with him was impossible. Five minutes after he was alone with someone who was not scolding and was not disgusted with him, he had climbed into his friend's lap and was pouring out a pitiful account of how he felt. He was telling of his discouragement and how utterly bad he considered himself and of his belief in the impossibility of being any better. It was impossible to avoid talking seriously and trying to help this boy from the very first.

Thinking with him: The worst thing of all was, he said, that though he used to derive physical pleasure from his experiences with the older girl, now there was little pleasure received from masturbation and he believed he was seeking for it all the time. It was just something inside him that would not let him think of anything else when he was awake and would not let him sleep. (His report said that he seemed always to be awake at night, no matter at what time or how quietly the room was entered.) He wanted to know why this was. He wanted to know why other boys were not like him. When told in response to questions that many boys older than he did not even know of any of these things, new flood-gates of his tears were opened, physically impossible as this might seem from the amount of crying he had already done. He wanted to know why he had to be the one these things happened to and why he had to feel as he did and to be so bad. He said he would like to kill the big girl and seemed actually to have some vague ideas of doing this if he ever saw her again. He could not remember how her face looked, but he had a very vivid memory of the appearance of her body and could never get away from the vision of her red hair. He thought he would recognize her by her hair if he should meet her. He could see this when he closed his eyes, and he wanted to know why this was.

Personality contact was complete before the end of the three rather long interviews, which were all that were possible at this time. He was accepting ideas and responding emotionally to them because they came from someone who could talk about the way he felt rather than what he had done.

The confession of behaviour as a therapeutic measure could be entirely eliminated from this case, for before I saw him in the clinic, this discouraged boy would commence to recount his behaviour as soon as a policeman, teacher, or any other adult whom he considered as having authority over him (and this included most of the adults he knew) commenced to talk to him. The psychotherapeutic treatment, which had to be carried on rapidly because of the impossibility of caring for him in the city, consisted largely in answering his questions in a therapeutic way and making him feel a thing which could not have been accomplished by arguments or in any other way than through the influence obtained by the deep psychiatric rapport. This was the idea that he might yet become a fine and happy boy.

Frank was hungry for love and affection, and it was judged that he had the potentiality of developing very good loyalties, but since he had never had the slightest chance to be loyal to any good person or thing, there was no way of being sure of this. When the treatment, which was carried on in much too short a time, was over, he seemed to be loyal to his new-found faith in the possibility of his becoming a boy whom others would like.

One fact about which much thinking was done was not discussed with this boy. This proved to be very interesting in the light of the final results. It was evident that, as a result of his experiences' occurring so early, he had developed a confusion of ideas about sexual and excretory functions. But his problems were so many that it was thought wise to ignore this at that time.

Was anything constructive to be accomplished by this *thinking about* and *with* the boy? Indeed, how could anyone think successfully for him?

Thinking for him: Considerable *thinking against* him had been done when the agency found him. *Thinking for* him, up to the time he was studied, had consisted mostly in ideas about hospitals, corrective institutions, and insane asylums. There was little reason to believe that any of these would be of much therapeutic help, though apparently they might be very necessary.

To the everlasting credit of the agency, it undertook, through the suggestion and encouragement of the clinic, the seemingly impossible task of finding a good foster-home for this boy. It succeeded in doing this. Quoting from the notes of the first conference held on him at the clinic: "It is interesting to find this boy is utterly frank and spontaneous and reaching out for help. On account of his attitude we feel that the prognosis is decidedly favourable if a good foster-home could be found for him. The boy is rather pessimistic about it himself, but the feeling of guilt and concern is probably on account of social ostracism."

His foster-parents, intelligent, middle-class people, were informed of his problems in a way that they could appreciate and understand. They came quickly to like him very much and were, and are yet, very loyal to him through all his ups and downs. His agency visitor takes an almost parental interest in him and has continued the psychotherapeutics in a very fine way.

Results: Frank is now (one year later) a happy little boy with many good interests. From the first day he was placed in his new home, he has never in any way attempted to tamper sexually with children or to talk about any of his former habits or delinquencies to them. He has in the one year made nearly three grades in school, though in the beginning he could not read one word. As was guessed, he has loyalties aplenty: to his friends, his foster-parents, his visitor, his psychiatrist, his school and playmates, and to sports and games. He is very loyal to the fact that he is becoming a good boy.

But it has not all been fine. Later developments have shown that probably it would have been best to have *thought with* him about the question previously mentioned that was not discussed or explained to him. During the first months of his life in the foster-home the bad excretory habits completely disappeared and the enuresis was greatly alleviated. Then another little boy, who had been living in this foster-home, was rather suddenly taken to his own home. Frank had made a firm friendship with this lad on the basis of sports and games in the home and he had learned to swim with him and had made him his real friend. Frank was unhappy and lonesome, and soon after he was left alone, these former undesirable things began to appear, and with them a most persistent and unusual type of lying concerning them, which, but for the patient efforts of his visitor, would have cost him his foster-home. He would not be frank with the visitor or his foster-parents concerning his instinctive life, though every way was tried to have him do so and to help him. Circumstances made it impossible for him to return to the clinic for a long time, but finally this was arranged.

Again we *thought about* him. This time he was not the discouraged boy of before. He was sorry that he must tell about his behaviour and sex life, thoroughly ashamed and unhappy; but he was entirely willing and expected to make a clean breast of it.

The details need not be recounted here. The story was of the old ideation about the red-haired girl, his inability to sleep, his surrender to his unfortunate personal sex habits, and the discovery that by doing other things at the same time he could obtain pleasure that was otherwise impossible. He told me of the days he would be discouraged and would consider himself no good and hopelessly lost. He told of his struggle with himself, both to overcome his desires and not to lie about his behaviour. (The lying seemed almost a part of the sex thoughts and acts in his case.) Many more questions were now answered psychotherapeutically, and sexual pathology and mental mechanisms were discussed understandingly with this little third-grade boy which would be impossible for many people who have three college degrees to understand. His visitor and his foster-father were taken into his complete confidence.

Results: This little boy is now well adjusted in the home of his father and stepmother. The improvement following the last series of interviews was rapid. The enuresis soon disappeared. His sex habits improved, first by being changed, at my suggestion, to the ordinary type of masturbation; and later with a good deal of encouragement he has almost entirely overcome his sex habits of all kinds.

He remained in the foster-home for a time after the treatment ceased, but his reputation there was too bad for him to live down. With fear and trembling I advised his visitor to try him in his own home. This proved to be good advice, as the boy made his best improvement after this change was made. He has been there more than a year now; he is doing much better in school and is a normally behaved and, we believe, a well-adjusted boy.

* *

The next boy *was* inferior, he *was* unloved and unwanted, and he *was* mistreated. Most people who knew him believed that he was to blame for being unloved and unwanted. He had never learned to· seek opportunities for expressing or utilizing his loyalties when none presented themselves. It is not often that a boy who is as much handicapped by poor health and unhappy situations as John was does this. But it is much the best way out of unhappiness for the child who has earlier learned the lesson of pleasure from human inter-response. For even though the lesson has been long forgotten, it is often possible to help him recall it. The constructive effect of understanding love and affection given to a young child has a real or potential value as long as life lasts.

.Case No. 25
JOHN WILSON

John Wilson, who was almost sixteen years old when first seen in the clinic, presented a most pitiful appearance. His eyes were red from crying. He was tall, but much underweight, stooped, narrow-chested, and sallow-complexioned, an unhappy, discouraged boy. He had many stigmata, asymmetrical features, a high narrow palatal arch, typical Hutchinson teeth, and very defective vision.

Mentally he was found to be slightly above normal in a testing period which the psychologist felt failed to do him justice because of his emotional stress.

The situation: The boy was referred to the clinic by a Sunday-school teacher and was brought in by his mother. She reported him to be a thoroughly bad boy. She said he lied, was disobedient, truant, hateful to his stepfather, ugly to his brother. He cried very easily and ran away to visit his father's relatives against her wishes. The mother said these relatives were undesirable people, just as the boy's father was.

The father had died suddenly several years before. There had been much quarrelling between the father and the mother during their entire married life. The mother believes that John's father suffered from syphilis and hints that this was the cause of his death. She says her present husband was a friend of John's father, and that he had been very good to the family before the father's death. This man has lived in the family ever since. She has recently married him. She would have done so earlier but that the man, who is a quite successful professional man, living in a suburban town, could not obtain a divorce. She told us that both she and the stepfather have tried to make a good boy of John. They had whipped and otherwise punished him much, all to no avail. She said the boy pretended to be ill because he was lazy and did not want to get a job. Physically the home was a very good one. There are two younger brothers. Her present husband had finished paying for the house. He is good to her, and were it not for this boy, she would be happy.

The mother catalogued John's personality traits as lack of affection, bossiness, crossness, disagreeableness, selfishness, laziness, irritableness, absolute lack of confidence and uncommunicativeness. She reported much dishonesty at home and in school. Before his father's death this boy was well-behaved except that he was rude to his present stepfather when he was in the home, as he frequently was.

As might easily be surmised, a check on this report showed that it was almost entirely unreliable. No dishonesty was proved. The school report was fine, as to both behaviour and trustworthiness. The grades were passing. The personality traits reported by his teachers and Sunday-school officers were entirely different from the mother's and many of them were good. The mother believed the boy should be punished at this time by being taken from school and made to go to work.

Thinking for the boy: The mother and stepfather, this unusual report, and the physical examination, all made it seem imperative that something should be done for him at once. It seemed evident enough that this unhappy boy needed many kinds of help. Not the least of these would be a good understanding of his mental life. Psychotherapy must be successful if any social success was to be obtained. To do this a good rapport would obviously be very important. It would probably be difficult to establish. For this reason much time was spent in establishing it.

Several interviews, mostly concerned with the boy's physical condition and trying to encourage him in the belief that he might attain good strength and health, provided the opportunity for establishing acquaintance, and through these interviews good personality contact was established. After much difficulty the parents were convinced that the boy was ill. They then allowed a physical examination by specialists and the beginning of a long-needed treatment. The parents being so unco-operative and the need of physical and mental treatment being so urgent, this could be carried out best if he were to remain temporarily at home. Nothing was said about his being placed in a foster-home at first, though this was a part of the original plan.

Thinking about him: The thinking about John had to be done almost entirely in connexion with the thinking for and thinking with him. There was but little occasion for a theoretical consideration of this boy's problems. The situation was too acute.

Thinking with him: John told his story very willingly after he had learned to feel that he was being understood. But at first he was hopeless. As he told about different things, each was discussed very thoughtfully and cautiously with him, for by that time he was accepting my ideas without stopping to think why he was doing so.

The boy's story follows. The reader will readily see how many things there were in it that must each be first thought about and then really thought out with this lad.

John remembers that as a little boy he was always happy. He was with his father more than with his mother and believes his father loved him very much. He was ten years old when his father died. He remembers very well many occasions when he and his father were happy together, but he remembers that even then his

father always seemed partially unhappy, and he thinks that he realized that his present stepfather was the cause of this unhappiness.
He believes that even then he hated his mother or at least blamed
her for this. His father died suddenly, being ill for only three
days. He was in the hospital. John was not told he was dangerously
ill and did not see him before his death. He was punished severely
at the time of the funeral for excessive crying and for saying that
he wanted to die too. Since his father's death he had had no one
with whom he could talk about his unhappiness, excepting his
paternal aunt, who lives in a near-by town and whose home he
was always forbidden to visit.

His greatest sorrow is the slurring and critical remarks about
his father that are openly made by his mother and stepfather. His
brothers also hear these remarks, but are younger than he and do
not remember much about their father and so do not resent them
as he does. The parents frequently say that the boy is like his father
and compare his weaknesses and shortcomings to those of his
father. If he resented these statements, as he formerly did often and
still does when they become unbearable to him, he was beaten
unmercifully. If he was ill or tired, as he frequently was, he
scarcely dared mention it because he was not believed and because
of these ugly comparisons.

The stepfather had recently decided that the boy must quit
school and earn his own living. John knew that his stepfather and
mother could well afford to keep him in school.

He did not feel that he should ever be successful. He said he
wanted to get good grades in school, but he did not believe he was
very smart, and besides this he was so unhappy at home that he
could not study there, and his mother would not allow him to go
to the library. He was trying very hard to take part in athletics,
but the other boys were all much better players than he. He was

sure that his defective eyesight would handicap him, no matter what he tried to do.

When his father was alive, John had a nice room. After his mother's remarriage he had a very small hall bedroom. He believed that his mother would love him if his stepfather would let her. (This was probably not true in any sense.) He realized that he was not good-looking. His brothers were. He had formerly tried to make up for this by dressing well and by being neat. He thought it was of no use to do so any longer.

The only thing in which he had had his own wishes granted, and this only on account of public opinion, was that he still attended and belonged to the church and Sunday-school with which his father was connected. He did not go to his mother's church, although she wished him to do so and ridiculed the church he attended. After John was told of his true physical condition, he had the new problem of the necessary long-continued and somewhat painful treatments to face. Also, the new problem of being told by his parents that his father was to blame for his physical disease. A valuable watch that had belonged to his father and that was to have been his on his sixteenth birthday had disappeared, so his mother told him, from where it had been kept. This watch meant more almost than life itself to John, but when he tried to deny his parents' accusations that he had stolen and sold it, he was punished and threatened with not being allowed to take his treatments or to come for interviews.

John told me he had never stolen anything, other than food from the kitchen, in his life. He had no bad habits. He remembers his father's talking to him about sex habits, and he says that no matter how badly he might want to do such things, they will never happen, because his father asked him to be a clean boy. John was *thought about* and *with* for a long time. This study showed that

while he felt himself profoundly inferior and while he in no sense
had the feeling of belonging at home, yet he had most firm and
strong loyalties. Some of these loyalties were not easily seen at
first, but during the treatment they became very conscious and
real to him and to others. He was loyal first to his father's memory
and to the knowledge that his father wanted him to become a good
man. He was loyal to his school and especially to the school
superintendent, who had shown interest in him and believed in
him. He was loyal to his church. During the treatment he became
very loyal to the idea of regaining his health and to the idea of
being self-supporting. He wanted to prove that he was not what
his parents said he was. He also became very loyal to my ideas and
friendship, but he showed no tendency to assume a dependent
attachment. He appreciated friendship and understanding, but it
was not in any sense to please me that he wished to make good.

The psychotherapy consisted largely in helping him to understand his own and others' emotional responses to the situation
and helping him to face unpleasant situations and admit the
truth—such things as the fact that he was unloved and unwanted
in the family, and that he must become interested in other athletics
than baseball, which was his greatest interest, as his vision was
too poor for him ever to play it well. By suggestion and in concrete ways he was brought to the place where he could feel that, after
all, he was not going to be inferior to others when he regained his
health and people understood him.

The thinking for John extended over several months. The carrying out of the plans was possible only because the parents were
obliged to co-operate when they realized that the situation was
socially serious. The mother and stepfather had many personality
difficulties of their own. Some of these were helped as this boy's
problems were solved. One of the fine placing agencies became

interested. They found an excellent foster-home in the country where the boy remained a year and attended school. His visitor and the school superintendent were very helpful and readily assumed the place in his life formerly occupied by the psychiatrist.

Results: John is now eighteen years old. Physically the results have been little short of marvellous. He has almost doubled his weight in two years. His eyesight is improved. His shoulders are straight and he looks his friends square in the face. He has a good job and is saving his money. After leaving his foster-home he lived in a Y. M. C. A. for a time and then found for himself, through church friendships, an excellent family where he rooms and enters into the family life. He occasionally sees his own family and now feels sorry for them. Both his mother and his stepfather have a much better attitude towards the boy. He appreciates what has been done for him as much as any boy possibly could.

At present John is a complete social and psychiatric success. The psychiatric success was made possible to a large extent by the fact that, while he had nothing else on the credit side of his ledger but his loyalties, he had many of these and they were excellent. It was attained by understanding the lad and his problems and helping him to understand them and, through this, to change his emotional responses to life. By suggestion and encouragement his loyalties were directed and augmented and his feeling of inferiority lessened. The success of the physical treatment had much to do with this, of course. Psychiatry was able to give much assistance to the social workers by helping them understand this lad and his problems.

John is a boy with whom many hours have been spent and who has been helped in many ways and on many occasions to face and solve hard problems. Great improvements have occurred in his physical condition, and many changes for the better in his personality responses have been made. Had John been treated earlier, the psychiatric task would have been easier and the results would be more certain of being lasting ones. In the summary he is classed as a temporary success.

*   *

The next boy I consider the most outstanding success of the entire group. With him the lack of loyalties, which was a large part of his problem, was directly based on his feeling of being unworthy and inferior.

Case No. 26
WILLIAM RICE

William Rice was eight inches underheight for his thirteen years, but a sturdy, healthy boy of normal nutrition. He was a good-looking lad, with dark expressive eyes. When he was first seen, his expression reminded one of the war-worn children of France. He appeared old, unhappy, and hopeless. He was tired, discouraged, and friendless. Mental tests showed him to be above normal. His I. Q. was 114. His mother, who died when William was five, was of German stock, his father an American. His stepmother is American.

The situation: William and his young brother are the only children of the father's first family. He has several younger half-siblings. He and his brother, one year younger, were seen in the clinic about a year before I knew him. They were at that time living a street life and stealing so extensively that his brother, who was much larger and considered to be the worse offender, was at that time placed in a school for delinquents. The clinic's advice at that time was strongly in favour of placing both boys, but this was not followed. After the mother's death they had been placed in several foster-homes until the father remarried, two years later. After his marriage the father refused to contribute to their support away from home and they were taken back to their undesirable home and to their stepmother, who was a rather weak character, busy and ignorant. Little attention was paid to the boys by either father or stepmother except frequently to punish and thwart them. They lived in a crowded tenement-house which was fairly well furnished. The church took an interest in the children. The father refused permission for the boy to take part in outside activities provided by church and school, but allowed him to run about the streets. Two weeks before I first saw William, he had been literally kicked out of the door and down a flight of steps by his father because of sex tampering with his six-year-old half-sister. He had been refused readmission and had lived in the alleys on the charity of the neighbours.

The boy was reported to be a day-dreamer, alert, emotional, untruthful, slack about clothes, seclusive, sensitive, hard to get acquainted with. He read much, was well-behaved in school, and liked school and church. He was not affectionate, but craved affection. The church worker believed he was ashamed of being so very small for his age. In the clinic a year earlier it was thought advisable that further psychiatric exploration should be undertaken to determine, if possible, whether or not the delinquency might be on the basis of an inferiority feeling, since his brother was much larger and better liked than he. At that time it was also suggested that personality help should be attempted. Neither of these things were done. Until the day before I first saw him, he had been living on the streets, night and day, for a period of two weeks. The church agency had taken him into a temporary home. He was interviewed for this agency.

Thinking about him: The first thing that one would necessarily think about, despite his remarkable history, would be his attitude and expression of dejection and sadness. These things were especially noticeable because of his very intelligent face. The story of his troubles and long-continued misbehaviours furnished much material to think about. The unnatural attitude of his parents made one think. It was especially interesting to think about possible causes of the unnatural and excessive sex drive of this boy, who from his size seemed to be eight years old and from his expression to be eighty. It was evident that the *thinking for* him was going to be of the greatest importance and that this must include a very thorough *thinking with* him if he was to be helped.

Thinking for him: The first thinking for him was easy and fortunately, through the co-operation of a very efficient church agency and a fine visitor, could be carried out. It was decided that if this boy was to be helped, thorough psychiatric exploration and much personality help must be given. He believed, and all who were interested in him hoped, that his home was closed to him. Of course some permanent plan had to be worked out eventually. But it was quite evident that an environmental change by itself was not likely to do much for this boy, especially when one considered the fact of his very unusual and strong instinctive-emotional reactions and his personality traits as they were reported to us. It was therefore first planned that he be placed in a temporary home where he would be cared for by the agency and where he might come to the clinic frequently. It was felt that a deep psychiatric rapport would be unquestionably indicated, but that it would be difficult to obtain.

Thinking with him: William felt that nothing mattered and that there was nothing to do about it. He believed that he was as bad as any boy could be. He said that, despite this, somehow he had never wanted to be bad and had always tried to think he was not. After his mother died, no one had liked him as well as they did his brother. He was never going to be able to overcome enuresis (a lifelong habit). He deserved all the punishment he had ever received and more. He did not blame his father for punishing him, but did blame him for not liking him. He said that he used to like his father very much. He believed he used to love him, but now he hated him. He said his father would never listen to him and did not understand him. From the first, William talked freely about his misbehaviour, admitting all the offences reported and many more that were not known. He was not particularly sorry for himself. He took most of the blame. He was a most thoroughly discouraged boy. After two or three interviews he became entirely frank. He could and did tell me of his emotional and instinctive life. Some of the interviews were held in the office, some on walks, and some during automobile rides to the woods or the shore. He told me of his day-dreams and his worries, and how sometimes, when he was bad, he could forget this unhappiness. As his confidence in my desire and ability to understand him increased, he was able to believe that it would be a good thing to try to think out all the unhappy things he had tried to forget. He said he had always tried to forget things that made him unhappy or that were bad. He did this, he said, because he really wanted to be a good boy, and it made him feel bad to think that he was not. Not only was he able to tell me how he felt about things now, but he could recall his early emotional life. We talked seriously about many things. We thought of his resentment towards his father, whom he first said he hated, later thought he loved, and still later made up his mind he only wanted to love because he was lonesome. We talked about his brother, who was better-looking, stronger, bigger, and better-liked than he. His brother could avoid getting into trouble better than he could. We talked of things in which he might possibly be considered superior to his brother. His feeling towards his brother was not one of loyalty. He admired him in a way, yet said that his brother was to blame for some of his unhappiness. He did not wish to see him again. We thought seriously about his dead mother and his few definite memories of her, which he treasured very highly. He dreamed about her and visualized her in his waking hours. Then there was the stepmother, who took her place in the crowded and unhappy home, and the younger half-siblings, who were better loved than he. His sex habits, conditioned by very early experiences, were one of the most important things we had to think about. This problem, like many of the others, showed a complicated situation and a complicated emotional response and must be thought out very carefully. William had had many wretched experiences of a sex nature, due largely to his bad environment. These had included mutual sex practices with his brother for a number of years, and he had, unfortunately, responded to them in a rather startling emotional way for one so young. He told us that what little happiness and pleasure he had in life were mostly obtained through these practices. Though he wished now never to see his brother again, he told me that he was strongly attracted to him. It was made very clear to this boy later, when he was willing to accept my opinions because they came from me, that nothing he had done had in any way injured his body and accounted for his very small stature, as he had feared. The thought that finally appealed to this boy was that the type of boy who indulges in such things was not the kind of boy whom people liked, because he was naturally ashamed and worried about them. It was a long time, however, before the latter idea could be given to him in this way, for it was found after several interviews that William had absolutely nothing in life to which he was loyal. He was not loyal to his environment, to his church (though it was the church that was now helping him), to his teachers, to himself, or to what he might some day be, for he did not believe in himself or in any of these others, nor did he believe that anyone cared for him. However, he was becoming interested in my effort to help him, anxious to come for his interviews, and eager for my approbation. And so this boy, while I was yet undecided whether it was best to go further than a personality contact or not, became dependently attached to me. And now, instead of telling him that others would like him better if his behaviour were different or if he felt differently about things, he must first be told that that was the way I felt. During the first part of his treatment it was the environment he wished to talk about. Seemingly it relieved him somewhat to confess all his misdeeds, after he came to trust me, but the remarkable change in his mood did not occur until he believed that I understood him, knew all about him, and still liked him. It was then that he became entirely frank in regard to his emotional life, and it was then that the most successful *thinking with* him about all his problems could be done.

He was seen every other day at first, and an hour or two would be spent with him each time. He told of many curious experiences and his feelings about them, things that he had tried hard to forget and still could not help thinking about sometimes. After a while he was told (and believed because it was I that told him) that a boy might do himself harm by trying not to remember things when he had not made up his mind about them or accepted the blame for them, if necessary, before he forgot them. Gradually, he came really to understand this and was co-operative in trying to recall and face his past life.

William was now becoming a different boy. The look of discouragement was leaving his face, and sometimes he seemed happy. He wished to come to see me very frequently and had to be told often of my confidence in his ability to make good and of the fact that I liked him. It was time to do a different type of thinking.

So his visitor and I *thought for* this boy again. First we thought that we must try to find a good home, and, more important than this, that in this home must be people who would understand and like him. The home was found; the church visitor made excellent contacts with the boy; the foster-mother was a very unusual person, but her peculiarities helped and fitted this boy. He came from the foster-home for interviews, at first often and later less frequently. I visited the foster-home twice and talked with his foster-mother and with the boy and mother together.

Later William was told frankly that I must now try to help other boys, and that while I should always be his friend and be very glad to help him if he needed help, other boys needed help more than he. A period of eight months ensued during which I did not see him. Occasional letters were written to him in answer to his interesting and healthy letters telling of his home and habits.

Results: This case is reported two years after all psychiatric contact has been broken. I have recently seen him at intervals of about six months. He is a fine boy, has grown ten inches in height, is happy, and has many loyalties towards his school, his excellent school record, his good health, his foster-mother, and, one might say, his entire environment. He is neat and clean and takes pride in it. There has been absolutely no delinquency of any kind. The enuresis ceased very soon after he went to his new home. He had earned some money and proudly brought it to me to ask my advice as to which bank was the safest. There were no demonstrations of affection whatever (although earlier he was allowed to make these), but he greeted me in a happy, care-free, boyish way with a good-natured grin and a hearty handshake. He says that there is some thought of having him live in the same foster-home with his brother. He says: "I should like that, but I don't know about it. Do you think, because we used to steal together and do other bad things, that it would be best?" Incidentally he said with a sparkle in his eyes that it had been several months now since he had even wanted to masturbate and that he had not done so since living in the foster-home. He remembers my former belief in the improbability of his being able to overcome the habit entirely and thinks the joke is on me. (Because it was felt that it would be very hard for this boy to get away from his bad habits he had been frankly told that his failure entirely to stop would not spoil his chances of making good and of being happy, but he was also told, of course, that if he did overcome the habit, it would be a very fine thing and would prove to himself and to me that he had good power of will.)

This boy's problems have been straightened out. The treatment has been successful. The social problem was serious and the solving of it might in itself have corrected his behaviour (it is doubtful if it would have done so), but his personality difficulties, involving, as they did, such a profound change of mood, could not have been solved by social adjustments.

The developing of good loyalties was the thing that brought success. This was made possible by establishing a very deep rapport with the boy and later being able to transfer the loyalties thus developed to other people and things.

William was in the beginning, of all the normal children the the writer has ever known, the most utterly discouraged and hopeless. He is now a fine, happy, active, and well-adjusted boy. Perhaps other methods of dealing with him would have been as successful. The writer feels that they would not have been, in his hands.

CHAPTER IX

MENTAL AND NEUROLOGICAL DISEASES

The Child who Lacks or Loses his Equipment for Life

O F all the children whom the psychiatrist tries to help, those with mental or neurological diseases are the most difficult and among the most to be pitied. Many times the problem only appears to belong to the psychiatrist until such a time as the physical diagnosis may definitely be made. Sometimes the physical and mental problems complicate one another. It is not the psychiatrist's privilege to say to the physician: "First give the child a well-functioning body and then I will attempt to do my part." For sometimes a little personality help may be given and a little happiness added to the life of these unhappy children with physical handicaps and mental defects by what the psychiatrist may do. In all of the six cases following, in this much more definite group than the others, the mental or physical abnormality was suspected before treatment was undertaken. In two—the second and the last—the diagnosis was definitely made before treatment had begun. In none of them was the treatment discontinued because a diagnosis of physical diseases was made.

* *

The first boy was suffering from a definite mental disease. Such children should be studied in an institution rather than in a guidance clinic, but until this becomes more generally possible, to observe

195

and try to understand their mental life and to help them meet their problems as best one can will at least do no harm.

Case No. 27
CHADWICK LUNT

Chadwick was a small but healthy little boy of Negro parentage. He was thirteen years old. His expression was sad. He was uncommunicative and uninterested. Mental tests, conducted with difficulty, rated him as of poor ability.

The situation: Chadwick was brought to the clinic for a diagnosis. His history was given by his unobserving and busy aunt, with whom he lived. This story told of peculiar solitary running away from home, of hours spent in the home in day-dreaming, of his frequent refusal to take part in play, and of vague statements that seemed to indicate that the boy was having auditory hallucinations.

Thinking about the boy: Chadwick did not talk and would answer questions only by gestures or monosyllables. Though, from the history and his behaviour during the tests, he seemed to be abnormal enough to warrant a diagnosis of a beginning psychosis, it was felt in conference that it would be at least very interesting, if not therapeutically helpful, to know something of what was going on in this boy's mind. (It was interesting that he had come to the clinic on the first day for his tests without his breakfast and remained in the clinic until almost two o'clock before this fact was discovered and before it was noticed that no one had taken him to lunch. He had said nothing about it, but seemed pleased when he was taken.) The history as given by the relatives was too vague to warrant spending much time *thinking about* him.

Thinking for him: Advice as to the social handling of the boy was needed. The better he could be understood, the better this could be given, of course, and it was decided, partially as an experiment and partially for social reasons, to attempt the establishment of a positive rapport.

Thinking with him: He was seen for three other quite long interviews. Very slowly he seemed to learn to trust me. At first I did all the talking and told him many things about the ideas and feelings of other boys I have known, which I guessed might be similar to those that he was experiencing. While he showed but little interest in this, he did listen and for some reason or other commenced to tell me about himself. I felt that, while the rapport was no deeper than that of a friendly belief, I actually had attained this, a definite accomplishment in the case of this peculiar ego-centric boy.

He told interestingly, but in an abstract way, of many things in his mind which he had confided to no one else. The hallucinations were very definite experiences. The words were vague, but he felt they had certain meanings. He said of his runaways that some of them were caused by thinking he heard the voices talking or by dreams that he had. When he had run away and was sleeping in cars at night, the voices would be more friendly than they were at home and he was not so much afraid of them. On his runaways he could and would enter into games among strange boys more than among acquaintances. He told these things in an abstract way, with no show of emotion.

He told of his shortcomings and delinquencies. These were but mild, and most of them had occurred much earlier.

The only thing to which he gave any emotional response at all was in regard to his religious belief. He connected these voices in some vague way with religion and God. He believed that lying is a very bad sin and said that one reason he did not like to talk when first seen at the clinic was that he did not want to lie.

During the next interview he seemed much more like a normal boy than he did earlier. It was evident that his habit of physical withdrawal from his environment accentuated his mental peculiarities, and it was easy to see that this boy would be happier and would get more from life when away from home among strangers, if what he said about being able to mingle with them better was true.

Chadwick's case is interesting in two ways. It demonstrates that it is possible to develop a positive rapport with a child who is developing a psychosis, and it also illustrates that the rapport itself is not always a therapeutic weapon and that it is a very difficult one to use in meeting such situations.

Results: The boy, a year later, is gradually becoming less accessible to others. Special arrangements have been made whereby he is not compelled to attend school. He will soon be an institutional case. The fact that I failed to help the boy when some degree of rapport had been established, in no way proves that help might not have been given with unlimited time and opportunity, but during the treatment I felt the hopelessness of it very strongly.

*   *

The next boy when first seen presented an unusual problem in that he was a very unhappy *feeble-minded boy*. Treatment was undertaken with a definite plan of trying to make him less unhappy. As the long treatment progressed and evidence of mental disease developed, I was given some insight into this deep unhappiness, which at the beginning seemed so unusual.

Case No. 28
MELVIN ANNETT

Melvin has been one of the clinic's regular visitors for more than four years. He was eleven years old when first seen. His health has always been good, his physical development somewhat above the age average. The change in the appearance of the boy may be judged from the notes in regard to this taken from his first and last physical examinations. The first describes him as "an active, healthy, good-looking youngster"; the last, "a dull, coarse, irregular-featured boy." The psychological examinations which have been made at intervals of about a year show a remarkable consistency in all respects. His intelligence quotient as first determined was 73, at the second test given him 72, and at the last two 73. This is particularly interesting because of the fact that the boy, in his appearance and somewhat in his responses, seemed to be gradually deteriorating. His school-work had always been below that of his mental age.

The situation: His first appearance in the clinic was for the purpose of receiving advice and social and educational adjustment. At that time and later there have been other interesting aspects to his problems. The environmental situation has remained quite the same. He has two younger brothers. These children are above the average in mentality. The boys all make their home with their father and stepmother. Their father and mother were divorced four years ago. The mother still sees the boys regularly. The home is physically good, and the stepmother kind and patient with the children, especially so with Melvin. A paternal grandmother lives in the home and is devoted to the boy.

At the time of the first study his personality traits were reported as follows: "He is independent, solitary in habits, excessively sensitive, remembering injuries and slights for a long time. He seems to be more alert and to notice more things said that might be interpreted as derogatory to him than one would expect. At times he is disobedient, always slow, but anxious to do things well. There are many days on which he seems to be more unhappy than usual. He is never happy. The change that is gradually occurring has mostly shown itself by a greater tendency to stay by himself. Recently there has been some active day-dreaming, which frequently causes him suddenly to laugh aloud."

Thinking about the boy: This boy is classed as a high-grade moron. There are many unusual and interesting things to think about in his case. He is very sensitive, often entirely misinterpreting statements or behaviour of others as reflecting on him. He has most unusual ambitions and a dogged stick-to-it-iveness that one cannot but admire, though one realizes that they add tremendously to his problems and to his unhappiness.

It is this acute, alert unhappiness that is the most remarkable of all his responses. When thinking about Melvin in connexion with other feeble-minded children, one is very thankful that those traits are not usually found.

Thinking for him: It was felt in conference that if in any way this unhappy lad could be made happier, it should be done. It was believed that if his mental life might be better understood, possibly better social and environmental advice might be given. It was also thought that if a good rapport could be established, the one who in this way gained his trust and loyalty might help him to face and understand life better.

Thinking with him: In psychiatric interviews Melvin responded differently from most children with his mental equipment. He reached the rapport of personality contact very quickly. Because of his responses he has been encouraged to maintain this relation and has been seen regularly during the past two years. He has given during that time and in that rapport much interesting material to think about. In his slow, plodding way he has thought with me about many problems that most children with an intelligence quotient of 73 could not recognize as existing.

Melvin has never been questioned deeply about his mental problems or urged to tell about them. He wants to do so, and at each visit he has new questions to ask and he asks the old ones over again, saying he has forgotten. But he has not forgotten. He likes to hear again such encouragement as someone whom he can trust may give him.

"Is there ever any boys who can't learn like me who maybe get so they can learn fast?" "Does an engineer on a train have to be smart?" "Are you sure you know I can make my living when I grow big?" "I wish I was big now, only I'm afraid I can't make my living." "How did my brothers learn to be smart?" "What makes folks like my brothers better than me?" "Does it hurt you to die?" "Can anyone always be good if they try to?" On every occasion I have seen him, he has talked about and wished he were older and could earn his own living. Over and over again he says he does not want other folks to have to give him money. He never has failed to thank me at the close of the interview for talking to him.

Melvin and I have thought about many practical things that might help him with his problems. (At one time we decided that it might help to make his home more pleasant if I were to see his brothers. Possibly this helped with the situation somewhat. The brothers willingly came. They proved to be intelligent boys who were anxious to help Melvin in any way they could. They had been noticing his increasing unhappiness and were concerned about it.) We thought about Melvin's unusual ability to find his way in strange places. He can be trusted to go from one part of the city to another, even though he has never been there before, as well as the average boy of his age or better.

When I first knew Melvin, he was just entering a somewhat premature puberty. At that time he was disgusted and worried about some experiences he had had with another boy, who had attempted to teach him sex habits. Recently he has been more concerned about these old happenings and about his own developing sex emotions. He says: "One reason I want to come and see you is that you will tell me more about these dirty things." He badly needs someone to think both with him and for him concerning his sex problems. At his last interview he told me that he could not refrain from hunting for news dispatches about sex attacks and sex murders. He would find them and persist until his grand-mother would read them to him. He says that the ones that tell about crazy men who perpetrate these attacks make him feel "awful funny and bad." He says: "They make me feel like if maybe I would do such things some time, but then I won't. I'd be afraid. Anyway, it's wrong." Melvin has never masturbated.

He has always talked about suicide. At first it was simply be-cause of an interest he had in it. More lately he has been think-ing about suicide. He says: "I might do it if I were not a coward, but I won't. It would hurt me, and I'm afraid."

One interesting thing about this boy is the fact that he is always happier and less worried and upset for a time after he talks with me. He is always anxious to come for an interview. He is very careless about his dress (though he is painstaking about most things) except when he is coming to the clinic, when he will dress himself with great care.

Results: His parents feel that his interviews do him so much temporary good that they are of great help, both to them and to the boy. He seems less discouraged and a little more extroverted for a short time after them. He seems to do a little better in his school-work. (He is working in an ungraded class and making but little progress, though he always tries hard.) I have tried to encourage Melvin in every way I could without doing so in a way that would make him unhappy later. He considers me a very good friend and thinks I understand how he feels. While this latter belief, I fear, is not true to any great extent, it is one that may be encouraged without later doing him harm.

The family believes that to some extent the boy's personality traits have been changed for the better. This is very doubtful. However, two definite things have been accomplished: one is that the boy has been made happier, and the other is that I have established myself in his and the family's confidence to the extent that if he becomes an institutional case, as he probably will soon, I may be of help to them in adjusting to the situation.

During the year following my first interviews with Melvin the boy was for several months in a foster-home on a large farm. Here he did well, but finally became dissatisfied and is now at home again. He sees either Dr. Bronner or me occasionally. He desires these interviews. He still has remarkable insight into his mental life for a boy who is presenting many definite psychotic symptoms. Perhaps if he can continue to have a little psychiatric bolstering up from time to time he may live always outside of an institution. But I feel that he will always be of potential danger to others as well as to himself.

If the psychiatrist keeps a numerical summary of his successes and failures and refers to it for encouragement, he will not find so much as he will if he remembers the children as individuals.

* *

The next two boys are representative of that very important and rapidly increasing group who suffer from organic changes due to acute encephalitis. These two boys, who were so similar in behaviour and responses that they seemed at times to be the same boy, are very typical of many of these unfortunate children.

Case No. 29
MANLEY HILL

Manley first came to the clinic nearly three years ago when he was eleven years old. He was a large, well-developed boy. His physical condition was then excellent. It was noticed, however, that he had a slight asymmetry of facial muscles. Because of this, at the time he was first studied, a neurological consultant was asked to see him. His report was negative. There was no history of serious illness. Mentally his tests at that time gave him an I. Q. of 95.

The situation: Manley was a distractible, irritable, over-active, and uninhibited boy. These traits and extensive stealing were making him a very serious problem in his home. He was the bad boy of a large family of otherwise fine children. His parents were intelligent and co-operative. His father was a professional man, residing near the clinic. It was possible to see and study this boy under the best circumstances. The parents reported that the boy had been for more than two years extensively delinquent at home and in school. He had been truant, disobedient, and impudent. He had stolen many valuable articles from his neighbours, friends, and strangers. It had been only with the greatest difficulty that his father had kept him from appearing in the juvenile court.

The parents, when first seen, said that his behaviour had always been bad; but later, after carefully considering the matter, they decided that there had been a rather sudden change for the worse about three years before.

Thinking about the boy: His behaviour suggested the possibility of a post-encephalitic reaction, but nothing in the physical examination or in the history tended to substantiate this opinion. It was best, therefore, to think about Manley as a boy with mental conflicts, and for several weeks he was seen and treated with this idea in mind.

After several weeks, however, and before the physical changes began to be observed, a diagnosis of post-encephalitic changes was made on his behaviour responses alone.

Thinking for him: Psychotherapeutic endeavour was really decided upon as the best method of diagnosis. It was felt in conference that the excessively upsetting behaviour of this boy justified this, even though, with his unusual personality responses, he was unlikely to receive help and might even become more upset by the treatment.

Thinking with him: During the treatment Manley displayed the same peculiar responses reported by his parents as part of the problem. On some days, and at times during only a part of a particular interview, he would be a serious, unhappy, thoughtful lad. He would be critical of himself and sincere in his desires to be a better boy. At other times he would be an uninhibited "devil-may-care" boy with the desire to shock people by brazenly telling of his behaviour and experiences in an exaggerated way.

This lad, however, reached a very definite personality contact with me, and there was no time during the treatment (nor has there been even yet) when I could not for a few moments at least, if alone with him, bring the quiet, serious side of his nature to the surface. At these times all the known and most of the theoretical sources of possible mental conflicts were discussed. The boy was frank and reaching out for help. He carried out my suggestions as far as it was physically possible, and he would temporarily accept my ideas. I believe that had this boy's behaviour been on any other than a physical basis, his personality responses could have been changed.

Results: He has now developed many physical signs of change in the central nervous system. The diagnosis is held in reserve and rests between a brain tumour and changes following *encephalitis lethargica*. He has developed a hemiplegia and has unequal reflexes. There are some slight eye-changes. He is deteriorating mentally and is being cared for in an institution.

The case is a failure, of course, as far as the end results are concerned. I still see the boy occasionally. He enjoys talking with me, and, even though usually boisterous and over-active or sullenly quiet, he will at some time during the interview become serious and thoughtful and tell me in some way that I have done a great deal to help him. He still believes that I will be the one who will cure him.

Case No. 30
REMP MALONE

Remp was a sturdy, happy, over-active boy of ten years when he was first studied, three years ago. His physical examination was then and is still entirely negative. Mentally he was of good average ability.

The situation: Remp was one of a family of twelve living children. He lived in a distant city. The parents were well-educated people who provided a fine home in every way for this large family. They said that if all the bad behaviour of the other eleven children and the trouble made by them were added together and multiplied by four, the result would still be less than Remp's record would show. Stealing, truancy, frequent runaways, and bunking out were reported as having long been a part of the lad's behaviour. More recently, following a period of truancy, he had absolutely refused to attend school.

Thinking about the boy: The boy's behaviour during interviews

furnished material for thought. He was distractible in the extreme.
His mood changed very rapidly. He would be crying bitterly because he had made so much trouble and was a bad boy and would
suddenly stop, go to the window, which was twelve stories above
the ground, and ask if he would be hurt if he jumped out.

He liked to talk about all his delinquencies, but most of all he
liked to tell of his sex knowledge and experiences. These were
known to be largely, if not entirely, in his imagination. He was an
excellent conversationalist for a lad of his age and could use the
most vulgar as well as the more acceptable sex terms in an unusually uninhibited and unemotional way.

Remp said there were two boys in his chest, and he always
pointed to his chest when he said this. One of them liked to be good
and one did not like to go to school. He said that this latter one
would not let him sit still. At times there was a feeling in his head
as though it were suddenly swelling and something inside his breast
turned round. He had great difficulty in restraining himself, at my
suggestion, from playing with the desk calendar. The bad boy
usually had his way, however, and it would be only for a few
moments that he could let it alone.

Thinking for the boy: There were no physical signs and no history of even the slightest illness. One could hardly feel justified in
making a diagnosis of physical changes or at least in being so sure
of the diagnosis as to decide not to attempt psychotherapeutic help.
For even if one fails to help a child in Remp's situation, one may
at least help others in the boy's environment who wish to do all
they can to solve his problem, by making them feel that attempts
are being made.

Thinking with the boy: Although Remp's moments of serious
thoughtfulness were few, they were interesting. His mother had
been told in his presence that he probably had some disease that

accounted for his behaviour. This was a serious subject for Remp to think about and he tried not to take it seriously. But at times for a few moments he would face his whole situation, and I believe that during these short periods he firmly intended to do better. His usual responses were not of this sort. He said he could not keep from truanting and that he would not want to be changed. It was the same with his other behaviour.

Personality contact was established with Remp, for during his sober moments he trusted me and wished me to understand him and believed that I did. He believed it so strongly, in fact, that he assumed I really did not expect him to change his behaviour. He asked me: "If you had those feelings and could not sit still, would you go to school?" Several interviews, considerably separated, were given this boy. At the end nothing seemed to have been accomplished. His behaviour would sometimes improve for a few hours following interviews and sometimes would seemingly be worse.

Results: The lad is now a very troublesome and unhappy boy, in an institution not suited for his care. A diagnosis of post-encephalitic changes has been made, almost entirely on the basis of personality responses and changes. Remp was a complete social and psychiatric failure. In the present state of his knowledge all that the psychiatrist may hope to do for these children is make them a little happier, and during the time I treated Remp I accomplished this.

While as yet we know we may do little to help these children, establishment of a good rapport with them may add to the understanding of their mental life and to our knowledge of their care, if not eventually to the therapeusis.

*   *

The next boy—or young man, more properly speaking—was definitely abnormal mentally when first seen. He is the oldest of the entire group and was treated mostly because it seemed that the contacts that would be made with him during the period of treatment might help in social adjustments.

Case No. 31
HUDSON ELLIS

Hudson's case will not be reported in any detail, but simply be mentioned as a complete failure both in establishing any therapeutic rapport and in giving any therapeutic help.

He was an older boy than is usually studied at the clinic. He had most excellent and successful grandparents. His mother died early. His father (probably suffering from paranoia) was peculiar and excessively cruel to him. The boy himself was diagnosed at the clinic as pre-psychotic. Because his life-story was particularly unhappy and his future so dark unless something could be done, and because it seemed that, no matter what his mental condition was at the time, there must have been many earlier mental conflicts, it was decided to try to establish a rapport, with the idea of giving him personality help if possible.

Thinking about him led only to the confirmation of the earlier diagnosis. The *thinking for him* did accomplish something in improving his physical situation and protecting him from unjust punishment.

Thinking with him was impossible. He became apparently entirely frank and told a most distressing story in an abstract egocentric way, but he did so because he believed that in this way he could sooner end his irksome visits to the clinic. He was in no way interested in the fact that others were interested in him.

Results: The boy is now being cared for in an institution. This case only further illustrates a fact frequently pointed out by Dr.

Healy: It is difficult to give personality help to any child in the group usually loosely called psychopathic personalities, and of all the various types within this group the ego-centric individual is the most difficult to help.

*   *

The last of this group is one of the four of the entire series who had his problems increased and his adjustments made more difficult by the attempts at therapy. The tentative diagnosis of psychogenetic epilepsy was made at the beginning of the treatment after a negative report from one of the best neurological clinics in the country, and this diagnosis is probably correct.

Case No. 32
FRANK WARD

When we first knew Frank in the clinic, he was fourteen years old. He was a tall, fairly well-developed, good-looking boy. He walked with an erect posture and had an open, pleasant, and direct expression. He had been studied in several good neurological clinics and treated extensively for epilepsy. He had both major and minor attacks. (This condition was considered to be of a probable psychogenic origin by others and by ourselves.) Early in life he had had illness with convulsions, and at the age of four the major attacks began. These always appeared very regularly, usually to the day, every two months. During the last two years he had developed various types of minor attacks which took the form of temporary unconsciousness, lasting about fifteen seconds, accompanied by a jerking of the head to the right. He never fell or had any accident as a result of these. They were always more noticeable when he was emotionally upset about anything, especially when some unpleasant occurrence in his past life was recalled. Mentally

Frank was somewhat above the average in general ability, and his school-work was excellent.

The situation: He was a refined boy, very particular in his personal habits and in his appearance. He was sensitive and unhappy because of his physical troubles, and the events of his life brought him greater unhappiness because of his attitudes. His grandfather, with whom he lived, reported him to be usually helpful and cheerful about the home, but subject to changes of mood and occasionally exhibiting spells of temper in which he said cutting and disagreeable things. He was somewhat neglectful of his duties. His interests were normally boyish and he played football successfully.

His parents were early unhappy, and when Frank was five, a separation occurred, the father running away with another woman. Since then his mother had remarried twice. Both stepfathers failed to like or understand the boy. An older sister who was much loved by Frank had been delinquent and was now a great source of worry to him. Frank was separated from his younger brother, about whom he also worried because he believed the boy had bad habits. His relatives always predicted and prepared for his major attacks, which usually came on the day they were expected to occur. (The boy was seen in the clinic during one of them. It was a typical *grand mal* attack, lasting an hour or more.)

Frank was brought to the clinic for analysis and an attempt to understand his mental life, and possibly to be given help by psychotherapeutic treatment.

Thinking about the boy: His physical condition had been studied and very extensively treated by others. The only thing to be decided in thinking about him was as to the advisability of attempting the establishment of a deep enough rapport to permit an exploration of his mental life and whether or not this was a wise procedure in so serious and long-standing a problem. There was no reason to do this unless there appeared to be some hope of helping him, for it was easily seen that such an experience might be an additional upsetting factor.

Thinking for him: Because of the seriousness of the situation and the desire of the family that everything possible be done, it was decided to undertake a mental exploration and psychotherapy.

Thinking with him: The boy was friendly and frank from the first. Good personality contact was easily established. He told of many instances in his early life that were of tremendous emotional importance to him, and he told how these experiences had depressed him and kept him awake nights. He said that he had always made great efforts to forget unhappiness. He believed me, however, when he was told that he might receive help by bringing these things to the surface and frankly telling of them. Because of his confidence in my opinion and of his desire for help he was entirely co-operative in this, though it was far from easy for him to be so. Associative memory interviews were held and many vague and half-forgotten experiences were remembered. An attempt was made always to think these things out with him, to give them their true value as they affected his life at present, and to encourage him to accept new emotional attitudes.

The fact seemed evident that this boy was profoundly lonesome and felt himself unloved and unwanted. It was remarkable to find how much responsibility he expected he must carry when he became a man. He believed that his mother would be dependent on him, and that he would have to support his sister and her family. He assumed that his entire life must be given over to this. His family loyalties were very strong in regard to all his relatives. Early in his life he had known of many things which he was trusted to keep secret. It was felt that this may have had a conditioning influence on his feeling of responsibility towards his family.

He really had experienced a number of very unhappy and upsetting things. For many of these it was difficult to offer any helpful suggestions as to his mental attitude, especially since all the members of his family failed to understand them.

What little was accomplished in changing any of these unfortunate beliefs and attitudes, with their resultant worries, seemed only to be done as he admired and became attached to me. While he was not encouraged, no attempt was made to prevent his assuming a feeling of dependent attachment, which he did. For a time he was happier and better adjusted to his home. Possibly his physical condition was slightly improved. His minor attacks nearly disappeared and he missed one of his regular major attacks at a time when his family was instructed to say nothing about it and not to prepare for it.

Unfortunately, through unavoidable circumstances the contact with the clinic was suddenly broken.

Results: After this for a time the lad wrote very friendly personal letters and then suddenly changed his feelings towards me and did not write. He said that he did not want to see me any more. He became even more unhappy than before. He was more of a problem in the home, and at last reports his physical condition was quite the same as it had been before he was seen in the clinic. His personality problems were greater.

Undoubtedly, the psychotherapy in this case was harmful. The sudden breaking of the treatments may have been to blame. It certainly was unfortunate, for perhaps something permanent might have been accomplished. But the greater probability is that it was an error to go so intimately into the mental life of the boy, who had such serious problems, when there was so small a chance of helping him. No one could be sure that his condition was not entirely a physical one. After he had told of his intimate mental life, it was very easy to find theoretical psychogenic causes, and it was felt that at least the form of the attacks, undoubtedly, was conditioned by his experiences.

In this case the *thinking for* him and the *thinking about* him were badly mixed. In the treatment the *thinking about* him probably carried too far into the *thinking with* him.

CHAPTER X

PSYCHIC TRAUMA

EW children, either normal or otherwise, go through life without experiences similar to those that act as serious mental and emotional traumas in many cases. The way the child responds, and not the occurrence itself, is the important thing. In fact, the same experience that causes serious trouble in the mental life of one child may be the thing that in some way causes another to take a more normal attitude towards life. Early sex experience for one child may cause a lifelong repression that makes for permanent unhappiness and even mental disease, while the same experience for another may produce a wholesome, healthy, childish desire to avoid such things, without causing him to worry or to feel guilty in any way.

*   *

The first boy to be described had an experience that was definitely traumatic, while this same experience has been for many boys of this series the thing that saved them from a life of failure and unhappiness.

Case No. 33
ROY WALDOCK

Roy is a boy who, once having been known, is not forgotten. When he was first seen in the clinic, four years ago, he was eleven years old. He was a very short, poorly nourished, desperately unhappy, but friendly lad. The examination revealed no evidence of definite disease, though he was wan and pale and appeared much below par physically. Mentally his tests gave him an intelligence quotient of 90. He co-operated in these, though he cried most of the time while he was taking them.

The situation: He was first referred to the clinic for study because of extreme home-sickness. Two months before this he had been removed from as bad an environmental situation as any child can have and had been placed in a church home for destitute children.

His parents had been arrested many times for selling liquor and drugs and for conducting a house of prostitution, where the lowest types of men congregated and where frequent fights and brawls occurred. The parents had been in jail a number of times. The hours this boy and his older brother had kept were very irregular. Frequently they were roused from their sleep that their beds might be used by inmates of the house. The food, while sufficient, was irregularly served. The children were encouraged to stay on the streets much so that they would be out of the way. During the period of two months that the boy had been away from his home, he had cried almost without ceasing. He slept but little. In fact, on several occasions he was known to have remained awake the entire night, quietly crying and moaning. His behaviour in the foster-home, however, was good. He co-operated as well as he could in the activities of the children, was helpful, attended school regularly. He received good grades, even though his tears seldom ceased during studies or recitations. He wanted his mother. He said it was not to go home, it was not because he was in the school, but because he wanted to see his mother and be with her that he cried. A short time before I saw him, the matron of the home had found him with a rope tied around his neck. It was evident that it was a serious attempt at suicide, for he was going about it quietly and in an unfrequented place.

(After his first interview the recommendation of the clinic to the court was that the boy be allowed to return to his home. The excessively delinquent mother loved the boy in her way and was very kind to him. This recommendation was given only because of the tremendous emotional conflict in the boy's life, which continued unabated after two months, even though his foster-home was as good as one could expect to find.)

The second study of him in the clinic, two years later, was made at the request of a different court. In this court he had been placed on probation because of gang delinquency. His family situation had changed but slightly. Again there was an unhappy emotional experience complicating his responses. His brother, one year older, of whom he was very fond, had been placed in an institution for the treatment of osteotuberculosis. This had been done against the wishes of his parents. Roy had been grieving and crying because his brother was gone, but his reactions were as nothing compared to his earlier ones when he had been separated from his mother.

The mother was seen at the clinic. She proved to be a most impossible person, with no redeeming qualities except the loyalty and love she had for this lad and his brother. This had taken the most unfortunate form of protecting him from all efforts of various agencies which were interested in the children and anxious to give them the help they so badly needed.

Thinking about the boy: One might think forever about this wretched environmental situation and why the boy responded as he did to it and to his mother, but unless one knew what was in the boy's mind, one could in no way understand the boy.

Thinking for him: His responses were evident enough, but one must know why he responded in this way before any constructive plans could be made or advice given to the social agencies. No boy could need help more than Roy did, and mental exploration was justified on diagnostic grounds alone. One could not feel that there was much hope of giving him personality help.

Thinking with him: Roy came to the clinic in the attitude of personal trust. He knew that it was through the advice given there that he had been allowed to return to his mother, and he hoped that his brother might now be returned to the family in the same way.

A personality contact was very easily established. He was asked no questions about his home situation, but when he became interested in my understanding of his thoughts and feelings, he told of many terrible things that happened in the home of which he was afraid and which he did not understand. He would tell of these things only as it became necessary to do so to describe his own experiences and worries and to tell of his own problems. He assumed that the things he told would not be repeated.

He became willing to consider my ideas and give them much more value than he would those of a person to whom he had not given his trust and confidence. There was a point, however, beyond which he would not go. He had the most deeply rooted, unchangeable loyalty to his mother that I have ever seen in a boy. He quickly convinced me that I could in no way change this trait even if I had wished to do so. The fact that the boy could see this was probably why he so thoroughly believed that I understood how he felt.

Roy was not distorting reality or denying the existence of his problems. He frequently stayed under the porch until very late at night, or even at times all night, to avoid being in the group of fighting and carousing men and women in his home. He had often pleaded with his mother to move away, or at least to keep out of the bad things herself. He believed that some time she would take him and go away as she often had told him she would, if he were a good boy. Roy told of the things that his mother had said to him. Her life's problems must have been very great. She would tell Roy and his brother that what she and their father were doing was very wrong and bad, and that they must never do such things. Immediately afterwards she would become drunk and drive the children from the house. But she was Roy's mother and he loved her, and she loved him. No ideas that others might give this boy could change these responses. These facts must be accepted and dealt with both in the *thinking for* and in the *thinking with* this lad.

When Roy was asked about his sex habits, his response was so spontaneous and sincere that one knew it came from the fundamental part of his mental life. He said: "Doctor, I'm just a boy and I'm little and I don't feel that way yet. I hope it will be a long time before I do. My mother says it will. I don't think any kid who sees those men would want to think about such things as that himself. I've had drunken men sometimes get into my bed and try to teach me to do such things and have had them do them to me, but it just makes me sick and makes me cry and I run away."

The only one of his problems about which I have tried to have him copy my responses and accept my ideas was that of his brother's necessary absence from home. I was successful in this, and the lad seemingly convinced his mother—a thing that I had earlier failed to do when I talked with her. Other than this the deep rapport was not used therapeutically. He was advised, encouraged, and praised, as he could have been had he felt only a personal trust for me.

Results: Again the advice of the clinic was against separating him from his mother. He remained in the same environment for a few months. Occasionally during this time he came to see me voluntarily. Though there was more trouble in the home, the boy was happier because of the fact that he could tell me his troubles freely, but more because his mother was now seriously considering going away with him. Finally the mother came to the clinic and announced that she and the boy were going by themselves to a distant city to make a fresh start. She was subdued and less impossible. Roy was with her and she seemed like a real mother who not only loved her boy, but who wished to help him.

They carried out this plan. Recently a social check-up on the boy, through an agency in the city where he now lives, shows that the boy is doing very well, seems happy, and has a good school report. His mother is working and the boy is helping after school hours. There is no mention in the report of any suspected delinquency on the part of either the mother or the boy.

This case is a success. Credit should mostly be given to Roy himself. Psychiatric treatments gave him some personality help and a good deal of encouragement. The psychiatric understanding led to the advice given to the social agency, which, though given with timidity, later proved to be sound.

One did not need to know the mental dynamisms at work in Roy's mind to help him. All that was necessary was to know what set the dynamisms in motion and to remove the cause. Psychiatry added its part to the solution of the problem only by recognizing that this boy simply could not live without his mother.

*   *

The next boy had so many sides to his problems that he could be grouped in any one of several of these chapters. His trauma existed in several widely scattered experiences.

Case No. 34
NATHAN POLUSO

Nathan Poluso, the thirteen-year-old brother of Cases No. 15 and

46, had many serious physical handicaps. He was three inches short for his age and underweight even for his height. His vision, corrected by glasses, was only one-third normal. His hearing was defective at times, while at others it was nearly normal. His face was asymmetrical, his small mouth mis-shapen, owing to the faulty alignment of his teeth. He squinted a great deal in an attempt to see better through the thick, heavy, noticeable lenses. He distorted his lips when he talked. Earlier he had had a bad speech defect and had been in a special class on this account. His mother reported that all his life, at irregular intervals, he had suffered from enuresis. At the time I first knew him, he had a lisp in pronouncing his s's and r's, but his voice was rather pleasant in tone. In spite of all these things his expression was noticeably intelligent, and he was liked by people who met him casually. He was very active and alert in all his responses.

He showed superior intelligence on age-level tests, in spite of the fact that he co-operated poorly in taking them. His I. Q. was 146.

The situation: His parents and siblings thought him the largest disturbing factor in a home full of disturbance, quarrels, unhappiness, and economic stress. His only delinquency, aside from his behaviour at home, was to keep for his own use a part of the money he earned by selling papers. He was searched thoroughly by his parents when he returned from paper-selling and was severely punished when caught holding out money.

His family reported that he was nervous, easily upset, and fond of street and gang life, but that he kept out of the gang's delinquencies. He was fond of music and had quickly learned to play several instruments. He played the banjo in the school orchestra. He was happy at one time and unhappy at another and always subject to sudden changes of moods. His school reports were excellent, as far as scholastic attainments were concerned. His behaviour in school was sometimes very good and sometimes very bad. He was first brought to the clinic because he himself had gone to the agency which had placed his smaller brother in a foster-home and asked them to place him. He said he did not believe it fair for his brother, who was so delinquent, to be rewarded, while he was compelled to stay at home.

Thinking about the boy: The question was why Nathan was behaving as he did. The most obvious answer was that he was compensating for his feeling of inferiority and attempting to make others and himself believe that he was not inferior. Another question was what were the lad's real feelings regarding the great efforts he was successfully making to overcome his physical handicaps. His teachers reported that his adjustments to school had been much better since he had been in the sight-saving class for the past year.

While it was quite possible that his disturbing behaviour might be on a basis of some obscure mental response to life, it might also be explained as quite a normal reaction of this handicapped boy to a very unpleasant environment. As with his brother, it was felt that this boy could not be thought *for* or *about* successfully until good *personality contact* was established with him, thus making possible an understanding of his emotional life.

A number of interviews failed to establish anything deeper than the rapport of *personal trust*. He was interested intellectually in my opinions and trusted me as his friend to give good advice. He told me many things which he did not expect me to repeat. But he did not develop any real desire that I should understand the way he felt. He seemed entirely frank, as far as his behaviour and experiences were concerned. I reached the erroneous conclusion that he was not having any worries or mental upsets and that the problem was largely a social one.

Thinking with him: Because of this conclusion I did very little serious *thinking with* the boy, although I gave him advice and suggestions and praised his successes. We did not discuss his handicaps as such. I made no attempt to change his personality traits or his emotional responses, because I did not understand them well enough to be sure that it was best to change them, even if I could.

Thinking for him: He was placed in a foster-home at some distance, where he was apparently much happier and did well in school over a period of several months. He made many friends among his schoolmates, and the adults in his new environment liked him. We seemed to have accomplished a social success. After a time in this foster-home he began to be dissatisfied and wrote letters to his visitor saying that he wanted to come home. He would give his visitor no reasons for this, either in his letters or in personal interviews. He said he would tell no one but the doctor why he wanted to leave. He wrote letters to me saying the same thing and expressing his desire for an interview. Circumstances made it impossible to see him for some time. When I finally saw him, he seemed for the first hour quite the same boy as formerly. (Later he said that I seemed different from the way he had remembered me and that he was afraid.) Soon he grew courageous and told his story. He was allowed to do this in his own way. I asked him very few questions and made few comments. Before he had finished, he was in most excellent *personality contact*. During the rest of our long interview Nathan "thought out loud" if ever a boy did. And this was a rare opportunity to think closely with a person. He said that the reason he could tell no one else was that he was afraid no one else would believe him and understand how he felt.

The boy's story was one of long-continued sex attacks by a homosexual man who frequently visited in the foster-home. To these attacks Nathan had at first responded. Then he began to loathe and to avoid them. With this story came an account of most amazing emotional responses to other earlier experiences of a similar nature which he had skilfully avoided telling us earlier. When I first knew him, the original frankness in discussing sex as well as other subjects had diverted my suspicion entirely from the possibility of this as a cause of his difficulties.

A report of the many distortions of reality and the peculiar phantasied beliefs that had become a part of this boy's mental life would be too long to give fully. For example, he believed very firmly that if the fact were known that he had had such experiences, no girl or woman would ever want to speak to him, nor would he have the courage to face people who knew these things about him. He had many other peculiar beliefs and emotional responses, with regard not only to his sex experiences, but also to his feelings about his father and mother, and especially to religion. He wanted to join a church of an entirely different faith from the one in which he had been raised.

In this case the original *"thinking about"* proved to be all wrong. It shows very clearly the futility of *"thinking with"* a child and considering factors which one has guessed at rather than definitely discovered when *thinking about* him. Because of his very acute desire to be understood, *personality contact* was very good when it was finally established. Nathan had no inferiority feelings at all. Had he been *thought with* seriously at the time of the earlier acquaintance, it would have been along this line, and it is quite possible that if this had been done, a real inferiority feeling might have been planted in the mind of this handicapped boy.

Results: The earlier attempts to establish rapport laid the foundation for the later developments. All the thorough *thinking with* him happened too recently to tell just how much it accomplished therapeutically. Very unfortunately, the social plan for the family has nearly collapsed, through no fault of the agency. Those who know Nathan are anxious to continue helping him if possible. It has been impossible to give him the desirable intensive treatment. We still hope that this will soon be possible. He is a very interesting boy to think about. It is likely that this boy may have the possibilities of developing into what the world calls a success. He has the natural gifts and the talents. What is it that will determine whether or not he will develop successfully? Is it in his environment or is it the influence of those he meets? How much will be determined by that part of his mental life over which others might have some conditioning influence? Is he likely to become an adult with serious sex problems? If so, can psychotherapy offer any help?

This case shows how very important is the selection of the degree of rapport to be established for successful understanding and for successful psychotherapy.

Subsequently the boy has been seen frequently over a period of almost two years. He still is in excellent personality contact, and this rapport is being utilized occasionally to help him with his many serious problems. He has now developed some very fine loyalties and a sincere desire both to understand himself and to face life. He has made some very definite personality changes for the better. His behaviour is good; he is an industrious, happy, normal boy, two years after all intensive treatment has been discontinued. But, above all, he is now much more anxious to win the approbation and affection of his very fine foster-parents than mine.

* *

The experiences the next lad had endured would be active as an emotional trauma in a very large percentage of children were they to pass through them. But be they serious as they may, the damage is not always permanent.

Case No. 35
ANDREW JACKSON

Two and a half years ago, when Andrew was first seen in the clinic, he was ten inches shorter than most boys of fourteen and a half years. He was healthy and well nourished, however, and because of his childlike face and physique one did not think of him as being an undersized boy of fourteen, but rather as a boy two or three years younger than he actually was. Mentally he was of poor general ability.

Andrew was brought to the clinic for advice as to placing in a foster-home. His parents were unknown. He had been abandoned as an infant on the steps of a hospital. His supposed mother was a young woman from a fairly good family who had been wayward and immoral since an early age. This was not known to be a fact. Andrew had been in several boarding-homes during the first years of his life. At the age of four he was placed for adoption in a good middle-class foster-home. Here he had lived until one year before we first saw him.

There had been no complaint of the boy for many years. More recently he was reported by the foster-home as being not dependable and slightly dishonest. He had been taught to believe that he was the child of his foster-parents. He bore their name. They had told him that he had lived away from home during his early years because of his mother's health.

Shortly before I saw him, the boy was given up by his foster-parents, their reason being the ill health of the foster-mother and her inability to manage the boy. The foster-father had, in a moment of exasperation, while punishing Andrew, suddenly told him that he was not their boy and that they did not want him any longer. Days of unspeakable unhappiness followed this announcement.

When the boy demanded reasons for being sent away, he was accused for the first time of being responsible for a fire that had destroyed his parents' home and household goods several years before, when he was six and a half years old. Other things of which the agency had never heard were charged against him.

Since leaving this home Andrew has been in three foster-homes, none of which had proved satisfactory. The reports have said he was unmanageable, but he was not accused of serious delinquency. He was suspected of being dishonest. His school-work had always been poor. He seemed unhappy. All who knew him believed he was rapidly becoming a bad boy.

Thinking about the boy: Andrew is a boy with a long history of fairly good behaviour. One year ago a real tragedy came suddenly into his life. It was the sort of experience that one thinks about as being likely to cause mental conflicts. It is a profound and upsetting experience for a child of thirteen to learn that those whom he had believed to be his parents and whom he had learned to love as such are not really his parents, and that they no longer want him. After this happened, Andrew's behaviour and personality responses became more disturbing to others, and he was more unhappy. Theoretical thinking would place this boy in the group of children with definite mental conflicts, based on psychic traumas.

Thinking for him: Thinking for Andrew was comparatively simple. Three different environmental changes had been made within a year. They were all failures. Other social remedies had been tried and had failed. It was evident that he must change his responses to life situations if he were not to become an unsocial, unhappy, and probably delinquent man. Someone must help him to do this if it was to be accomplished. One might feel justified in doing anything one could to help this boy. This includes establishing as deep a rapport as necessary for diagnostic and therapeutic reasons.

Thinking with him: Andrew was lonesome, and he believed himself to be unloved. He had many unanswered questions in his rather dull mind. One can usually establish a deep rapport very easily with a child of this type. The wish to be understood is already in the child's heart.

When a good rapport was established, two things quickly were found. First, this boy still had a remarkable loyalty to his supposed parents. Second, when he became entirely frank, he appeared very much more intelligent than before. It was noticeable that when a third person entered the room or talked with the boy in my presence, he lost some of the alertness of mind which he had when he talked with me alone.

There proved to be many things about which it seemed desirable to *think with* this boy. Some of them had been half forgotten and half denied. Many of them were important things. When I told him that he might be a happier and better boy if he would remember them and tell me about them, he believed me and was willing to try to do so. Andrew was a boy who asked many questions about how things would seem to me if I were a boy and what I should do in various situations. Early in the treatment I believed that a feeling of dependent attachment to me would probably be necessary to accomplish psychiatric results, but when the excellent loyalty to his early foster-parents was found, it no longer seemed necessary or desirable.

Had I had good ideas or a good solution for more of Andrew's problems, the results might have been even better than they were.

Though I might not always *think for* the lad, it was well for me to *think with* him. He had long needed someone to do this.

We thought about his having lost his home and whether or not his foster-parents had ever loved him. We thought about whether he was to blame for what had happened. We thought about the fire that had happened so long ago, which Andrew had forgotten, but which now came very vividly to his mind, often in his dreams as well as when awake. He had been in the house alone when the fire occurred. He remembers that when he saw the stove door open and the fire falling on the floor, he had been exceedingly frightened and had tried to do something, but he is very sure that he was not to blame. It was necessary to think of the best excuses possible for these people and their behaviour towards the boy; for one could not destroy loyalties in this particular boy without doing him harm. He needed all he had. He had laboriously written several letters to them without receiving any reply. He was worried about his foster-mother's health.

His name had recently been changed to the one given him as a foundling. He would have liked very much to keep the name of his foster-parents. He blamed others whom he thought could have prevented the change, and we were obliged to think about this.

Andrew wanted to know why other children did not like him. This made possible a discussion of the things in a boy that other boys did not like when I was young; also the fact that when a boy becomes happy, as I believed Andrew was going to be, he was apt to be liked more by his playmates. It is not often well to give a boy excuses for his own bad behaviour, but this unhappy boy needed some encouragement.

There were many other things to think about. None of them seemed to be easy or pleasant for Andrew to talk about, and for none of them were good ideas easy to find. Andrew was ready to accept my ideas when they were given to him, however, and with some of his problems I could help.

Andrew wished to know many things. Why was he so small for his age? Why was it hard for him to learn in school? Who did I suppose really were his parents? Why had he not been told more of the facts of his birth? Did I suppose his parents were still alive?

At the time I knew him, Andrew had no sex problems. They had been met early in so healthy and normal a way that it is of interest to give a report of the facts. Three years earlier he had learned masturbation from hearing other boys talk about it. For two years he practised it rather frequently. He knew that it was considered wrong, and that he would be punished were it to be known. He did not know why it was wrong or that it would be harmful, until one day about a year before. He was playing in the woods alone, as he frequently did, near a little shack he had built, and he was seen masturbating by a young man eighteen years old. The young man was a friend of his foster-parents, though Andrew knew him but slightly. The boy was greatly frightened, believing that his parents would be informed. Instead of this the young man talked with him in a frank and friendly manner about what he had seen. He warned the boy of its bad effects and told him he would keep this secret and asked Andrew to promise to try not to do it any more. Andrew was impressed, both by what the young man said and by the fact that he was not going to tell his foster-parents. He stopped his bad habit entirely as a result of this incident, though, of course, it took a very noble effort on his part. He still thinks of this young man as one of his best friends and always thinks of him when he is tempted to indulge in his old habit.

Andrew was an undemonstrative boy. I saw tears in his eyes only once. This happened one day after an interview which had been rather trying for the lad. As I stepped to the door to open it for him, he held me back and threw his arm around me and pressed his face against my shoulder. He held me very tight for a moment; then he looked straight at me, so that I could see he was crying. He did not say a word. It was his way of saying that he appreciated my attempts to help him. He did not do this after the manner of a child who is dependently attached to a person, but rather as an adult who is willing to show his friend his true emotions.

Results: Andrew has been seen at infrequent intervals during the two years I have known him. Attempts to have his former parents take him back proved impractical, but he still has his loyalties to them. I believe that destroying these would have been fatal to my efforts to help Andrew.

He is now loyal to other people. He is in a foster-home and has a fine foster-mother who is not only interested in the boy, but really likes him and is patient with him. His behaviour is much better. He is sincerely trying to take a better attitude towards his playmates. Both Andrew and the foster-mother feel he is succeeding in doing this. The boy gets much satisfaction from it. He always has many questions to ask when he comes to see me. He is a boy who does not forget his friends.

When one considers that this boy has made these improvements without many real changes in the things that had made him so unhappy, one appreciates what loyalties alone will sometimes accomplish for a child. The case is a success, both psychiatrically and socially. Possibly the psychiatric success should be mentioned first, for without some change in his responses to life, even the very patient work of his visitor and his agency would have been unsuccessful.

It is easier to *understand* how Andrew feels than it is to change his feelings. He is a good example of those children whose response to a psychiatrist is excellent, but for whom it is difficult to do constructive thinking.

*   *

The last boy of this group is one in whom the trauma was only surmised, but the beneficial effect of social treatment based on this diagnostic guess seemed to support the supposition.

Case No. 36
LAMONT ROGER

It is seldom that all the people in the clinic agree that any child is good-looking, but Lamont Roger was called beautiful by them all. His seven-year-old body was straight and lithe. His fine black curly hair, dark-blue eyes, clear skin, regular classical features, and frank open expression all added to his good looks and attractiveness. Mentally he was highly superior, but his tests showed irregularity.

The situation: Lamont came to us from a distant city in Connecticut, and he could be seen but a very short time. His mother was dead. He had formerly lived in the fine home of a paternal aunt, who was reported as cultured and refined, but a very peculiar personality. His week-ends were spent with this aunt at the time of this study.

For some months he had been living in an excellent private boarding-home. The reports from this home seemed impossible to apply to this very attractive and apparently fine lad. He was excessively disturbing to other children and to adults. He fought with smaller children and was cruel to them. He was cowardly and revengeful to the older ones. He suffered from both nocturnal and diurnal enuresis and frequently soiled himself in the day-time. He had severe, long-continued, and destructive temper tantrums, and at these times he would indulge in very filthy excretory habits, seemingly in a revengeful way.

He was a sex teacher and, according to the reports of the other children, a chronic masturbator.

There were periods, sometimes of many days' duration, when not one of these problems, except the enuresis, was in evidence, and, according to the report, at these times he would be even a nicer little boy than he appeared to be when we saw him.

The evident potentialities of this boy and these good periods enabled him to stay in a fine situation which one would naturally expect to be closed to him.

Thinking about the boy: He was in the city for only two days, but during this time he was in the clinic nearly all of the regular clinic hours.

He was on his good behaviour all the time, so that none of the reported unhappy personality and behaviour traits were observed. He talked reluctantly about the things of which he was accused and reported no other ones. He did not wish to lie, but used all the powers of his pleasant and engaging personality to help him avoid unpleasant subjects.

One could say that this was a conflict case, without doing very much theoretical thinking. Since no deep rapport with so serious a problem child would be therapeutically justifiable for such a short period of treatment, all the advice that could be given to his teachers and foster-parents must be based on the theoretical *thinking about* him.

He was very friendly and would chat freely about pleasant subjects and show that he had some normal boyish interests. It was through the things he said while talking in this way and through one particular occurrence in the office that we based our guess as to the cause of his conflicts.

It was noted that in talking about his former home he talked freely except when his aunt was mentioned. This seemed always to bring a resistance and to cause him to want to change the subject. He happened to make a remark that told me he had always slept with his aunt when he lived with her. He was embarrassed when he realized he had let it be known, and he did not want to talk more about it.

The observed behaviour was reported by a young and attractive psychologist who was alone in a room with the boy. He attempted to kiss her several times and later tried to put his hands under her dress, and when she prevented this, he said with a knowing look: "I guess if we were in bed, you wouldn't act that way."

Thinking for him: The need for establishing deep rapport and a long-continued period of treatment was very evident in this case, but it was impossible, as he could not remain in the city, and there were no psychiatrists available near his home. Under these circumstances definite advice based on a combination of guess-work and his rather definite information was given to those who had charge of him. It was suggested that the boy be prevented even from seeing his aunt over a considerable period of time, and that he be told in advance that this was to be done. These suggestions were carried out.

Thinking with him: The rapport was very superficial, and no attempts were made to establish a deep one. Consequently he was not *thought with* in regard to his mental life, and he was *thought with* very little in regard to his behaviour. All that one might have said in the way of advice or scolding had been said many times before by others who were in a better rapport with him than I. So the boy and I simply talked in an ordinary way about his school and the possibility of his having to leave his present home. Lamont believed that I was a good doctor and his friend, but he went no further.

The results: The results have been good, comparatively. They have been obtained largely through social efforts, but the psychiatric study (there was no treatment in Lamont's case) aided in effecting the social adjustments that made success possible.

A year later his behaviour is reported as much improved. There is little evidence of interest in sex. He is more normally gregarious and is doing better in his school-work. The enuresis and soiling have ceased. He still quarrels and shows a tendency to be bold and self-assertive at times, and his temper frequently is the cause of trouble. His teachers and foster-mother are fond of him and are lenient with him because they feel he is making a distinct effort to be a better boy.

If at some future time this lad for some reason takes someone so deeply into his environmental values that he tells him his problems and his mental life, this is what I think will happen: if by that time he has not suppressed the memory of these early unhappy years, he will reveal to that person that his aunt had used him sexually in some way to gratify herself, that he had both liked and disliked the aunt and the experiences, and that he was confused by the affair and wanted to know what it was all about.

The *thinking about* this boy accomplished something. Had this been mixed with the *thinking with* him, and had this boy unwillingly told these experiences to a person who had not established himself deeply in the lad's life, nothing would have been gained and his problems might have been made worse. The real credit due to psychiatry in this case is to the fact that psychiatric advice and not treatment was undertaken.

Many people over-value the importance of traumatic experiences on the mental welfare of children. Much of this over-estimation is based on just such theoretical ideas as those held about this not-understood boy. There is not the slightest doubt that profound emotional experiences do cause serious and often lifelong malad-justments, but it is also true that relatively few children who show behaviour disturbances have psychic traumas in their history.

CHAPTER XI

UNCERTAINTIES

The Child who Doubts his Parentage or Parental Affections

HE children who believe for any reason that they are being deceived regarding their true parentage or that those who should be dear to them do not love them are very often problem children. Life is a problem for all of them. They are of course only a part of the larger group who feel themselves in any way rejected or inferior. My experience has been that this particular uncertainty produces unhealthy emotional reactions or unfortunate behaviour with much greater consistency than does any other.

The children who have these uncertainties are very likely to have formed, long before they are seen by a psychiatrist, the habit of distorting and avoiding their situations and mental responses and are difficult children with whom to establish a good psychiatric rapport. Many of these children do not wish to be frank regarding their true emotional response to their parents. They do not wish to understand themselves, because the understanding makes them at first more unhappy.

*   *

The first boy of this group is placed here largely because I felt very sure when *thinking about* him that the explanation of his behaviour and peculiar attitudes lay in the fact that the boy loved his father very much and believed his father did not love him. However, since I failed to *think with* him, I am not sure that this was his problem.

Case No. 37
NELSON JACKSON

I knew Nelson first when he was twelve and a half years old. He was a well-developed, healthy, restless, emotional boy whose sharp face and protruding ears gave him a peculiar appearance. Mentally he was of good average general ability.

The situation: Nelson came to us against his will and against the wishes of his parents. He was referred by his school principal, who, because of the fact that the boy had been excessively truant, was in a position to insist that he be either brought into court or studied at the clinic.

The truancy was concomitant with prolonged runaways from home. During the preceding eighteen months the runaways had averaged two or three a month. The duration of the runaways varied from two to ten days. He was in the sixth grade of school and making passing grades in spite of his frequent absences.

Two years earlier he had been in court with a group of older boys for breaking and entering. Since then no delinquencies other than his runaways and truancy had been known.

Nelson's home conditions were good. His father is a bank officer. He has one sister two years younger than he. The mother reported that the father has always whipped him very hard and sometimes treated him cruelly in other ways. Many other kinds of punishment had been tried to correct his misbehaviour, all to no avail.

The personality traits were reported by the parents as distrust, uncommunicativeness, ugliness towards his sister, who he said hates him, constant fear of his father, whom he tried to avoid. He was "tense and nervous," disagreeable and impudent to his mother, but often pleaded with her for favours or ran to her for protection. In the home he was helpful and could be fully trusted. He lied only in self-defence.

Thinking about the boy: Nelson was a most interesting lad to think about. I had many theories about his mental conflicts, but since I failed to really understand him, I have no assurance they were sound. Despite the rather strained relations between him and the clinic, he became interested in the mental tests. During the first psychiatric interview he was friendly and talkative.

No effort was made to establish an immediate rapport or to get deeply into his emotional life during the first interview, but his re-ported behaviour and his peculiar beliefs and emotions seemed to make an intimate knowledge of him very desirable.

Thinking for him: His situation in school was critical. He would have to be helped to solve it or be removed from his home. The clinic did not realize the extent of the parents' objections to having the boy studied, and believed that, through the school authorities, interviews might be arranged for the boy's treatment.

Two more interviews were had with the lad. Though he did not like coming to the clinic, he seemed glad to talk, once he had ar-rived. His truancy and behaviour temporarily improved. The par-ents, first by making excuses and later by pleading his improved behaviour, successfully prevented his keeping further appoint-ments.

Thinking with him: Because of the interesting things this usually uncommunicative boy told me, I felt that a good rapport was slowly being established. I decided to postpone the *thinking with* him until I was sure the necessary depth of rapport was established. Therefore I did not seriously discuss many of the things he told me. He reached the stage of personal trust during the second interview and I hoped to have him reach that of personality contact before we discussed his behaviour and emotional responses.

Nelson said he did not believe runaways were wrong or uncommon among boys. He believed that he was justified in them. He told of much severe punishment in the home, of much nagging by his mother, and of constant scolding by his father. He thought that under these circumstances any boy would run away. He said he liked school and did not want to avoid school attendance directly. Sometimes he took one of his school-books with him so that he might keep up with his class. He usually spent the time away from home in some such way as this: He would go to a distant part of the city where he could find shelter at night in parked cars. He said that he usually slept but little at night, as he would get up very early and find a job to earn money for food. He often helped clean restaurant floors or small hotel lobbies. Sometimes he helped the vegetable-pedlar or the milkman. Often in the afternoons he would sleep.

He stayed by himself, he said (we had some corroboration of this), and he never made friends on the runaways. He seldom spoke to another boy unless he knew him. He had never run away with another boy. He often cried when he was alone, but he did not cry because he had run away or because he knew he would be punished on his return home. He cried because he was unhappy. Ordinarily he returned home voluntarily. His usual method of doing this was to go to the home of the minister of his church and have this man either phone to his home or accompany him there. (The boy seemed sincerely interested in church and Sunday-school.) He never failed to say his prayers at night when on his runaways. He prayed about his troubles a great deal always. He was shrewd in escaping detection and only recently had it been the police who returned him to his home.

He never played or had any fun when away from home. Sometimes he was so successful in earning money by odd jobs that he would have money saved to bring home at the end of the runaway.

During the last interview Nelson was becoming anxious to have me understand him. He was almost convinced that he did not really understand himself. At that time he said he really thought he did not know why he ran away, for he had no fun and was always punished. Besides, he had to work hard in school to catch up. He volunteered no promises of better behaviour to me, however, although he did this constantly to his parents and teachers.

He said he remembered that he used to want his father's attention very much, and that even now, if he were not afraid of his father, he would try to get it. At night when away from home, he imagined and wished he were in bed with his father and that his father would put his arms around him, but he never dared to show any affection towards his father when he was with him. He remembered he used to make unsuccessful advances to him. He sometimes kissed his mother, but she did not seem to like it.

At the time of the last interview he told willingly, but in confidence, of home situations and quarrels that he had not mentioned before. It was interesting that this twelve-year-old boy, evidently with genuine sincerity, said that one of the things he felt bad about was that the doctor might bring a new baby to his home. He said: "I never let boys talk to me about babies or other dirty things." He said that he had always gone away when the boys commenced to talk about such things. He knew vulgar and profane words, but did not like to hear or repeat them.

Nelson was still frightened during the last interview, though he was much more frank. Many of the things he told me were in confidence. He said his parents had warned him against talking too much in the clinic. At the end of this interview the lad was very near the rapport of personality contact.

A serious mistake was made in not trying to help Nelson understand his problems earlier. The plan to allow him to reach a good therapeutic rapport was sound. The failure resulted from poorly estimating the social situation when *thinking for* the boy. Nelson was a boy with many mental conflicts, which it would have been well for him to understand and face. The treatment as carried out may have given him a little encouragement. But, on the other hand, it was unfortunate that no sooner had he reached the place where he wanted to be understood than his parents' poor co-operation cost him the opportunity. This may have caused him to withdraw more into himself and made future attempts to give him the much needed personality help infinitely more difficult.

Results: Since the parents on plea of improved behaviour were able to prevent the boy's treatment, direct contact was lost. A follow-up report through the school shows that for a time his runaways stopped and his other behaviour improved. Later he became worse than ever and was placed in an institution. Nelson represents both a social and a psychiatric failure, owing largely in both ways to lack of opportunity for treatment because of poor parental co-operation.

* *

The next boy to be described failed to respond to me, and he, like the preceding case, was not well understood. Perhaps the conflict over his parentage and parent relationships was not his real problem, but it seemed to be.

Case No. 38
GEORGE RICHO

George Richo, who had been known in the clinic for two and a half years before I saw him, was a boy of almost thirteen. He was somewhat short, but well nourished. He had always had a pleasant smile and looked directly at the one to whom he was speaking. His eyes were noticeable, both because of their vivacious intelligent expression and because of their bright-blue colour, contrasting noticeably with his swarthy skin. Except for periods when he was in foster-homes, he was always dirty, ragged, and unkempt. He was in good health. Mentally he was of low average ability.

The situation: His home, owned by his parents, was crowded, in a poor part of the city; it was well kept, but poorly furnished. There were several children, both older and younger than George. It took several good social agencies, working over a period of three years, to learn the real facts of the home situation, and even now they are probably not fully understood. There had been no love in the marriage of the parents. Superstition had always played a prominent part in the home life and atmosphere. For example, the mother believed that she had successfully used "love charms" to capture her husband's affection. Jealousy developed on both sides. The children were whipped severely. No encouragement was given them to stay at home. There was always economic stress. Throughout his life George had shown excessive family loyalties, but had very little conscious affection for either his father or his mother.

The lad's delinquencies had all been various types of stealing. He had stolen from his home, school, boys' clubs, and the streets. He had been dishonest in transactions, such as selling papers. In foster-homes he had been somewhat better-behaved generally, but still periodically dishonest. In his own home he was a quarrelsome and unhappy boy.

Thinking about the boy: It is interesting that never, either from his family or from his foster-parents, had we received what we considered an unbiased report of the lad's behaviour and personality. People always seemed to be either whole-heartedly for him or very much against him. He was such a dynamic boy that he was bound to be either liked or disliked. He was subject to sways of mood and to changes of emotional responses. He usually lied first and later told the truth about his delinquencies. When in foster-homes (he had been in two for a total period of a year), he had done very much better school-work than when in his own home. His personality had effected, however, just as many difficulties in the foster-home, and he was always desperately home-sick when separated from his family.

Many interviews with this rather attractive, friendly boy have shown that it is rather easy to understand all his delinquencies, but very hard to understand why he is as unhappy as he is and especially to understand why his good family loyalties have not proved to be assets in any sense.

Thinking for him: A full report of all the thinking for this boy that has been done by various agencies and workers would be much too long to give here. Possibly some permanent results have been obtained in the social field, but even this is doubtful. Early in his attendance at the clinic it was indicated that psychotherapy was much needed. The ineffectiveness of the *thinking for* him was probably due to the fact that he had never got successful psychotherapy.

Thinking with him: A number of interviews were held with George more than a year ago. Later friendly correspondence was carried on with him for some time, but a rapport deep enough to understand or help him could not be obtained. He believed that I could give boys good advice, and that I was his friend, but despite every effort he never arrived at the point where he trusted me. We did not acquire that degree of real *personality contact* which certainly would have been necessary for me to understand this boy's mental life. He had always talked in a most friendly manner. He described his interests, but he never asked personal questions and he did not want to talk about his emotional life. He did not tell of his troubles or his delinquencies unless they were already known, from other sources. Three different psychiatrists and two good social workers have known this lad and tried to understand him better, all with the same results. None of us could really *think with* him, and so it was necessary to *think for* him as best we could. This, plus the fact of his great home-sickness, led to the advice that he be tried again in his own home.

Results: Thus far nothing was accomplished. He continued delinquent in as many ways as before. He quarrelled and was openly defiant in his home, especially to his father. Recently a second effort was made to establish a psychiatric rapport with this boy, still with the hope of understanding his mental life. During the second series of interviews he arrived one day in a very unusual emotional attitude. As soon as he was given a chance, he said that he had just heard his father openly accuse his mother of being immoral and declare that George was not his son. After this confession George responded to questions and related other occurrences in the family which had undoubtedly been the basis of worry and of possible mental conflicts and repressions on his part. Even after telling these things, he did not want to tell me how he felt about them. His motive for talking was evidently not to tell the truth for its own sake, but only to say what he thought would most benefit him; not for the sake of being understood, but for the sake of justifying his own behaviour.

Possibly this was the beginning of a genuine *personality contact* with George, but probably it was not. It was more likely the boy's simple reaction to the anger his father had aroused in him.

Treatment was a failure, owing largely to the inadequacy of the rapport. In *thinking about* George one may feel reasonably sure that his behaviour is on the basis of an unfortunate, unhealthy mental life. Had this boy really thought with me, as he would have done had the rapport been deeper, about the same things that we discussed superficially, he might easily have been helped to be happier and more normal; or if I had been able to make him want me to understand him, I might have helped him.

* *

The next boy is one on whom much time and thought has been spent. He is apparently making good adjustments to his environment, and shows improvement. But the essential problem of his parental situation and the conflicts centred in it have not been liquidated. For that reason he is classed in the summary as only a temporary success.

Case No. 39
LEE ROFFERTY

Lee was eleven when first seen in the clinic, three years ago. He was a healthy boy, somewhat large for his age. His boyish face, round and smiling, and his friendly responsive expression made him appear happy. He was rated in the superior group by mental tests.

The situation: The problem for which a solution was first sought in Lee's case was that of trying to understand and to help him overcome very extensive and shrewd dishonesty. This had been going on for many months before it was detected. He had successfully conducted many business affairs for one so young, and mixed his dishonest practices with his business. He had defrauded a newspaper company of twenty dollars in a way that could not be detected. He had stolen a total of sixty dollars by withholding several times a part of the money he was taking to a bank for his employer. He had covered this up so well that it was not detected until long after. The Sunday-school treasury was short eighteen dollars on a ticket-sale for an entertainment. Lee had been the general ticket-agent. At that time he was not suspected. In addition to this he was becoming a disturbing factor at home, unco-operative and "grouchy."

The home situation as reported by his relatives was rather unsettled. They believed, however, that Lee knew little of this and doubted that this could be a cause of his misbehaviour. Lee was an illegitimate child who had been brought up by his paternal grandfather and grandmother as their son. The grandfather died. The real father, whom Lee called "uncle," had later married and continued living in the home of the grandparents and the boy. There were two half-brothers, young children. The father paid little attention to Lee, but his wife, who knew the facts, believed that he distrusted and disliked the boy. She did not allow his father to help support him. Since the income of the family was small, Lee's success in his small businesses had been something of a factor in the family situation.

There were other upsetting things in the home. The family reported that since the discovery of his delinquency Lee had seemed unhappy and in many ways strange and queer. He had adopted the habit of withdrawing from the others and not talking to them. He seemed to be eavesdropping constantly and attempting to overhear conversation not intended for him. Formerly he had been friendly and frank with his family and with his friends, but now he was exactly the opposite of this in every way.

Thinking about the boy: When first he came to the attention of the clinic, he was seen only once and no psychotherapy was attempted, although it was recommended. It was impossible to treat him and at the same time follow the social advice given at this time.

The advice given was that he be placed in a foster-home where he could not engage in gainful business or work or handle money. He was to be told by the family, preferably by his grandmother, of his true parentage. All but this last advice was followed. The grandmother later reported that she had tried to tell him of his parentage by telling him to call her grandmother instead of mother and saying that she would explain to him when he got older why he was to do so, but he reacted so badly to this that she never again mentioned the matter to him.

On his return to the clinic a year later there seemed to be no reason to spend time theoretically considering his problem, and the decision was made at once to try thoroughly to understand this boy and, if possible, to give him psychotherapeutic help. One thing was absolutely necessary: namely, that some person who was thoroughly in this boy's positive emotional environment tell him the facts of his birth. It was quite evident that the family could not do this successfully, though they were willing it should be done. During the year between his two appearances at the clinic he had adjusted poorly in what seemed to be an excellent foster-home. He was becoming more antagonistic to his family. He was unduly interested in sex and was suspected of bad sex habits.

In other words, there were plenty of known problems to justify establishing deep rapport and there was every reason to believe that more problems would be discovered if this could be successfully done. The decision as to what depth of rapport I should strive for was important. The first few moments I talked with the boy showed how thoroughly unhappy, discouraged, and self-critical he was. His anxiety to have some understanding person listen to his story and answer his questions was apparent. This fine, intelligent, really talented boy knew vaguely that he must have help from someone. He wanted much more sympathy and indulgence for his shortcomings than one likes to see in a twelve-year-old boy well along in adolescent development. He had very excellent loyalties to his family and to his abilities and his ideals. Consequently it would be undesirable for him to become attached to and dependent on a psychiatrist. Although in this event his behaviour might improve more quickly and his problems be understood more thoroughly, it seemed best that these results be accomplished without allowing him to enter this deep rapport.

For more than a year Lee was in a deep personality contact with me. During a considerable part of this time our only association was through the writing of letters. His case was considered important both because he was of such excellent material and because mental conflicts seemed to be the largest part of his entire problem.

Simply to enumerate all the things in this boy's mental life and his reactions to his environment of which he freely and gladly told as soon as he believed he could trust me and I could understand him would make this report impossibly long. Much more important than the things themselves was the manner in which they had to be thought out with this boy.

I became the substitute for all the people he had formerly been loyal to and he became very loyal not only to me, but to my ideas. It was necessary carefully to *think about* the boy and the various things he told me, before I discussed them with him.

He said he had suspected for a long time that his supposed uncle was his father. He had searched for and read old hidden letters, he had listened to whispered conversations, and he had interpreted veiled remarks made in his presence ever since he could remember. When he finally made up his mind that the family were lying to him about his parentage, he decided that he was no good and that no one would ever like a "bastard." He believed that the family did not like him for this reason. He did not think his dishonesty or any of his other delinquencies were half as bad as being an illegitimate child. In his peculiar way he considered illegitimacy in the same class with crimes. He had, through loyalty to his grandmother, pretended that he did not know about himself. He loved her and wished very much for her to tell him the truth and he had tried to give her an opportunity to do so. He was embarrassed and ashamed to ask about it. When she tried to tell him in the way she did, he was hurt, for he decided she thought he was a baby, and she did not understand how he felt about it. At that time he lost his last loyalty.

He said that for the past year he had not cared to be good and had not tried to be happy. He had not committed many dishonest acts, partly because opportunity did not present itself and partly because he was afraid of punishment. However, he had indulged very excessively in masturbation during this time. He had known of this habit, but had not practised it earlier. He received much physical pleasure from it. "It makes me feel like I am a man." He had thought about having relations with girls and had made some crude unsuccessful attempts to accomplish this. He believed that such things were wrong and harmful, but the sex drive was very strong. (He was a rapidly developing boy, who seemed at least two years older than he was.) He had lost the belief that he could be good and he did not care much about good health.

He both loved and hated his father. He loved him because he was his father and "everybody loves his father," but he hated him for not owning him and for not giving him as much care and affection as he did the half-siblings. For these siblings he had the same ambivalent response. When he saw them for a short time, he would enjoy being with them, but then he would feel like treating them roughly and getting away from them. Lee had always had strong religious feelings, which he had not lost, but he was doubtful and suspicious of the church in which he was brought up, because it was the one accepted by those towards whom he felt so aggrieved. He had been brought up in a Protestant church. He always attended church and prayed about his troubles and unhappiness. Now, whenever he could, he attended a church of another Protestant denomination. He knew nothing of the Catholic faith or doctrines and had attended Catholic services only once, but he said he wished he might join this church.

He had always wondered who his mother was and whether she were dead or not. He wondered of what nationality she was, and above all he wondered if she would love him if she were living and he were to find her. He wondered what she looked like and if he looked or was like her. The question of his education was disturbing Lee. Earlier he had believed that he would go to college. He still desired this, but believed if his illegitimacy were known, it would be impossible. He seemed really to doubt that an illegitimate person could go so far towards success as to get a college education.

These were some of the things which Lee and I thought about in our letters and about which he finally accepted my ideas and beliefs. I was the one person to whom he was loyal during this most trying time.

Results: His visitor and his friends believe that most of his problems have been solved. His behaviour is much improved and there has been no delinquency during the past fifteen months. He seems happier and better adjusted in his group. He is doing very well at school. He shows no tendency to dishonesty at present, as far as those who know him can determine, although he is working and in his work is entrusted with considerable amounts of money.

I am not so sure about it all. It seems to me that he is failing to take anyone else who will understand him into his environmental values. I have tried to build up, as best I could, a loyalty to ideals and ambitions, but there has seemed to be no person in his environment upon whom the lad could depend or whom I could honestly advise him to trust to help him. This explains the prolonged treatment, which is in itself a confession of incomplete therapy.

In Lee's case there have been some problems about which I could not think with him because I had no solution of which I was sure. He was too quickly accepting my opinions and ideas for me to give them to him as an experiment. Among these was the problem of his religious beliefs. The problems centred in his religious ideas I had to ignore entirely.

One mistake was made, though not all of it was mine, concerning the problem of masturbation. He got from me too strong suggestions about the desirability of his overcoming masturbation. He succeeded in stopping it very quickly, and when during the past year it has been occasionally resumed, he has had altogether too much feeling of guilt and inferiority about it. He writes self-accusing letters, wording them in an over-emotional fashion, confessing his faults, and promising never to do it again. The boy has taken his foster-father into his confidence in regard to these things, owing to a suggestion I gave him, without my first thoroughly understanding the foster-father, and this proved a mistake also.

Something has been accomplished. I am still trying to help this fine lad. He is classed as a temporary success in the summary.

While this case on the surface seems to be both a psychiatric and a social success, I believe that unless some understanding person comes into this boy's environment, his personality problems are very likely to reappear.

*   *

New variations of the problems parents may create for their children is shown in the case of the next boy to be described.

Case No. 40
LOUIS JULIO

Louis was a thoroughly Americanized boy of foreign parentage
who had been known to the clinic for two and one-half years. He
was a good-looking fourteen-year-old with good physique and development. Mentally he had fair average ability.

The situation: When first seen, Louis was a very unhappy boy.
He had always had an excellent reputation for good behaviour
both in school and elsewhere, but at that time his quarrelling family
said that he was becoming disobedient and otherwise hard to control.

His home during the eight trying months preceding the clinic's
first acquaintance with Louis had been in process of disruption,
and Louis had been the cause of much quarrelling. Each of his
parents wished to keep him and had been persuading the boy to
move about frequently. He had been living first with one and then
with the other and had been obliged frequently to change schools
against his will. He had been brought into court on a *"stubborn
complaint"* by his father because he refused to change schools
again to accommodate his father's new move.

Thinking about the boy: Louis said: "I wish I knew how to make
them both like me. I know there is no chance of their caring for
each other, but I love them both and don't like to have them quarrel over me, because they will hate me if they do."

Louis told the often-heard story of the child who is the subject
of quarrels and contention in divorce proceedings. He admitted that
he was discouraged and that he was in many ways a bad boy. He
said he had been unhappy for a long time and that he was going
with the kind of boys he used to avoid. He was tempted to stay out
late at night because in that way he would hear less of the family's

quarrels and less criticism from whichever parent he happened to be with. His brothers and sisters were divided over the family disagreement, and Louis felt that none of them liked him, because he was the only one who had been trying to maintain friendly relations on both sides.

He had learned bad habits from street friends and was worried about them, and he was worried as to what was the best thing to do. He was most worried, however, because at times he could not help believing some of the very bad things of which each parent accused the other. Louis was loyal to a large number of people and he was trying to follow all their suggestions. Nothing was making him any better, and everything seemed to be making him more unhappy.

Here was a fine boy in the process of being made into a bad and unhappy one.

Thinking for him: Louis was a boy for whom one might lay definite plans and feel that if they could be carried out, success would result. What he needed was someone in his environment whom he could fully trust, someone who would decide upon the best plan of action for him to follow. This person must also be able to influence the boy's mental responses, so that he might persuade him this plan was best.

The social agency made a very thorough and complete investigation of the family situation, and on the basis of this and of the things learned from the study of the boy a plan of action was decided on.

Thinking with him: Louis was a boy who was frankly facing his problems, but he could not understand them; he had very good loyalties, but he was beginning to doubt their worth. He did not need any more people deeply in his dynamic environment, but he did need someone whom he could implicitly trust. It was not difficult to have him reach the rapport in which he could trust me. With this unhappy lad one had to be careful that his responses did not go further.

(When a boy of this sort trusts the psychiatrist, the latter may be certain that serious, complicated mental or behaviour problems may be recognized from simple association with the boy, although they may not be thoroughly *understood* or well *handled* without a deeper contact. If he finds them, there is then plenty of time for the psychiatrist to go further with the rapport.)

Louis and I thought and talked together about many things. We began with problems common to all adolescent boys. I proved myself to Louis in this way, and then we thought about his own particular problems.

Since the social workers were very sure of their findings, one could take definite steps. Louis and I thought the matter out and decided that if there were unhappy facts that a boy must sooner or later face, it was best to do so at once, even if it meant rejecting some loyalties and affections that had meant a great deal to him.

One of his parents was guilty of the things charged by the other, and one was innocent. Louis was told the facts, which were bad enough to disturb any boy. They were not pleasant for him to face, but they were something definite and he could feel that in facing them and in solving the uncertainty he was accomplishing something permanent. He did this better because he had found an understanding friend whom he could trust, and whose emotional response to situations was of dynamic interest to him.

Beyond that point the boy did most of the therapeutic thinking for himself, and advice was given him only as he asked for it.

He went to live permanently with the worthy parent and ceased to see the other. He made permanent school arrangements. His decision involved placing himself in a social position where he must work and help support himself. He was told he could come back to me when he wished for short interviews. At first he did so frequently, the character of these talks changing from the *"thinking with"* kind to ordinary friendly visits. These became infrequent, but they have never been discontinued.

Results: Two and one-half years later Louis is an industrious, well-liked, and happy lad. He has not forgotten the old family life and the tragedy that occurred, but he does not worry or grieve about it. He believes he has done the best he could.

His mother, with whom he lives, has taken a new lease of life's enthusiasms, largely through the personality help given her by this boy. He has a job and is going to night-school and learning a trade. The gang is forgotten and no one who knows Louis ever thinks of him as having been a bad boy.

An interesting sidelight on this boy is that not long ago he was offered a considerable sum of money to take part in an illegal and disreputable business. He refused this, but came at once to the clinic and waited a long time to see me and talk it all over.

Louis is a social and psychiatric success. Perhaps he is more of a social success than a psychiatric one, for social adjustment without the help of a psychiatrist might have successfully solved his problems, while the psychiatric treatment could not have been successful without correlated social investigation and help.

* *

The next boy, whose case is taken as the last of the group, is one of the most interesting of the entire series. He is interesting both because of the type of his problem and because the good results were obtained largely through good rapport. The theoretical *thinking about* the lad was not highly successful.

Case No. 41
JACK WHITE

Jack White was referred to us by a clinic in a distant city. He was a red-haired, freckle-faced, active boy of thirteen. He was thoughtful and reserved and made a very favourable impression on everyone. He was small for his age, but of normal nutrition and in excellent health. He had good general ability on mental tests and a good school record, except for occasional truancy.

The situation: Jack was a normal boy. He liked wild-West stories and wild-West games. He was an imaginative lad and a leader in imaginative games, in which he and other boys were cowboys, Indians, soldiers, and highway robbers. He was loyal to his friends, who were usually boys somewhat younger than he. He wanted to be, and was, their leader. He had never yet been beaten in a fight, though he had had many. Nearly all of them were the battles of his friends. He went to school as a matter of course and got his lessons, but since school interfered with his play, he did not like it very well. He was truthful except for occasional lying to get out of trouble. He was honest in his home and his school. However, Jack was a very bad boy. His delinquency, which covered a period of more than two years, had always been the same. He specialized in breaking into vacant, unfurnished, or closed houses and marring and destroying property in them. He always took younger boys with him. He himself never stole anything and usually prevented his companions from doing so. They broke electric light bulbs, ransacked drawers, and drew pictures on freshly decorated walls. They committed many other acts of wanton destruction. He had been apprehended in these acts and brought to court several times. The police were tired of him and insisted that if he continued to make so much disturbance, they would force some sort of disposal of the boy, so that he could no longer bother them.

His mother reported that he had always had temper spells. These lasted but a short time and he would usually *do* something to show that he was sorry, but he could not be made to *say* that he was sorry. Recently he had been defiant of his mother's authority, swearing and saying that he would not obey. He always did obey, however, if left to himself.

Jack had a very comfortable home in a small city in Vermont. He had a mother who loved him and who used very good judgment in trying to help him. His father's work took him away from home many days at a time. When he was at home he punished the boy severely. Formerly the father spent much time with the three boys, of whom Jack is the second. The other boys had never been delinquent in any way. His mother reported that Jack was very fond of his younger brother and always anxious to see that he had a good time. She thought that the smaller boy would have been involved with Jack had Jack been able to trust his brother not to tell their mother of their escapades.

Thinking about the boy: Between the first and the second interview Jack committed a new and serious offence. With two other small boys he broke into a private art collection that had been closed on account of the death of the artist. Here they found an old rifle and cartridges. They fired this several times, doing considerable damage. They ransacked drawers and cases. Among other things Jack took an old dagger and ran it through the heart of the portrait of a man. He left the dagger sticking into the picture. The only thing stolen was small scales used to weigh mail, and this was taken by one of the other boys without Jack's knowledge. Some money was found, but it was left untouched. Certainly there must be some pleasurable motivation for such unusual acts of vandalism, particularly since they were likely to cause such serious trouble for him. It might be any one of a number of things. It was easy to think of his behaviour as symbolic, but Jack insisted that he did everything for fun. Now that he had behaved this way, he was very sorry. Although he was friendly and pleasant, it was apparent that he was a bright, quick-witted boy who was planning his own battle to get out of trouble and who considered himself the best one to do this job.

Later inquiry into the family situation made it appear that the lad might have some mental conflicts about family relationships.

During this crisis interviews were held frequently. The boy willingly told of all his delinquencies and of his bad behaviour in the home. He seemed to be relieved to confess things of which no one knew. He cried about them and appeared sincerely sorry. He regretted that he was in trouble rather than that his behaviour was bad. He soon developed a sincere personal trust in my opinions and advice. But his poor behaviour continued towards his mother, who was very closely supervising him. He frankly said he knew he would do something worse when he got a chance, no matter how hard he tried not to. At no time did he become entirely frank about his emotional life. He said he hated his father, but he would discuss it no further. He was never going to speak to him again, and he actually did carry this threat out for some time, refusing to speak or even to cry when he was severely punished by his father. He had no desire to feel differently towards his father. He said his mother did not love him and he did not care. He was going to run away and take care of himself. He could do it all right if they would just let him alone.

Thinking for him: Jack was really a big problem. The family was being disgraced. The boy was being kept out of court only by his father's liberal payments for the damage he did, and this could not be kept up much longer. Jack was living his life without any help and was putting everyone out of it. There was no question of the necessity of establishing deep rapport with this boy, in the hope of understanding his mental life and of entering his environment sufficiently to influence his emotional responses.

Thinking with him: While his personal trust was sincere, nothing further could be accomplished in the way of establishing deep rapport. He said he would rather talk about his troubles and confess his shortcomings to me than to anyone else. He was much interested in any plan I offered to get him out of trouble and to prevent his being sent away to school. He seemed sincerely co-operative and insisted that he was being frank and telling me his feelings just as they were.

But this was obviously not so. The boy was always on the defensive and always considered in advance the effect of anything he said about his situation. The questions he asked all concerned his getting out of trouble. The following incident happened in one of the later interviews: During a particularly good moment this statement was made to him: "Now for a moment, Jack, just be honest and square with yourself and think how you really feel towards your dad and what you would like to say to him if you dared." He was thinking, for his eyes filled with tears and he looked away. "Now, come and tell me what you are thinking, for I have to know if I am really to help you." Jack suddenly burst into angry crying, jumped up, and said: "Where's my hat? I'm going home. I won't have anyone talk to me like that." This was the first time he had been anything but friendly towards me. He had even requested his mother to bring him to the clinic more often than his regular appointments. His mother, who was in the outer office, stopped him in his hasty retreat and asked me what to do. I told her to take him home. She tried to make him say good-bye, but he refused. Ten minutes later I heard someone outside my office. Jack was waiting to say good-bye. He shook hands and looked very gratefully at me when he saw that I was not going to scold him. But he did not say he was sorry. Later I learned that he had decided to come back without any further suggestions from his mother, and that he had left her on the street to do so. So far the *thinking with* him had mostly been a failure. It was possible to do much *thinking about* him, but he had not allowed one to think with him seriously.

It seemed necessary to do more *thinking for* him at this time. Because he had made good resolutions and promises, he was allowed to try his own school again, but his bad behaviour continued. In his home he was more disturbing. Soon he broke into a neighbour's house. He was then sent to a military school, from which he promptly stole a car and ran away. Although he had driven a car less than a mile in his life before, he drove it seventy-five miles at a very rapid speed, trying to get home. He was then placed in a very strict military school as a disciplinary student. Here he was under constant control and supervision and never allowed to leave the grounds. Much physical work was also required of him. At first he bitterly resented all this and made a bad record. He wrote me several letters asking me to visit him. After he had been in the school several weeks, I went to see him.

Thinking with him: He was very glad of the opportunity to talk again, and in the first five minutes of this interview, in spite of the fact that we were in a large room with people coming and going, I established the personality contact I had been attempting for so long. Possibly this was because the boy was lonely and wanted a friend, possibly because of things that I had said to him before, possibly because he had had time to think. He now told me his real troubles.

As a little boy he had believed that his father loved him the most, and he had reciprocated this affection. Nothing else meant so much as being with his dad on long excursions or at home. For a long time he had felt vaguely that there was something separating them. He had felt that his father paid less attention to him and punished him frequently without much cause. Jack had hated to think of this, and he had done everything he could to forget it. He now realized that he had been trying to make himself believe he hated his father, but since his confinement in the school the realization of how very much he loved his father grew upon him. His father had visited him here once before our interview, and the boy had experienced a tremendous struggle with himself, which did not result in his breaking down the barriers as he wanted to. He believed now that if his father had remained ten minutes longer, this would have happened.

Now he asked me questions about his home situation and about the relations between his father and his mother. He suspected they were not happy, but he wanted assurance that they were.

The first serious whipping his father had given him was for breaking into an empty house with other boys in order to borrow snow-shovels with which to earn money. He had not considered this wrong at the time. In fact, he had hoped to please his father by bringing home some money he had earned. His father had given him no chance to explain and had punished him. He felt that this was unjust and found it very hard to forgive him.

He told also of conflicts about his natural love and affection for his younger brother. He told how he had tried to avoid accepting the knowledge that his father treated this little brother better than he did him, and that he probably loved the little boy more.

It was now possible to *think with* Jack. I saw him four times during his year in school. His behaviour immediately improved and he soon became a very fine and diligent student, though he was home-sick and unhappy.

The psychotherapy consisted largely in utilizing the value of the confession and particularly in evaluating the excellent loyalties that he really had towards his father and the other members of the family. He changed his statement of the real reason for wanting to be good when he would get the chance outside the school. He said that although he had previously stated that the reason was his not wishing to make his mother unhappy, he realized now that his major reason for wanting to be good was to win back the love of his father. I helped him in his attempt to divide his affections between his mother and his father, and at the end of the treatment his loyalty to his mother and his love for her seemed to be more genuine now that he admitted his real attitude towards his father.

Results: The boy has now been at home for eight months. There has been no delinquency of any sort. He has on a few occasions been angry when he has been denied privileges, but on the whole his attitude is very good and his behaviour in the home is fine. The mother reports that no child could be better. Since his return home another thing has been done to help Jack. He has been told frankly the unpleasant facts in the domestic situation and he has been made to see that he himself can be of help to both his mother and his father in meeting their life-problems. Up to now this boy has been a complete success. The credit, of course, should be divided between the psychiatric understanding and treatment of the case and the fine comprehension and help given by the school. Again, in this boy the loyalties made the results possible, but these loyalties might have been entirely lost had not the boy allowed someone to enter his environment sufficiently to help him understand himself.

It is very essential for those who are interested in child welfare to study and understand children whose problems are similar to those described in this chapter. For if the psychiatrist can teach parents and others how to understand and solve these problems, he will have added much to human happiness. And it is very important to remember that in this situation, more than in any other, theoretical ideas and instructions may do the utmost harm.

CHAPTER XII

DISTORTED LIVES

The Child who Misses his "Age of Innocence"

ARLY abnormalities in the sex life frequently appear in the records of children who are later considered "peculiar" or "unstable." These early aberrations may indicate some peculiarity inherent in the child at birth. But, on the other hand, some external factor may have conditioned the early distortion or precocity of the sexual life, and these distortions may later cause the peculiarities in the more mature responses. The question of prenatal, natal, or postnatal determination is important, but it can be answered only by very careful and long-continued research.

Theoretical *thinking about* these children is not so productive in planful therapy as it is with some other types of problems, and my experience has been that when I help the type of boy represented by these five cases, I do it without having as clear an idea of what results have been obtained as I might wish. It does not seem to be so much what one says to the child that helps him as what place one holds in his dynamic environment at the time one says it.

*   *

The study of the first group, a boy whom life had treated badly, is particularly interesting and instructive. It shows well that very early superlatively unfortunate experiences, involving the most

264

fundamental emotions, are not always serious in their ultimate effects.

Case No. 42
CLAIR FORDFIELD

Clair was seven years old when first known to the clinic, three years ago. He was a boisterous, romping lad with attractive features and an innocent childish expression. He was friendly, but somewhat suspicious. He talked with a funny little lisp that made him seem to be talking "baby talk." Clair had normally developed a healthy body. At the time of his first visit to the clinic his mental test gave him an I. Q. of 92. He was only in the first grade in school, but his teachers reported that he could learn easily when he was not too busy being a bad boy.

The situation: His mother had died three years earlier. He and a brother, two years older, had been cared for in two different unsupervised homes. Their board was paid sporadically by the father, who seldom visited them and apparently cared but little for them. In the last home, where they had been for two years, they received plenty of food and fairly good clothes, but poor attention and no love or affection.

Several people reported his personality characteristics as activity, disobedience, and skilful dishonesty. He was reported as being untruthful, easily repentant, affectionate, interested in boyish activities, sly, revengeful, daring, and very fond of adventure. The delinquencies were all those that go with the unsupervised street life of a tenement district. He was a seriously disturbing element in the school, settlement house, and home because of his skilful and often successfully hidden dishonesty.

Thinking about the boy: The boy's superficial story, a knowledge of his environment, and reports from his disturbed neighbours and playmates all seemed to fix the cause of Clair's problems in his environment. He seemed to have done things because he had been taught to do them and because through them he had obtained pleasure. If one put oneself in his place, it seemed quite easy to understand all of his behaviour and many of his personality traits.

Thinking for him: An attempt was made to have the father allow an agency to place the boys elsewhere, but this failed at first. Finally the father was persuaded to move the boys back to a former foster-home in a different town where they had lived two years before, although the father insisted that their present home was much better and in a better neighbourhood.

Thinking with him: Two or three short interviews were held with Clair after this was done, to encourage him to keep some of the good resolutions he had made under his father's threat to have him committed to a school for delinquents. A deep rapport was not considered desirable or necessary, and he did not exceed a feeling of friendly belief in his responses towards me. As one might expect under these circumstances, he reported himself free from any sex habits. The treatment consisted entirely in encouraging him towards better behaviour and in attempts to get him more interested in normal activities through explaining them to him and proving to him that he would have more fun in this way than he was having in his delinquencies.

Results: A few months later he again appeared in the clinic, this time through an agency that had taken him from the court. We learned that for a short period after our former acquaintance his behaviour had improved, but now all the former disturbing factors had returned fourfold. He had begun to run away very frequently and to involve others in serious affairs, such as breaking into and entering stores, destroying property, and "fishing" drunken men.

Though but seven and one half years old, he was a leader in several of the affairs. One of these with another boy occurred at a distance from his home, and though the money was found where Clair had hidden it, neither he nor the other boy could locate the shop so that it might be returned.

In addition to this he was showing some very peculiar personality traits. He was quarrelling with his brother, a thing he had never done before, and refusing to let his brother be a member of his gang. The leadership of this gang he shared with another boy, whom he called "Hair-Breadth Harry." The most interesting of all of his new traits was that he very frequently reported imaginary delinquencies to the police. These stories would involve innocent boys and often even imaginary ones. Adults in the neighbourhood were not exempt from these accusations, and he had created many disturbing situations for his acquaintances. Policemen had spent many hours running down these clues, often taking Clair with them and giving him in this way long automobile rides, which he thoroughly enjoyed. He had been able to do this over a considerable period because sometimes he would report genuine affairs in which he had been involved, and through his help some crime was actually traced. But even at that he was really skilful in carrying out these deceptions and he had received much emotional satisfaction from his success.

Thinking for the boy: His recent difficult behaviour and the necessity of making some social decision for him justified an attempt to explore Clair's mental life. Since he was on probation, we could now be sure of seeing him regularly for study and treatment.

Thinking with the boy: It was more difficult to establish a personality contact than is usual with a boy of this age and type. Probably this was due to my coming so far from understanding his problems the first time that it was difficult for him to believe that I could understand them now. He was not consciously unhappy in his present way of living; therefore it was not easy to make him believe that a frank statement and understanding of his problems would be desirable.

This boy had, however, one very important problem which he yearned to confide to someone he could trust. He finally decided to take a chance with me. After he told his story, the good rapport came quickly, as a result of the confidence rather than as a cause of it, as is usually the case. The story itself cannot be told in all its details. Dr. Healy, in a conference report, said that in all his experience he had never known another child of this age with as extensive sex experience and as complete emotional response to it. He and his brother learned sex habits from older boys in their foster-home, and between the brothers homosexual relations had continued uninterruptedly for two years. Clair told of this as though he were describing an attachment between adults. He told of feelings of jealousy that had existed between him and his brother and of terms of affection, kisses, and other expressions of endearment practised by the boys when they were alone together. His physical response to this intimacy seemed, from his description, to have been much more complete than usual in so young a child.

When the boys had been moved out of this former foster-home, the brother made a sincere effort to avoid delinquency, but Clair, whose good resolutions were not kept so well, soon became involved with a large gang of street delinquents. In this gang were depraved girls older than Clair, who first taught him to have normal sex relations with little girls and later taught him all sorts of perverse sex practices. These children had constructed an observation post from which they could watch the sex activities of promiscuous adults. It was through going there that the boy's interest in these girls was first aroused. Because Clair insisted on joining this gang, and his brother wanted him not to, but to continue their former intimate relationship, the brothers had quarrelled and their intimacy had been destroyed.

This gang was made up of two parts, the older group being leaders and teachers in sex affairs, and the younger, with "Hair-Breadth Harry" and Clair as captains, thinking more about breaking and entering and other forms of stealing. It is interesting that nothing of the bad moral situation, aside from the stealing, was suspected by the police or social workers, who knew the boy so well.

Perhaps it was fear of punishment, perhaps it was his former acquaintance with me, but more probably it was the conflict in his mind over the emotional separation from his brother that inspired Clair with a sincere desire to get away from this gang. It was only after a considerable time that he would say that he wanted to overcome all his sex habits. He did not consider his physically expressed love for his brother to be abnormal or wrong.

I thought with Clair long and earnestly about his situation and behaviour and about how a boy could not be happy if he did such things. We were able to talk frankly of his behaviour, and he finally came to the point where he accepted the ideas I wanted him to, not because he believed them, nor because he felt that they were true, nor because he wanted to give up his bad habits, but because they came from me and because he believed that I was his understanding friend, who wanted to help him and probably knew best.

Clair did not understand how there could be any direct connexion between his sex habits and his other bad traits, for he had been punished for his delinquencies even though no one knew of his habits. Because of the good rapport which I had with him, I could tell him that this connexion existed. Even though I could not be sure this was the literal truth, there was at least therapeutic truth in this statement. He believed me when I told him that it would be easy for him to stop stealing if he overcame his bad physical habits.

Results: This proved to be true. The boy, instead of being sent to a school for delinquents, was placed in a foster-home in the country, with a wise foster-mother who had several small boys in her home. During the next few months he was seen twice in this home. He soon felt that he was stronger, healthier, and better because he had stopped his bad habits. He became loyal to this ideal and to his foster-mother and quickly ceased to feel dependent upon his loyalty to me. He has been in this home a year. Except for occasional masturbation during the first six months, he has indulged in no sex practices or sex talk, and he says he has little sex ideation. He is in good enough rapport with me to be depended upon to tell me the truth. We have an additional check on him through two other little boys in the home who report to the foster-mother the slightest misbehaviour on the part of the other children. Clair has not stolen anything from his home, though he is freely trusted with money. He has not attempted to run away. He is happy and well-behaved except for an occasional fight with his companions.

He is still retarded in school, and his teachers consider him somewhat dull. He has never been retested psychologically.

This case is a psychiatric success. The social adjustments of course enter into the general success he has obtained, but the fine work of the foster-mother is largely psychiatric rather than social.

The academic acquirement of the psychiatrist counts for very little in a case like this, but common sense, his ability to accept the boy, to feel with him, and to avoid being disgusted with him are the essential things. The value of the confession was very great, for the boy probably had a certain desire for loyalty to his brother, which he wished to re-establish. He probably realized unconsciously that telling of his affairs would free him from his gang; after this was accomplished, he learned by experience that he was happier, and thus he could go on to better ideals.

This success was possible because the confession was made to someone who could successfully redirect his loyalties into more normal channels.

*   *

About the next boy's mind we *know* practically nothing. The best psychiatric guess, or at least the one that has been most frequently made, is that his behaviour was conditioned by some abnormality in his sex life.

Case No. 43
MARVIN ATKINS

Marvin was a large boy for thirteen years. He was first known in the clinic three years ago. Neglected teeth, nasal obstruction, tonsils, and adenoids handicapped him physically. He had a dull, sullen expression and was rather inactive. Mentally he was of low average ability.

The situation: Earlier Marvin had been placed in various foster-homes because of street delinquency, often repeated, and because his environment and home situation were very bad. He had adjusted poorly to all of the foster-homes, of which some had been good and some had not been suitable for the lad. Marvin's personality traits have always entered very largely into his problems, and the patient, long-suffering visitor could predict quite accurately how the boy would react to a new situation. He has always seemed an unhappy boy. He was never affectionate, trusting, or confiding. He was irritable and often excessively quarrelsome. He resented authority, was easily offended, and considered himself discriminated against. Among his few good qualities was truthfulness. During the years before I saw the boy, he had been in the clinic three different times and had been seen by three different psychiatrists. To each of these he had unwillingly confessed some unfortunate behaviour important in the situation at that time. He had reluctantly reported his sex habits and sex ideation. Many abnormal responses were found in this boy relating to sex. He derived pleasure from driving nails and sticking knives into wood. He usually did these things when he masturbated. He was brought to the clinic, at the time I saw him, to find out, if possible, whether or not he was a sex teacher in the foster-home.

Thinking about the boy: The social situation seemed to demand that the truth be known about his present behaviour. On each of the former occasions when he had been seen in the clinic, the partial information he gave had always been used to make social adjustment. No positive rapport seemed to have been reached at any time. The boy's history, with its peculiar and only partly known sex responses, and his superior and antagonistic attitude made it evident that he very much needed personality *help* rather than investigation of his behaviour.

Thinking for him: One had to mix one's *"thinking for"* this boy with *"thinking for"* society in general. We know from experience that sufficient cross-questioning could finally force Marvin to admit the truth. One could be just as sure that Marvin would permanently exclude his questioner from the place in his emotional life where the questioner might give personality help if he told his misdeeds for any other reason than because he wanted to, or, in other words, without having entered a good rapport.

As many mistakes as it is possible to make in any one case were made with Marvin. It was an error of judgment for me to think that I might be the detective first and the psychiatrist afterwards. Theoretical *"thinking about"* was badly mixed with *"thinking for"* him. When the boy, quite naturally, reacted negatively to me, I reacted negatively to him instead of remaining neutral. Then instead of refusing to obtain his confession under these circumstances, as I should have done had I remained neutral, I cross-questioned the boy and finally obtained his confession.

Socially that was possibly the correct procedure, but had I *thought for* the boy more thoroughly and insisted on a prolonged period of treatment, perhaps I could have established *personality contact* later and have given him psychiatric help.

Thinking with him: Since no rapport was established, we did not think together at all. I faced him with damaging evidence I had, and obtained his reluctant confession, which was accompanied by the statement that it is not easy to ignore or forget. He said: "Yes, those things are all you people think of and talk about. You are no better than I am. They say they bring me here to get help. I'd like to know how it helps me to just talk about it all the time."

After this interview it was insisted that Marvin come back for further attempts to help him. He refused to come unless he could be assured that he would not have to talk to me. He came once more and another psychiatrist saw him. A good rapport was not established and he has not been seen in the clinic again.

Results: This boy was made more unhappy, his bad personality traits were more firmly fixed in his life, and anyone else's attempt to give him help will be the more difficult because of my interview with him.

Very patient social work has accomplished something for Marvin.

His visitor through long and diligent efforts has been able to reach the boy to some extent and to have some small influence on him. His behaviour is somewhat better. He is now working and is keeping out of serious trouble. He is still an unusually peculiar and grouchy boy, with many unfortunate and disagreeable personality traits.

*   *

The next boy asked many, many questions; from the nature of his questions and from his behaviour one felt strongly that some abnormal twist had occurred in his instinctive life. He may adjust to life well even though he is not understood or helped.

Case No. 44
NED ROSS

Ned was ten years old when first known to the clinic. He is now nearly fourteen. He is an alert, bright, likable chap with a healthy body and normal development. But he is over-active and distractible. Mentally, on tests, he shows good normal abilities.

The situation: Since he was first known to the clinic, Ned on numerous occasions has said many interesting things and given interesting glimpses of an unusual mind. But after he was seen two or three times, he disappeared, leaving those who were thinking about him still baffled in their attempts to understand him. When he was first known, his home was a good average middle-class one, well furnished and comfortable. There had always been some economic stress, however. He was the only child by his father's first marriage, and he had several younger half-siblings.

Later Ned's father, who was a shopkeeper in a small way, was killed in a motor accident. He had been inconsistently over-indulgent and then neglectful, first protecting, then accusing the lad. Since the father's death the mother had been assisted by various agencies, whose good offices she utilized in every possible way. She taught the boy the art of getting something from everyone. The parents were never co-operative in the boy's attendance at the clinic. The mother especially, since she can see no concrete advantage to be gained, believes it is useless for Ned to keep his appointments with us.

On two or three occasions before his father's death Ned appeared in the juvenile court for petty stealing, and at one time he stole four dollars from his church poor-box and with the money purchased a toy revolver and some handcuffs. He put the handcuffs on another boy and, providing himself with an eye-mask, paraded his friend down a crowded street, announcing that he was Gerald Chapman, and that he had subdued and handcuffed this detective who was sent to capture him. Because he disturbed the peace (or possibly it was a policeman he disturbed by doing this), he was again in the juvenile court.

He had been reported earlier, by his father, as irritable, but affectionate and pleasant, jealous of his half-siblings and exhibiting temper tantrums towards them, but always friendly and pleasant towards others. His father said that he was non-confiding, usually obedient, willing to work, not easily impressed. (The reports showed that the boy considered his appearances in the juvenile court a huge joke.) Others reported the boy as aggressive, talkative, sly, and a skilful liar. He showed tendencies to run with a bad gang, but he usually kept out of any of the gang's criminal activities. His school reports have always been good. He is much interested in church and attends the church school and services regularly. He never neglects to say his prayers. Ned's voluminous record, with its many conflicting reports of his behaviour and his personality traits, reads as though it were that of two or three different boys!

A detailed report of this boy and his remarkably functioning mind, containing all the interesting details, would be impossibly long. He had been seen by three other psychiatrists before I knew him. Some of the facts brought out by these studies are best mentioned under the situation as I first met it.

One of the interesting periods during which he had been known in the clinic was at the time of the dramatic crimes, arrests, trial, conviction, and the execution of the notorious criminal Chapman. For days this boy seemed to be living a life of fantasy in which he, in a peculiar way, identified himself with this man. His remarkable imagination, the details of which he always freely reported to everyone, is illustrated by the fact that, though he was home in bed, the death of his hero, Chapman, in the electric chair, was as vivid and vital to him as to those in the death chamber itself. And it probably had as much emotional value to him as to many who were actually present. His description of the execution, gained from reading the papers and augmented by his imagination, surpassed in gruesome detail and in colourful sidelights the efforts of the star reporters. The boy asserted he had been awake all of the night of the execution.

Another very interesting thing was that although it later developed that he was not being frank and truthful about some of his more serious problems, he succeeded in convincing all those who saw him that he was. Despite this apparent frankness, however, no psychiatrist who saw him felt that he had in any way really understood him or influenced him towards more normal personality traits. There was and still is plenty of concrete evidence that no one has influenced any of his behaviour patterns for the better.

His sex problems he had always discussed in a half-frank, half-disgusted, childlike manner that seemed to indicate that they were of minor importance.

Several attempts to give him psychotherapy had been made. These were unsuccessful, largely because he would break appointments. Finally he would drift entirely away from the clinic.

Thinking about the boy: At the beginning of my acquaintance with him he was talkative, boastful, and given to fantastic lying. He asked me remarkable questions, often irrelevantly interrupting our conversation. Here are some of them: "What is the difference between a dead man and a dead animal?" "Do doctors see dead people all over after they are dead?" "Do they see inside of them?" "Why does anyone go to sleep?" "What is anything when it is right?" "Do you believe some people can see thoughts?" "How much does it cost to learn to be a doctor?" "Who first thought about having money?" "Why is money worth anything?" "Is a criminal's dead body different from anybody else's?" "What do people want to learn things for?" "How do we know there is a God?" "Would they let a boy go into the morgue if he was not dead?" "What does a morgue look like inside?" Many other questions about ordinary things were interspersed with these. He always reached for the answer and always remembered what was told him. I knew him first previous to his father's accidental death, and this type of question was asked before this occurred. In the early part of our acquaintance no direct sex questions were asked.

There was abundant material in Ned's mind, superficially available for the construction of theoretical ideas that would comply with the specifications of any one of the schools of mental philosophy.

Thinking for him: Ned was becoming more disturbing to his family and the authorities, although he was not seriously delinquent. He was becoming a chronic complainer and a successful applicant for the privileges and benefits of organized charity. He was growing more unusual all the time. Recently he had shown some tendencies to withdraw from his groups. There could be little danger of making him more unsocial or of further upsetting him emotionally by establishing a deeper rapport. It seemed essential to explore Ned's mind, particularly when we considered the social aspects of his problems.

Thinking with him: There continued to be many broken appointments but these were often offset by his appearing for interviews when we did not expect him. He gradually became more sincere in conversation and lost some of his over-vivaciousness and distractibility. Whatever rapport was established with this boy was effected largely through his curiosity. He became convinced that I was sincerely trying to answer his questions, and gradually he asked more intelligent ones. He began to state his questions more frankly. He began to trust me, because he believed that I was being frank with him, and that I was trying to help him. Ned is still being treated. At times he says and does things that make me hopeful of a good personality contact, but as yet this has been unsuccessful. He is, however, more frank and less boastful than he has been with others. One may not be sure that he is revealing all of his emotional or behaviour life.

Ned in his more recent serious and sincere moods still shows fantastic and peculiar mental reactions. He has always believed that he will be either a criminal or a doctor, and he imagines himself one or the other of these very frequently. Recently he says that he had about made up his mind to be a doctor until he found out how much it costs to get a medical education. He is now thinking somewhat of being a criminal first and in this way accumulating enough money to study medicine later. He thinks that if he were successful as a hold-up man for two or three years, he might do this.

There has been a long-drawn-out damage suit as a result of his father's death, and he has many fantastic ideas of how to force those he believes negligent to pay the damages to his mother. Once during a pause in the discussion of quite another subject Ned smiled to himself and glanced shrewdly around the room. When asked what he had thought about at that moment, he said: "I thought that if I had those two men who killed my father [the men owned the truck in which the accident occurred] here in this room, and I had a gun, how slick I could kill them. I don't think you'd say anything about it, for you know they're guilty."

He frequently imagines himself to be small and inside of the various parts of the human body and able to watch the way the body works. He says that these imaginings have been the reason he has wished to know so much about the human body. He is particularly interested in the brain and heart and asks dozens of questions concerning the anatomy and physiology of these parts.

He believes that his stepmother loves his half-sisters more than she does him. He misses his father very much and often imagines that he is still alive.

He has many unusual and peculiar ideas and thoughts about religion. These do not concern his own personal feelings so much as they concern his wondering why the different religious sects believe as they do. I have tried sincerely to think with him about these and many other things, even in the superficial stage of rapport which we have reached. Possibly something in the way of influencing his personality traits and mental life has been accomplished by meeting him on his own level and answering his questions frankly, but it is probable that if a deeper rapport could be established, much more could be done.

I have probably helped him with his sex problems. Formerly

he had lied skilfully about his sex experience. He now says that two years ago a little Jewish girl, two years his senior, had told him about sex things, and that he has frequently had sex relations with her. He had learned to respond to and to long for her advances ardently. For the past few months his racial and religious feelings have made this seem very bad to him, and he has been trying hard to resist the temptations. The girl lives in the same tenement and still frequently makes approaches to him. He says that for the past three months he has successfully overcome his desires. The boy says that he is able to do this because I have told him the entire truth about sex life, especially the facts of sex diseases and of sexual hygiene; I have encouraged him to believe that to stop his unfortunate behaviour will show that he has a healthy body and good will-power.

Ned has few good loyalties to people or to ideals. It is very interesting to note that the one real loyalty, aside from the earlier one to his father, that has been found in this boy has been of the greatest help to him in this matter. There is a little girl of his own race and creed whom he has known for the past few months. He believes she is a very nice little girl and he thinks that she likes him. He would not want her to know of his bad habits and is ashamed when she sees the little Jewish girl speaking to him. He asks me if I think it will be all right for him to tell this little girl that he likes her—providing he is good for a while longer in the mean time.

Since Ned has become confidential about this part of his life, his questions have lost much of their peculiar archetype character. He still asks me questions, but they are much more answerable, and his train of thought does not fly about as formerly. Doubtless his conflicts about his sex life have been brought to the surface. One can easily believe that he has many other conflicts, but the rapport is not sufficiently deep for me to describe or evaluate them.

Results: Ned is still being treated, and it is difficult to say just how much help has been given him. He has reached the point where he probably does not lie. His street delinquencies, which he seems to report freely, are conditioned by his personality traits, and the way he looks at life in general has been altered but little. At present he is a very interesting boy to think about, but it has been very difficult to *think with* him successfully. Speaking generally, the psychotherapy has been a partial success. It is possible that he will become a serious social problem unless I or someone else can help him to face his problems and better to understand himself and life.

* *

The next boy presents a peculiar personality response to life situations. Again one may theorize from his behaviour that his sex life is abnormal. It was not possible really to understand him.

Case No. 45
ELMER ANDREWS

Elmer Andrews has been known to the clinic for three years. He is now fourteen years old. Elmer is boyish in his facial expressions and in many of his responses and interests. He is distinctly premature in his general and pubertal development. His face is smooth and dark-skinned. He is healthy and well-proportioned physically. He has a pleasant boyish smile and a very friendly attitude. Strangers consider him and treat him as a child, though in physical development he is practically a man.

The situation: Elmer has lived in an unhappy situation, but he says that he has always been happy. For several years his father has been an inmate of a state hospital for mental diseases, diagnosed as *dementia prœcox*. For a time the mother kept the children together in a semblance of a home. Elmer has three younger sisters. His mother has been living as a common-law wife for some time. Elmer has never felt bad about this.

Because the home was finally broken up, this boy and his three younger sisters were taken by a placing agency and put in a very good foster-home. He is reported by his foster-mother as being reserved, quiet, sometimes slightly disobedient, but always very helpful and neat about the home. He is kind to his sisters. She says that he is a moody boy who often says very little when quite serious situations arise, but who at other times is frank, explanatory, and sorry for things he has done. He was brought to the clinic as a psychiatric problem and for advice in placing elsewhere. Recently it has been discovered through the confessions of one of his sisters that for a long time Elmer and two of his sisters have been indulging in sex play of a serious nature. One of the girls is much upset about the matter and has developed chorea—possibly on the basis of her experiences. While sex relations did not actually occur, it amounted to the same thing emotionally for all of them.

Thinking about the boy: The unhappy home and the lack of parental care and affection must be considered. Since Elmer presents some of the symptoms that might be considered as pointing towards a later psychosis, the question of hereditary influence seems important. He shows a very peculiar blocking in his conversation. Much study of this reveals no connexion between the blocking and the unpleasantness of the subject being discussed at the time. He talks quite freely about a subject and then suddenly is unable to give any answer to some simple question, or he suddenly stops in the middle of a sentence. If nothing is said to him, his face assumes a far-away look, and he often smiles to himself.

He tries to tell what his thoughts were when this happened, but he either cannot or will not tell what actually is in his mind. He is a day-dreamer and much interested in reading. The most notice-able thing about this lad is his very distinct under-emotional atti-tudes. This is especially true in regard to his delinquency and its re-sults. He knows his sister is ill as a result of it, but he does not feel bad or blame himself very much, though he says he is very sorry it has happened. He knows he must be removed from his sisters and says he does not want to be, but he smiles about it. He becomes interested in knowing where he will go. He shows slight emotional response to the knowledge that his friends and foster-parents must be told of his behaviour. He thinks that since he has been discovered in his misbehaviour, he will be treated better if he makes a clean breast of the whole matter.

Thinking for him: Elmer is another boy who must be understood thoroughly if he is to be helped. His is a case in which the estab-lishment of a deep rapport was justifiable, even though we might not give him psychiatric help, for we should know as much of his mental life as possible if we are to predict his probable future behaviour. Only by doing this could we give valuable advice to the placing agency.

Thinking with him: From the first, Elmer wanted to be friendly, in his peculiar reserved way, and it was a very simple matter to establish a good rapport with him. He wanted to get out of trouble for selfish reasons, and he believed I might help him. But through-out the time of treatment and since, while he seemed, in most ways, in excellent personality contact, he failed to give much emotional value to our acquaintance.

He was entirely frank in telling the story of his life. He asked many questions. He always wanted to come back for further inter-views. He would write friendly notes and letters, but despite all this he was entirely unable to be frank in regard to his emotional life, although he was very friendly and at times even affectionate in a shy and reserved way. He said he had never loved any member of his family enough to feel bad about being separated from them. His father's being in the state hospital was a bad thing, but he could see him occasionally, and so he saw no reason to feel upset about this. His sister might eventually be mentally ill as a result of his misconduct, but he did not worry about it.

In response to questions as to how any particular experience made him feel, he would reply with a frank open smile: "Why, just no way, I guess. I don't think about it that way."

He told us that older companions had taught him sex practices of various sorts when he was very young, and he had continued them. Since they have now got him into trouble, he is glad to find someone who can talk to him about them and tell him how he may avoid them, for he wants to get out of trouble. He is neither boastful nor ashamed of the things he has done. He says he is very sorry about them.

We have spent a great deal of time together. Elmer is always co-operative. An attempt was made to go deeper into his mental life by using associative memory. He was entirely co-operative, but nothing was obtained. The psychotherapeutics consisted largely in good advice and in some rather serious criticisms of his behaviour. Elmer did all the things that a boy in good personality contact usually does, but his emotional responses were those of one in friendly belief.

His superficial loyalties might be judged very good, but they were loyalties of words and deeds rather than emotional ones. In his way he was loyal to his foster-parents, to his school, and to his undeserving mother. He was loyal to his promises of better behaviour. His behaviour steadily improved, especially as it involved other children. When he did something he thought he should not do, he confessed to it voluntarily in interviews. Sometimes he wrote his confessions to me. What he wrote seemed much more sincere, for the indifferent tone of voice and the pleasant superficial smile were missing from the written words.

Nowadays he is anxious to return to the clinic for talks. I have visited his foster-home on several occasions. The case has been followed partly on account of interest in the diagnosis of his mental condition. The psychotherapeutics throughout have been carried out as best they could be in this peculiar type of rapport.

Results: With the exception of one short period when the surrounding circumstances offered much temptation and opportunity for sex activities, Elmer has indulged in no mutual sex behaviour with other children. He is constantly struggling with himself to stop masturbation and is succeeding in a large measure.

His interests seem more normal than they were. He is doing good school-work and is earning some money by helping in the church and Sunday-school as janitor. He saves his money. He is becoming very neat and careful about his appearance and seems to have some social interests of a good type.

It is impossible to say how much of his improvement has been attained through the efforts I made to give him personality help. The boy himself credits his clinical contacts with a great deal. He says that he is sure he is a better boy because of them. Without question we are dealing with a very peculiar personality in this boy. Possibly he should be classed under the group of psychopathic personalities. The social results have been as satisfactory as one could possibly have expected. The boy is well cared for and not doing harm to others. He seems to be happy. Certainly he is being given a very good chance to adjust himself to life, though his very unusual traits, which have probably not been modified to any extent, make the final outcome very doubtful. One might guess that whatever has been accomplished, has been done through his loyalties to his physician, though in the personal interviews I cannot feel that there is any direct evidence of this.

*   *

The last lad of this group is another boy who had a multiplicity of problems. His problems have been solved. Perhaps his behaviour at the critical moment served as an outlet for him and helped him to straighten out sex problems that might have overwhelmed him.

Case No. 46
SANDOR POLUSO

Sandor Poluso, who is now eleven years old, has been known to the clinic for three years. He is a small sturdy Greek boy, round-faced, with small bright eyes and dark skin. He is friendly and active. He has good general mental ability; I. Q., 118.

The situation: About one year ago, when psychotherapy was first undertaken (though it was advised much earlier), Sandor represented in his small person nearly all the forms of juvenile delinquency in the calendar. He was a successful thief of long standing, often successful in stealing considerable sums of money, sometimes stealing things he did not use. He was a skilful liar, frequently involving his best friends in difficulties by his lying and often doing it in a vengeful way. He had long-continued bad sex habits and was a sex teacher. He was a chronic truant from school and had run away from his home very frequently. He began this at the age of four. He was an especially skilful street beggar, telling pitiful lies to gain his ends. Very often he destroyed property wantonly, both at home and on the street.

He was all this, while his two older brothers and his younger sister, who had lived in the same undesirable neighbourhood and under the same bad home influences as he, were non-delinquent. The older brother was a very fine boy, of good moral standards. He was adjusting well to a very difficult situation (Case No. 15). The next brother is reported as Case No. 34 of this series. He was not delinquent, but had as many personality problems as Sandor had behaviour problems.

There was much economic stress in the home and much cruelty to the children. They were taught and encouraged to seek charity and to criticize and condemn those who tried to help them. The social situation may be reflected by the statement that this family has been known and helped by not less than twenty-two public agencies.

Thinking about the boy: The notes of the first conference held in the clinic on this boy say that it is entirely uncertain what dynamic mechanisms are active in him. He was a great talker, but little reliance could be put on what he said. A psychiatrist study was discussed and recommended, but was not carried out at that time. During the two years following his first appearance in the clinic he was placed in no less than six foster-homes. In most of these he did very well at first, but later became dissatisfied and then delinquent as a means to returning home or to getting a new foster-home. Much excellent personal work and attention was given to this boy by the agency visitor. When in a foster-home, Sandor wanted constantly to go to his own home; and when he was allowed to do so, he soon became dissatisfied and delinquent, got into court, and had to be placed again in a foster-home. He would then be ready and begging to go to a new home. Since I could rely very little upon what he said until after personality contact was established, most of the *thinking about* him had to be done on the basis of his history and reports.

Thinking for him: When I first knew him, the *thinking for* him resulted in a decision to make an attempt more thoroughly to understand him by psychiatric study.

Thinking with him: He was then about nine years old. He was friendly, bright, and active. Just then he was in trouble, and he wanted very much to get out of it. It was not easy to reach this lad in a way that really meant anything to him. It was most evident that it was not best to do things for him. To have things done for him was what he expected, because this had always happened in the past when others had tried to help him. He first became interested when he found that his opinions and statements were being considered seriously by someone who could tell when he was lying and who, instead of thinking it "cute" or "bad," was thinking about this lying as though it were a disease. Sandor did not like to feel that there was anything the matter with him. At least he did not want to admit this, though later it was shown that he really did think there was very much the matter with him.

He began to tell the truth, and then he found that he was getting sympathy and friendship from someone who was interested in the real boy, Sandor, underneath the surface. Before this no one had ever known him as he really was. This was the beginning, and then shortly he made excellent personality contact. He not only stopped his lying, but often in conversation he would go back and correct mis-statements he had made in previous interviews. He asked many questions and listened to the answers. For the first time he cried about things; he cried about things he had not wanted to think about. He became entirely frank in regard to his emotional life.

The treatment was much more prolonged than it is in most cases. In fact, it is still being carried on. At first, interviews were frequent. Later they occurred about once every two months.

By *thinking with* Sandor I found that he had many conflicts. I can mention here only some of the things over which he had both conscious and repressed conflicts. It was very easy to believe that all of his misbehaviour was in direct response to these. Each conflict seemed to account for some particular form of his misbehaviour. He was much confused and worried over sex problems. These were really very serious in his case. He had a very strong sex drive for one so young. He had distorted ideas in regard to the facts of his sex life. From early life he had engaged in many forms of sex activities. He had worried about his health because of this, but he denied sex habits to the other boys, who told him he would go crazy, and he denied his worry to himself. His lying, which often bordered on the pathological, seemed to be based largely on this particular conflict. Sandor and I always think very seriously on this subject when we see each other, and so far it is the one that is furthest from solution.

His conflicts in regard to hating and being jealous of his siblings seemed to account for his stealing. This was nearer the surface of his mind than the sex conflict, and this type of misbehaviour was the first to improve. He has shown very little dishonesty since the beginning of the psychotherapy. He seemed to adopt my emotional attitudes towards stealing very readily.

Although it was really true that he had indulged in a great deal of self-pity, he did not like to admit this to himself. He very easily became jealous of others in his foster-homes and was very sensitive of his treatment by other children in his various environments. This was also comparatively near the surface of his mind and could scarcely be called a mental conflict, although it seemed to account for his wanton destructiveness. This type of behaviour was also much improved soon after treatment commenced.

Buried deepest in his mind and coming to the surface only after he tried sincerely to be understood was his feeling of being inferior. He really hated himself and considered himself inferior, both morally and physically. This was probably largely on the basis of worry over his sex habits, though it also involved the attainments of his highly supernormal brother, the next older than he. Sandor felt that this brother, who was very gravely physically handicapped, was in every way a superior person to himself. This brother's behaviour was sometimes cited as an example for him to follow. He hated him and quarrelled with him constantly, although at first he insisted that he was the best friend he had. He believed that people always liked his brother better than they did him. All this had appeared in the boy in the form of a brazen and debonair attitude towards his delinquencies. He had adopted a supercilious attitude towards all who attempted to help him and towards the members of his family.

While this boy did not seem to reach the rapport of dependent attachment, he certainly approached it, and at one period of the treatment it seemed that it would occur in spite of my efforts to prevent it. It is true, however, that he probably is even now more loyal to me largely through my ability to understand him and to make him happier by talking to him than he is to any other person or ideal of life. He writes very interesting personal letters and insists on making confessions of misbehaviour to me personally rather than to his foster-parents or visitor.

Much time has been spent in *thinking about* and *with* this boy. He has been a most interesting boy to think about, and one from whom much could be learned in regard to the mental life of children and their emotional and behaviour responses.

Results: Sandor is still very different in his responses when there is a third person present at interviews from what he is when we are alone together, but this difference is gradually becoming

less. I have not yet found anyone to take my place in his scheme
of loyalties. How far I have permanently modified his personality
traits I cannot estimate at present. Apparently I have effected
large temporary changes in regard to many different things. (Recently he has had one of his home-sick spells, but it did not result
in serious misbehaviour, and one interview changed his attitude.)
He returned willingly to his foster-home after a two-day visit to
his own home and voluntarily wrote his visitor that he was glad
he had done so.

The results in modifying his behaviour have been excellent,
except for his bad personal habits, which are much improved,
but not entirely overcome. During the past eight months he has
been very good—wonderfully so, in fact—as compared with his
past behaviour. There has been no stealing and no truancy. His
vengeful lying has disappeared. He is more willing to work. He
does not express dissatisfaction, and his school record is better
than it has ever been. For all these things much credit should be
given to the help of his very intelligent and faithful agency visitor.

Without doubt Sandor is facing his problems of life much more
frankly, and his feeling of inferiority is disappearing.

The proportion of psychiatrists to the general population would
have to be very high if all the children who need help were to be
studied and treated as Sandor has been. If we are to acquire knowledge and understanding in the field of child-guidance that we may
utilize both therapeutically and educationally, however, we must
do it by a thorough study of the individual child.

CHAPTER XIII

RUNNING AWAY FROM LIFE

The Child who is Sorry for Himself

ERHAPS the most common unhealthy mental attitude found among children is a desire to avoid meeting the new situations of life as they appear. Modern psychiatry teaches that it is serious mental behaviour, especially in early life. The psychiatrist who is interested in children presenting "problems" is more often concerned with those children who in their childhood are trying to avoid the more concrete problems directly connected with their environment. Those whose cases are here grouped are of this type. They present the exaggerated form of a behaviour that is found to some extent in nearly everyone, the concrete behaviour that has as its mental equivalent self-pity.

As a group they are understood earlier and helped more easily than most of the boys and girls seen in a child-guidance clinic.

* *

The first boy had a rather hard situation to meet. He had never learned that there was any satisfaction in meeting hard situations, so he simply did not try to meet them. He finally learned this very necessary lesson, but he found it a difficult one.

Case No. 47
STEPHEN FRANKWORTH

Stephen has been seen frequently at the clinic for the last two years and a half. He is a healthy, well-developed boy with good posture and swarthy complexion. When he was first known, he had just reached his fourteenth year. Pubertal development was nearly complete, although he was boyish in his appearance and in many of his responses. Mentally he had only fair general ability.

The situation: Stephen was a member of a large family. His home was one of poverty, and his experiences with the better things in life had been very slight. His physical wants had been poorly supplied and his moral and character training entirely neglected. One will seldom see a so thoroughly neglected boy as Stephen.

He was reported lazy and unambitious in his work, but active and vivacious in his play. He was a follower. His tired, widowed mother had many good things to say about Stephen. He was always truthful, kind-hearted, and affectionate. He was disobedient, however, especially in regard to her wish that he keep out of a very bad gang of boys who lived in his neighbourhood, with whom Stephen had got into difficulties.

When I first knew him, these difficulties had resulted in several serious court charges against the boy. He had been twice apprehended with other boys in rummaging- and stealing-expeditions in closed summer homes, and he had been accused of being involved in an oil-station robbery. Besides this he was charged with making a sex assault on a little girl.

Thinking about the boy: Stephen was frightened and unhappy. He was frank and truthful. (An acquaintance of two years and a half and the shrewd opinion of his most understanding agency worker have convinced me that this boy never lies. Sometimes he refuses to tell things he knows or to admit delinquencies, but if he says anything at all, it is the truth.) He gave his unhappy history and reported his many temptations and misdeeds freely during the first interview. Nothing in his story and in the reports about him pointed to any emotional conflicts in his life. Life was hard for him and he was trying to avoid its responsibilities. He was denying neither of these facts. He was a bad boy and he knew it. He was easily led and he recognized the fact. He was in trouble and he wished to avoid the serious punishment that he knew, in justice, should be given him. He had loyalties, largely selfish because of his poor training and environment.

Apparently one did not have to search his emotional life for an explanation of his delinquencies.

Thinking for him: Stephen needed concrete advice and help. He needed encouragement to better living, and someone who could help him see life in a practical way. He needed to be convinced that happiness would come through better living. He needed someone who could see the assets in his character and in his environment and who would then direct his loyalties towards them. These things could best be done for him by a person whom he could believe and trust. I could see no reason to think that it would be best for that person to enter his environment in any emotional way. Any advisable degree of rapport could have been attained easily, but it seemed best to prevent, if possible, any deeper rapport than that of personal trust.

Thinking with him: He had reported truthfully in court about his gang stealing. He had not been involved in the oil-station robbery, but he had not been believed when he denied it. He had refused to tell in detail of the sex affair, but he had not lied about it. When he trusted me, he freely told the facts.

This boy, very mature for his age, had been with a gang of

older boys who, during the past year, had taught him bad sex habits. They had boasted of sex experiences with girls, ridiculed Stephen because he had not had any. He said that, not only on the occasion when he was accused by a lady who happened to observe his actions with a little girl, but also on other occasions he had tried very hard to persuade girls to permit him to have sex relations with them. He said that he had never been tempted actually to force girls to accede to his demands or even thought of it. The older boys had taught him that if a boy hugs and kisses a girl long enough, she will always consent. He had been observed and arrested while following out these suggestions. Stephen and I discussed in a practical and serious way what difficulties, punishment, and probable unhappiness such behaviour would lead to. We also talked about what his indolent habits would lead to in the way of practical life results. We talked and thought of the foolishness of making good resolutions without their being backed by practical helps such as avoiding temptations by doing something to keep busy. We discussed the fact that all boys have sex temptations, and that many of them control themselves in such a way as to make their own lives better, and that in the end this brought more real satisfaction and happiness. By very practical arguments I succeeded in convincing him that it was better for him to leave his present situation now and make a new start in a foster-home. At first he insisted that he wanted to stay at home and try to keep out of trouble. Then, if he failed again, he would be sent to an institution. He thought he would rather do this than leave his environment and his wayward friends at present.

I have known Stephen for a long time. When he gets into trouble or new problems come up, both of which things have happened rather frequently, he wants to talk with me and get my advice, but he comes to me as to a doctor who is interested in him and who knows about him rather than as to a friend from whom he can expect sympathy or protection.

Results: Finally Stephen willingly entered a foster-home, where he has done very well during the past year and a half. No serious delinquencies have occurred. He has stolen a few small articles. He has run away from his home twice for short periods of time. In this home he has been thrown with other boys who have had much better training than his in the refinements of life, and he has resented some of the things that have naturally arisen from this situation. From a behaviour standpoint, Stephen is a success. Much of the credit is to be given to the social handling of the case and to the interest and personality help given by his visitor.

The case, however, is not a complete success, as he is still lazy, although he has improved even in this respect. If this is corrected, it will probably be through the influence of some other person who enters his environmental values in an emotional way, but in this case, as in most others in which the mental and personality problems are not a large part of the situation, it is much better for this person to be someone other than the psychiatrist. Stephen has not yet fully realized that happiness will come through meeting and facing the problems of life, but eventually he will appreciate this. He may easily again become delinquent, and while the case seems to be largely successful, it is classed as a temporary success in the summary.

*   *

The third boy of this group also had a hard situation to meet, but his early training was better than Stephen's. He was handicapped in his efforts to learn his lessons of life by his very definite dislike for physical exertion. He is the only boy of this series whom the writer thinks of as fundamentally lazy. If there is such a thing as natural laziness, Henry is a sparkling example of it.

Case No. 48
HENRY ALLEN

Henry was fourteen years old when I first knew him. He had a splendid physical development, was lithe, quick in his responses, and open of countenance. He greeted everyone with a pleasant smile, although often he showed a serious, sad expression. He was normally boyish in most of his characteristics. He demonstrated himself by test to have average mental ability. He was friendly and frank in a reserved way. He wore well on acquaintance and made a very favourable impression on all who knew him.

The situation: The boy's father gave an immensely long history, which we afterwards learned was unreliable and full of self-justifications. Henry had been brought into court for stealing money from telephone boxes. He had been away from home for two weeks, bunking with another delinquent boy in an old house. This was the fifth time that Henry had stayed away on long runaways, and on numerous occasions he had remained away from home overnight. It was surprising that when he was on these runaways, he nearly always attended school. The father made much of the fact that the boy smoked excessively. As the lad's own story was checked up, it proved to be more reliable than the father's. Henry confessed to much stealing that had not been known before, and he made clear the peculiarities of his family situation.

The circumstances of Henry's birth and early life were unusual and were the basic cause of a large part of his problem. His father and mother were married when he was nearly two years old. At times after the marriage the father admitted paternity, and then denied it. Henry knew there was something secret about his parentage. His father had told us that he did not believe Henry was his son, but he had denied having told Henry this. He made

remarks to Henry in my presence, however, that would make any
boy suspicious. He never allowed Henry to speak of his mother in
any way. His mother had died when Henry was six years old. He
was living in the Western states at the time, and he continued to
live with his maternal grandparents for a year. He then came to
Cambridge, where he lived with his father, who remarried shortly
after his first wife's death. His stepmother has never liked Henry
and was not good to him. The younger half-sisters were favoured
in the family, by both the father and the stepmother. Henry had no
playthings and earned or stole what money he had to spend. His
father whipped him excessively for his delinquencies. The father
was an ordinary working man, and the family was in poor circumstances.

Thinking about the boy: At the first interview Henry was a
much discouraged boy, so discouraged, in fact, that he said he
wished to be sent to an institution for delinquent boys. He was
perfectly resigned to answering questions because he believed that
it was his duty and it might lead to this adjustment. Because of the
very unreliable report we had of him, it was necessary to *think
about* him while talking with him.

Henry said he had never been happy since his mother's death. He
remembered and told, with many tears, the circumstances of her
death and of his father's ill-treatment of her. He said there was no
one in the world who cared for him. He had frequently written to
his relatives in the West, asking to be allowed to go back to them,
but they knew through his father of his delinquencies and would
not take him. He told me that being bad never made him happy,
and that he received little satisfaction from the money he had
taken dishonestly. He had often hoped he would be arrested on
his runaways and "sent away." He would have much preferred
this to going home again.

Henry had strong religious beliefs and expected to be punished for his misdemeanours in a future life.

He had never done any "dirty" things in his life, though he had been with a very low gang on the streets and knew much about the lowest kind of street life.

He said he did not hate his father and had tried at times to be good, hoping that his father would love him. He had never tried to be friendly with his stepmother because she was never good to him and because she had made slurring remarks about his mother.

After the boy told his story and two interviews had been held with the father, I felt much better equipped to *think about* the problem.

Thinking with him: The memories of his early life, which he was both distorting and brooding over, had to be thoroughly thought out and faced by this boy. He was pitying himself and justifying his behaviour on the basis of this self-pity. To this lad, who blamed his father for everything, the half-siblings were not human beings with emotions, but things that added to his problems. They were in the world just to make him unhappy.

In *thinking about* Henry one might decide that his father deserved no loyalty and his stepmother no consideration, but in *thinking with* him it was best to try to develop in him some loyalty and respect for them, as well as some understanding of his present situation, regardless of the past. To do that kind of *thinking with* him and to alter his personality responses enough to get him not only to believe but to *feel* that he owed them loyalty and attention, I should have to establish a deep rapport with the boy. Several interviews failed to do this. He grew to trust me in a personal way, but the rapport went no deeper. My ideas must have proof before he would accept them. He believed that I was sincere in my efforts and honest in my thoughts, but he would not essay my ideas simply because they were mine, and I could advance no proofs of their feasibility, at least none that he considered valid. I could not reach the desired rapport, though I spent considerable time with him.

The social situation must be solved at once, and since I could not influence or change his personality so that he would make further efforts in his present environment, the next best thing was to change the environment.

Thinking for him: Serious thought was given to the problem. Several later interviews with the father convinced me and the social agency that he was not likely to change his unfortunate attitude towards the boy. He said that he wanted to be entirely rid of him, that the boy was thoroughly bad, and that he was sure he was not his son. He said he was unable and unwilling to support him.

The plan was made for this boy to be placed in a foster-home in the country and be supported by a very excellent agency that was interested in him. A plan was made to give him psychotherapy even though a deep rapport could not be established.

Henry had many excellent, praiseworthy traits. Much of his misbehaviour disappeared as soon as he faced his situation in a practical, understanding way. I advanced good arguments for discontinuing his stealing. He listened to them, accepted them, and has not been dishonest since. I had good arguments for his going to school, and for two years he did so. Deeply rooted in Henry's personality, however, was a disinclination to work. Work had never brought him any pleasure and he did not believe in it. My arguments for it were not valid. I failed to influence him enough even to try working, and on this very practical point my psychotherapeutic efforts were a failure.

Results: This boy has now been followed and seen at infrequent intervals for three years. The final results are far from perfect.

All his delinquency has disappeared. I doubt that he will ever become delinquent again unless he is forced to it by hunger and physical wants. Many of his personality traits are improved. His laziness certainly is not. If a deeper rapport could have given me an insight into the basis of his extreme dislike for work, or if I had been able to develop in him a loyalty to me so deep that, at my suggestion, he would have tried out a more industrious mode of living, I might have been successful in helping him. As it is, I have failed in a large measure in my efforts with this boy.

I hope he will make a law-abiding, happy, and useful man. He may reach the first two of these goals, but he will never reach the last one unless someone enters his dynamic environment deeply enough to help him change from his indolent responses to life.

* *

The next boy was afraid of his environment and sought to run away from it largely on a basis of the unhappiness caused by this fear.

Case No. 49
MARTIN JONES

Martin Jones was fourteen years old when first known to the clinic. He was a short, sturdy boy, good-looking and friendly, with a somewhat serious and worried expression. Physically he was in excellent health. Mentally he was of average general ability.

The situation: Martin, who came from a good middle-class home, had been a thief for many years. Twice he had been in serious trouble for stealing from a Sunday-school, once alone and once with companions. For years he had been a successful petty thief, stealing from his home, from stores, and from companions. He was occasionally truant and on a few occasions had stayed away from home for a day or so. While his home situation was physically good, there was much unhappiness there because the father was a habitual drunkard and abusive. Martin had been punished in many ways, including excessive whipping. None of these punishments had resulted in any improvement in his behaviour. His mother had died when he was a small boy. He had one full brother, two years younger than he, and several half-siblings. The stepmother was very fond of him and eager to help. At this time there was some question of Martin's being committed to an institution for delinquents, and he was much worried and upset about this.

Thinking about the boy: Martin was an unhappy boy, seriously delinquent. The delinquency was mostly stealing, and at no time had the boy really needed the money or the things he stole. Almost all these offences had been committed alone. The family situation was disturbing. Since the other members of the family had all handled their situations in a good way, however, and none of the other siblings were delinquent, one must suspect that explanation of his behaviour lay in his mental life. From his stepmother's report and the conversation of the boy, it seemed clear that his repentance never went further than a fear of punishment.

Thinking for him: There was every reason to believe that Martin, unless he could be helped, would have to be placed in an institution. The family, especially the stepmother, had been very patient and had tried in all sorts of ways to help the boy overcome his bad habits. The minister in the church had also been very kind and had attempted to help him in various ways. In Martin's case as deep an exploration as possible seemed justifiable in the effort to help him change his reactions to life, and even if it failed to help, one could feel reasonably certain that the exploration would not add much to his problems. It was decided to try this.

Thinking with him: Martin was not an easy boy with whom to establish rapport. He was rather suspicious of all those in authority over him and classed the psychiatrist with these. The rapport seemed to be established subsequent to his finally becoming frank and discovering that the person with whom he had been so frank did not think less of him than before. After a few interviews a very good personality contact was established with him and he became interested in my opinions because they came from me. His story uncovered many definite problems that had to be *thought about* with this boy—problems for which definite solutions must be offered.

Prominent among these was rather a remarkable attitude towards religion. Martin was not afraid of many things, but he was distinctly afraid of God. He believed firmly that God would punish him for his misdeeds and he felt especially guilty because much of his stealing had been from the Sunday-school. He said that many times when he would decide to be a better boy, he would think that there was no use in this because he had already been so bad that he was doubtful about being forgiven. Probably this was partly due to the memory of early religious teachings given by his mother.

He believed he knew things about his father that reflected on his character and behaviour of which other members of the family were unaware. There had been some mental conflict, especially when his father would punish him severely for telling these things. There was also a knowledge of recent occurrences in his home life which were serious and which he reported to us confidentially. The boy had been threatened with serious punishment were he to tell anyone. His attitude towards his father was ambivalent. Even though he felt resentful and full of hate towards him, there was also a feeling of loyalty to him. My *thinking with* him about this resulted in developing loyalty to the idea of helping his father out of some of his situations and thereby creating for himself a real place in his father's life.

The rapport was good enough so that the boy accepted as justifiable my criticisms of his behaviour, especially of his staying out late at night, although he had bitterly resented this criticism from both his father and his stepmother. He became very frank in discussing his affection for his stepmother. He wondered whether he was in a way disloyal to the memory of his mother when he responded to her, and he seemed to develop more healthy emotional responses in regard to this problem.

Together we *thought about* his real situation and the seriousness of it, and the boy came to the point where he was willing to abide by any decision made by the clinic as to the best way for him to overcome his bad habits and be more happy. This attitude was brought about by helping him feel that in this way he could really make a place for himself in the hearts of his parents, for when the boy had become entirely frank, it was easily seen that his basic problem was a feeling of being permanently separated from the circle of his family by his misdeeds, and the belief that no amount of good behaviour would reunite him to those he loved. This was, of course, considerably confused with his feelings of guilt in his religious life. It is interesting to note that this boy had no sex problems of any kind. He had handled these things in a very normal and frank way and derived considerable satisfaction from the realization that he had done so.

Results: The boy was placed through a church agency in a good foster-home. He wrote to me regularly. His stepmother would occasionally write very appreciative letters, asking that I continue to write to the boy and encourage him, as she thought he was being helped in that way. He remained in the foster-home for five months and has been back home for the past year and a half.

The success seems to be complete. The boy is now trusted in the family and in his place of employment. He is earning and contributing to the family and doing very well in school.

Many of his personality problems have been solved. His state of mind is quite different. He is now very happy and continues to be dynamic and active. Recently he returned to the clinic for a follow-up interview. When he came, he excused himself for not having been to see me before. He said: "I should have come, but when a person does not need help, he is apt to forget. It isn't because I don't appreciate what you did for me. It's a good thing there is a place like this for a fellow to come to when he is in trouble."

It is gratifying to see that this boy has in no way lost his religious interests or loyalties by having the basis for his religious fears explained and understood.

The redirection of misplaced loyalties and helping him to take a different emotional attitude towards his own abilities are the things that have helped Martin. This was possible because he accepted me into his environment and emotional values sufficiently to be willing to try my ideas and see whether they were worth anything. Many of these same ideas had been given him before by others to whom he had not responded emotionally, and consequently he had not even been willing to try them.

Martin and his parents were thoroughly discouraged at the beginning of his treatment. He has made a fine success of meeting life and facing it. He had very excellent personality traits to help him out of a serious situation.

*   *

The last boy in this group had a different problem from those of the others. The situation which he could not fully meet was created by his own and others' personalities rather than by concrete situations in his environment. His problems were harder for him to face and for others to help him solve because it is harder to change *people* than *things*.

Case No. 50
SIMON SILLER

Simon Siller was first known to the clinic four and a half years ago. He was then twelve years old. I knew him first when he was thirteen. He is a healthy boy, somewhat small, but well-developed and of normal maturity. Tests grade his intelligence as well above average.

The situation: Simon's story is much too long to be told here. Extensive social efforts have been made for him and for his family. All the members of his family are well known in the clinic and in other social agencies. Their peculiar personalities are an important part of Simon's problems. He is the second of four siblings, of whom the younger two are girls. His father died when Simon was eleven. A fairly comfortable home has always been maintained by the mother. She has constantly sought aid from various sources and has accepted it as a matter of course. Soon after his father's death Simon began to get into scrapes with other boys, nearly always stealing-escapades. None of the other siblings had ever done anything like this. Several minor offences of breaking and entering appeared in Simon's record. These have occurred in the company of older boys. His mother and Simon have fought, literally on many occasions, and figuratively at all times, for the past four years. He has been whipped excessively. On several occasions, on our advice, the agency has arranged placement in a foster-home for him, but always both the mother and the boy have withdrawn their promises to accept this, and the plan has never been carried out. Apparently both preferred not to have the opportunity for quarrels removed.

(The mother, who has a good reputation with the neighbours, received emotional satisfaction from the sympathy and attention she was given by them during her emotional upsets. These frequently suggested hysteria and were brought about by the worry and unhappiness the boy caused her.)

Simon was first studied four years ago as a school problem, and since then he has been seen at irregular intervals in the clinic. Many of his visits have been on the occasions of fresh difficulties. Often the lad came to see us of his own volition. His problems have gradually taken on new aspects from time to time without dropping any of their old ones. An appraisal of him includes school history of nearly constant failure, stubbornness, insubordination, truancy, and stealing (which has been somewhat controlled), serious disobedience, defiance of his mother, resistance of all authority, staying out late—even all night—associating with disreputable people, often much older than he. He has lost several good after-school jobs through being late to his work and careless.

All who knew Simon said that ever since his father's death he has been a very unhappy boy. Despite all his delinquency, everyone who knows him, except his immediate family, believes that he is not essentially a bad boy, and that in a broad sense he is not much to blame for his misbehaviour. All his acquaintances seem to like him, though he is not a particularly attractive boy. His employers, who had been forced to discharge him, had done so with regret, remained his friends, and continued to help him.

Thinking about the boy: It is fortunate that it has been comparatively easy to *think about* the boy, for most of the conclusions I have had to carry over into the *thinking with* him I reached in this way.

He is a profoundly unhappy boy, inordinately fond of his emotionally unstable mother. He is deeply jealous of his older brother.

After the death of his father, in whom the boy probably found refuge from his early family difficulties, Simon tried to use the older brother as a father substitute. The older brother, himself emotional, unstable, "over-moral," and "mother-fixed," failed to respond in any way to Simon's advances for friendship, probably on selfish grounds. Careful check-up has shown that always a part, and recently many, of his new delinquencies have not actually occurred until after his mother has accused him of them. His mother often does such things as destroy books which the boy borrows and brings home. She cannot read English herself, but she is sure that any book that Simon would read must be unfit. She calls his teachers and employers on the telephone and inquires into the most minute details of Simon's arrival, departure, and behaviour. She reports to them his insulting behaviour to her. Despite all this and despite the almost incredible things he says to his mother when they are quarrelling, he does not want to be separated from her, and his excessive love for her is quite in his conscious mind. He says: "I hate her until I could almost kill her, but of course I love her because she is my mother."

Simon has gradually arrived at the conclusion that he is essentially inferior, both in intellect and in business ability, that it is a hopeless thing ever to expect the desired mother love. He has very unfortunately reacted to this by an attempt to hold his mother's attention and, at the same time, to punish her.

Unhappy as Simon is (he has seriously considered suicide several times), nothing that has been done for him has in any way helped him to be willing to try life away from his family. In several serious crises he has sincerely promised to accept placing in a foster-home, but when he sees his mother alone, he decides he cannot do it. He has threatened to run away eventually, setting the time for his departure, but always in the future, never today. He was going to run away when he was fifteen, but he did not. Now he says he will run away when he is sixteen, but he will not.

He has had much adolescent sex stress, but has remained sexually moral, despite his associations. He says this is because of his mother, but, of course, there may be other reasons. Both she and his brother accuse him of immorality, and it is not entirely clear why he has not been guilty, as he has done the other things of which he has been accused.

Simon is a boy with mental conflicts, resulting in a seriously distorted personality, driving him to delinquency. In him these conflicts are magnified and open to study and to understanding. In him the dynamisms and resultant behaviour can be understood, while in many other children with similar responses they are very obscure. It is not hard to reconstruct theoretically Simon's early handling of his father-mother situation. This is one thing that has not been directly *thought about* with the boy, because it was felt that an understanding of these things, without a separation from them, would only serve to lower his few ideals. Possibly by itself it could not result in emotional responses strong enough to change his behaviour. The boy and his emotional family, though often exhausting and at times exasperating, are instructive and interesting in many ways.

Simon's various responses to the different depths of rapport established with him, were very interesting.

Thinking with him: When the first systematic psychotherapeutics were undertaken three years ago, it was decided, after considerable thinking with him, to attempt a deep personality contact with him. This was accomplished quite easily and he became very loyal to me and accepted my ideas because they were mine. It was a highly successful procedure for understanding the lad's mental life, but it was a failure in improving his behaviour or making him more happy, for another conflict arose as this boy was torn between his desire to remain loyal to his mother and stay at home with her, and his desire to be loyal to me and hold in his mind the new understanding of his situation that he was accepting on the basis of my personality influence. During this period he alternated between much better and much worse behaviour. One day he would obey implicitly whatever his mother told him. She would call on the telephone in ecstasy to tell us that Simon was cured. The next day he would be as bad a boy as he knew how to be. Sometimes he would come for interviews more frequently than he was supposed to, and at other times he would break appointments. Nothing was being accomplished, and the rapport was gradually broken, though in order to do this it was necessary really to deceive the lad as to how I looked upon some of his mother's attitudes. Friendly relations, however, were continually maintained.

A few months later the mother again insisted that Simon be treated, as she believed he had been given much help before. He was again in rather serious difficulties. This time we have reached only the rapport of personal trust, and somewhat better results are being obtained. No additional problem is being added. In this rapport I may not think seriously with him about the chief problems, but we can think out many of the superficial ones, and I, a person he trusts, can give him encouragement and practical advice, which he needs very much. Now, when he accepts advice and ideas, it is because, while he trusts me, he sees the reason and logic behind them, and not because they come from a particular person. Together we *think about* many things, but we avoid the mother-son situation as much as possible and we never discuss it seriously.

A recent instance will throw light on this boy's personality response to the present stage of rapport. He came for an interview voluntarily, evidently to tell me something of which he was ashamed and unhappy. He told of having hired himself out at a good salary. His employer proved to be a homosexual man who very soon made advances to him. On the first occasion, though displeased and disgusted, he submitted partly because he wished to keep his job, but on the second occasion he struck the man in the face and quit his work. He has been forced to lie to his mother to explain why he lost his job, as he has not known how to tell her. He has been blamed and punished by her and by his older brother for quitting. It was a very good thing that Simon had someone whom he could trust enough to unburden himself. It is unfortunate that the older brother does not hold that place in his dynamic environment. While Simon was normally disgusted and shocked by this experience, it was perfectly easy to see that his mother's entrance into the situation gave it its real emotional value for him. Our thinking together resulted in a plan for Simon's giving the man a sound thrashing, and a decision that his mother must be frankly told, so that she would no longer blame him. Very fortunately the offending man was small, effeminate, and a coward. A few evenings later the man was taken to a hospital, suffering with minor contusions of the head and face, caused by a "hit-and-run" driver, according to what the man told the policeman who found him. Since the thing happened in an alley, the police concluded that it must have been some daring criminal who was driving so recklessly. The sparkle in the boy's eyes the next time I saw him made it seem probable that one potential mental conflict had been liquidated by an actual physical one.

Results: Constructive thinking for Simon has been a failure as far as social adjustments go. It has been largely a failure from a therapeutic standpoint also. Had his environment made it possible, he might have been a very hopeful case for constructive personality help. From the standpoint of psychiatric interpretation, he is a case in which results in *thinking about* him were highly successful. From the standpoint of behaviour, they are a complete failure. He is now working, but he continues to be excessively pugnacious with his mother and brother. He has a few better interests, but these are more than neutralized by his poor companions and his recently developed habit of petty gambling. However, the boy and his mother both say that his treatment in the clinic has been of help to him, and the boy voluntarily comes for advice when crises occur. A mistake was made in the early treatment of this case by the establishment of too deep a rapport. The mistake was not through a misjudgment of the rapport needed, but through my inability to appreciate that I could not remove him from his home in spite of his unhappiness. As the case stands, all that psychotherapeutics have accomplished is to make Simon a little less unhappy. Had I been able to maintain a good rapport with this boy for a sufficient time while he lived in a different environment, the results would probably have been very satisfactory.

CHAPTER XIV

THE UNLOVED AND UNWANTED CHILD

The Lonely Child in a Hostile World

HEN one thinks of how large and untried the world looks to the child, when one remembers his own childhood, whether or not it was a happy one, he realizes that lack of love and protection is of all things the most tragic. One who works with problem children soon realizes that a child who lacks love and protection faces the most serious of the emotional difficulties of childhood.

Many of the children in this series could be placed in this group. The five boys whose cases are grouped in this final chapter were unloved and lonesome children, though they presented other problems. Such children are nearly always consciously unhappy. Many of them are trying to do something about their situation, and, fortunately, many of them are not denying or distorting the facts. Because this is true, these children can usually be helped through an understanding of their mental and environmental life. They are much to be pitied and are unlikely to become happy adults if they are not given help of some sort.

*   *

The first boy was most unhappy, because he had no place in the heart of anyone.

313

Case No. 51

PETRO ANJIOSSI

A little more than three years ago Petro came to the clinic for
one interview only. He was dirty, unhappy, unkempt, at first sullen,
but later friendly. This little Italian boy's red hair and blue eyes
lent him unusual charm. He was twelve years old. He was healthy
and of good mental ability.

The situation: Petro was a chronic runaway. The police in his
small city were tired of finding him and delivering him home. Over
a period of three years he had been running away once or twice a
month, sometimes staying away for only a few hours, at other times
staying as long as two weeks. Very often he attended school while
he was on these runaways, and his unkempt appearance made his
teachers suspicious that he was not sleeping at home.

Petro was running away from a poverty-stricken home. His father and stepmother were both working. The parents bore a good
reputation in the community.

The reports given by the members of his family and furnished
by the probation officer were that Petro was always treated well at
home and that his parents were much upset by his chronic runaways. He was reported helpful and kind in the home, affectionate
towards his half-brothers, and especially fond of animals. He was
said to be a good worker, and when he earned money, he gave it to
his stepmother.

The probation officer felt that the runaways were entirely explained by the fact that the boy was naturally bad and wanted to
make trouble. He reluctantly admitted that the boy was not known
to steal or be delinquent in any other way while on these runaways.

Thinking about the boy: The reports on Petro were incomplete
and unreliable. His parents' attitude and the way in which they

made their statements discredited the history they gave. The boy's statement threw no direct light on his situation. He could be seen only once, and he did not want to talk about his environment. He would only say that he was a bad boy and unhappy and that he wanted to get away from home. He talked earnestly about a foster-home, and discussed farm life, for which, he said, he had always longed. When I asked him to tell me more about the things that made him unhappy, he said: "Oh, doctor, my head is so full of everything, I can't be good. I'm a bad boy and I can't think about it."

Petro was very unhappy and lonesome for friends and wanted to be frank and to be understood. But he was afraid. I have never seen any other boy, without any encouragement on my part, make his desire to take me into his emotional environment so apparent.

Thinking for him: The only constructive thing I could do for Petro was to advise the agency that had temporary custody of him. This proved valueless, through no fault of the agency. He was on probation in a court that was suspicious of psychiatry. I was not justified in urging Petro to give me his confidence, for I had no reason to expect to see him again. Since this was true, nothing would be gained if I urged him to tell me his story in confidence, even though I might be successful in obtaining it.

Thinking with him: Thinking with this lad, about whose true situation and mental life I knew practically nothing, might easily have made him more unhappy than he was. In the process I might have sympathized with him or scolded him. Sympathy or censure, of themselves, seldom help children even if one knows which of them to offer. Petro was entirely frank about his personal habits. He was glad to *think with* me about his boyish sex problems, which were not great and which he had handled in a healthy fashion. We spent the rest of the time talking about farm animals and about his little dog, which had died recently. When he left, I told him that if he ran away again and wanted to, he might come to see me during his runaway.

Results: He was taken by the court from the society that was sheltering him temporarily.

His parents were present at the lad's court hearings. Petro told the judge that his mother and father were good to him, and that he ran away just because he was bad. He also told the judge that he could not be good at home and asked to be sent away. The court decision was that he was to go home with his parents, as they requested, and the parents were advised to thrash him soundly, once to mark the beginning of his reform, and repeatedly each time he ran away again.

A few weeks later he travelled forty miles to the clinic, mostly on foot, and asked to see me. He said he was "on a runaway," and that he had been away from home for four days. He was dirty, tired, and hungry, and on his body were many marks of severe whippings. Before I saw the marks of punishment, he asked me if I would promise not to repeat the things he wanted to tell me. I promised!

Petro's home was some distance from any of the neighbours' houses. This made it possible for his stepmother to inflict upon him, without being detected, very severe and unusual punishment. The boy had been threatened with death if he reported these things. Once the stepmother had thrown her chair at him and injured him so badly that he had been taken to a doctor for treatment. He had been forced to lie and say he had fallen on a sharp stick. These punishments were inflicted many times because the boy objected to stealing wood, coal, and garden vegetables from the neighbours. Another thing for which he was often punished was bringing home stray cats and dogs. He said that he could not resist the desire to adopt and to bring home any stray dog and cat that he saw, especially if it was being mistreated or seemed hungry. There were many depressing details to the story. The dog which he had formerly told me about had not died as he had said. The stepmother had killed it. He had kept this little dog hidden and had divided his food with it for several weeks before his stepmother discovered it. Several months had elapsed, but he was still grieving about the incident.

I could now *think with* Petro, and I did so to the best of my ability. I *thought with* him about many things, but I could not *think for* him, for though he was in personality contact with me now, he would not consent to my telling the authorities what he had told me. He said that he believed his parents would kill him if they knew, and he also said that he did not want to get his parents into trouble. He said that if I reported what he had told, he would lie and deny it. He was not afraid that I would break my promise, however, and I did not.

The plan he usually used when he returned from runaways, and which he said he was going to use that night, was to go to a street near his neighbourhood where a policeman would pick him up and take him home. He said that if he returned in this way, the heat of his parents' anger would subside before the policeman left; then he would not be punished so severely.

When I asked him why he had come back and told his story, he said it was because he did not like to think that he had lied before and because he thought that I would believe him.

Perhaps Petro was right. It might have been unwise to try to help him by reporting his plight to the authorities. The lad was telling the truth, but he had no proof of it, and he was still on probation to the same court that had advised further punishment.

Petro is a complete social failure—a recent indirect check-up on the situation shows that it remains the same. But he is not a complete psychiatric failure, for, temporarily at least, his happiness increased in the feeling that he had found someone whom he could trust, someone who understood him, someone who liked him. It will be a long time before Petro forgets me.

Petro needed a friend, and even though the understanding friendship I gave him was a very brief one, it may have given him permanent help. I did not sympathize with him or encourage him to think that he might repeatedly see me; it was not for these things he came back to see me. He came back because he had not told me the truth before, because he needed kindness and wanted to feel that he deserved it. I gave him advice about practical things, such as how to get proof of his mistreatments; I made other suggestions which I could now give him because he came to me as a trusted friend who knew all about him. I utilized every possible advantage of this good personality contact in an attempt to help him face and understand his problems. My major motive was to steel him against possible mental conflicts.

Even if Petro becomes a delinquent boy, his intimate experience with one real friend will make him a little less unhappy and a little better adjusted to life than he would have been without this psychotherapy.

The saving grace for Petro is that he is an extroverted boy who is not going to give up and become discouraged. He is not going to distort reality. I sincerely hope that he finds someone to fill the very vacant place in his life. The personality and character of that friend will be of the utmost importance to the child's welfare.

*   *

The next boy is a brother of Case No. 42. Although the brother was as "unloved" as was John, he had even greater problems and hence he is not grouped here with his brother. John was selected for psychotherapy at the time his brother was treated. Considerable social effort was made over a long period of time to make his clinic attendance possible. These efforts were a failure.

Case No. 52
JOHN FORDFIELD

When he came to the clinic three years ago, John was nine years old. He had suffered earlier from chorea. He was "nervous" and excitable. He bit his finger-nails excessively and complained of abdominal pain and headaches. He had many facial tics. His vision was defective. He had an alert, friendly expression that was at the same time a bit sly. Mentally he has good average general ability.

The situation: He was not treated intensively in the clinic, but he should have been. His case report completes the picture given in his brother's history, and shows well how environmental factors can completely nullify the efforts of psychotherapy. One cannot consider the brother's case without thinking of John. John was in the clinic at the time of the first study of his brother and at that time was considered as a very similar problem. Both boys were given the same advice, and physical attention was especially recommended for John. John was considered the less delinquent of the two, but, because of his physical condition, more intensive social work seemed essential for him. Later, because his brother reported John's early and excessive sex experiences with him, an attempt was made to have John brought to the clinic for further study and treatment. By then both boys had been placed in separate foster-homes. My interview with John took place against the wishes of his foster-parents; they grudgingly consented, however, to my interviewing him in their home.

Thinking with the boy: Because of the importance of the case, I attempted in this first interview to establish a rapport deep enough for the boy himself to want to come to the clinic. Though he was friendly, he naturally associated me in his mind with those who had changed his environment, who not only had caused him the loss of his brother's affections, but also had removed his brother from his environment. These things, the circumstances of the interview, and his parents' unco-operative attitude rendered a good contact improbable.

It was very interesting that in reply to ordinary questions about bad habits he told me that he never masturbated. He volunteered that no one could say his brother did either! Of course, I did not tell the boy that I knew he was being untruthful. It would have been a serious mistake, probably, for it might have resulted in much emotional upset and might have initiated in him the development of unsocial ideas. It is unwise to *think with* children about their problems before gaining a positive rapport with them.

Results: I have never seen the boy again. A subsequent social report states that his health is better. He has been in court two or three times in the last year for street delinquencies and as a neglected child. His foster-mother says that he is unhappy and bad, disobedient and disrespectful. She attributes this entirely to his having been separated from his brother.

John has not been helped, whereas his brother has. The reason is that he is still unloved, while his brother has found someone who cares for him and to whom he is loyal.

*   *

The next case is that of a fine little boy alone in a hostile world. If he is not helped, he will some day be making unhappiness for others as others are now making it for him.

Case No. 53
DAVID JUSTIN

David Justin when first seen in the clinic, a little more than three years ago, was eleven years old. He presented many physical problems. He was undersized and underweight. He had very defective vision, diseased tonsils, and teeth that had been from the start deficient in enamel and had since been miserably neglected. He was an active boy, likable and friendly. He had fair average mental ability.

The situation: This ragged, unkempt boy came from a home of the worst sort. His father had died before David was born, and his stepfather and mother quarrelled excessively. David had been kept in ignorance of the fact that the man was not his own father. At times the stepfather was very friendly with him, but at other times he was antagonistic. The parents had been frequently arrested and had even served jail sentences, during which time the boy had to live with his grandparents. These brief residences in his grandparents' poverty-stricken home were the bright spots in David's life. David was a skilful petty thief, dishonest in many ways, excessively truant, and at times a runaway from home for short periods.

He was living a street life in the congested district of a large city. The school had despaired of him, his parents were indifferent, the police were insistent, and his playmates were contemptuous of him because he was a physical coward.

Thinking about the boy: I saw him only once when I first knew him, three years ago. At that time he was not frank and no attempt was made to establish a deep psychiatric rapport. This little boy, with all his physical defects and his terrible home situation, insisted that he was happy, and, indeed, he seemed to be. The environmental aspect of the problem seemed the most vital at that time.

Thinking for him: A good agency and an excellent visitor became interested in David, and a good foster-home with excellent foster-parents was provided for him.

Results: He was unhappy in this home and behaved badly. Two other homes were tried during a period of eight months. Two of the foster-mothers made special efforts to help the lad and became deeply interested in him. His visitor worked long and hard to do his part. Despite all this the boy's behaviour improved only in so far as constant supervision necessitated. And he was complaining, disturbing, and unhappy in all of his foster-homes, although he received good care, had playthings and opportunities he had never before enjoyed, and associated with a fine group of youngsters.

His visitor, though very reluctant to admit defeat, finally decided not only that David was not profiting at all from his foster-home, but that he was adding to the problems of other children in the foster-homes and the neighbourhood and disturbing normally calm school situations.

Thinking about him: Eight months later David was again *thought about* in the clinic, and this time a good personality contact was established. He was very unhappy and he reached out for understanding. He now spoke freely of his experiences and emotional life. The things he said were tragic enough, but hardly so bad as one might have expected. Telling them seemed to relieve him very much. David said he really hated his father and mother, and he thought he always had. He said he would be glad if he were never to see them again. (Although formerly he had reported their misdeeds, he had insisted that he loved them, and that he wanted to be allowed to stay with them. He now said that he had made these statements only because when he was at home, he could spend some time with his grandmother and grandfather.)

He told us that his parents had involved his grandparents in some court actions. The grandfather, who was non-delinquent, was made unhappy by this, and David had given much emotional value to it. He said he loved his grandmother and grandfather more than all the rest of the world together.

He told of early sex habits, mixed with stealing, and of other street delinquencies that he shared with older companions. He told of bullying and fights that had probably inspired the responses that now evidenced themselves as extreme cowardice. An important point is that although there was plenty of material for mental conflicts and distortions of reality, considerable mental exploration during an excellent psychiatric rapport did not reveal any that he could not easily resolve.

Thinking for him: His visitor and I thought about this boy. Other foster-homes were now considered useless, if not impossible. He was not sufficiently delinquent to be committed to an institution, even if this sort of treatment held the solution for him.

What were his assets? He had only two. One was the long-standing loyalty to his grandparents, and the other was the more recently established loyalty to me. His new loyalty was based entirely on his belief that he was understood. We decided to try to build on what we had. The boy was placed with his grandparents. He was seen regularly for a period of two months.

Thinking with him: Together David and I thought about his past problems and his future welfare. We finally came to the point where we could think about his parents. We believed that they were trying to do better and that probably, after all, they really loved him. We thought about his cowardice. We considered the fact that boys who had not learned to be good in their foster-homes rarely learned to be good when they returned to their old environment. We lauded the courage of any boy who could do such a difficult thing. We talked about the necessity of very close supervision for him, and during the first four months David himself insisted upon the necessity of this. I still see him occasionally.

Results: A year is perhaps too short a time to know what the final results will be, but it is a long period for David to have maintained such excellent behaviour. His school record is the best he has ever had. His teachers report him as co-operative, a good worker, and fairly bright. He has not been delinquent, and he has not been away from his home in the evenings except with his visitor. He has not been away at any time without permission. He has not been truant. He is now trying to help his parents, whom he sees frequently, and he says he does not hate them.

David's problems are not all solved. He is still somewhat of a coward. He has too little confidence in himself. He assumes that were he to go with the old gang, even once, he would get into trouble. Perhaps more *thinking with* him will strengthen his affirmative attitude.

In so far as this case may be called a success, it is a psychiatric success. Here environmental changes and very good associations had failed to accomplish an improvement. The success was made possible by developing new loyalties and augmenting those he already had. He was in good personality contact, and suggestions were readily accepted. At present the loyalties of this boy are being quite easily transferred to the agency visitor. The final success depends upon whether or not there develops a mutual understanding between this boy and the people in his environment. Through such an understanding he will reach the goal of normal love and loyalty.

Later acquaintance with this boy shows that he is still doing very well. His grandparents are pleased with him, although he probably does not get from them quite as much affection and attention as some children get from their parents. This very affection is the thing that will carry him through to a happy life-adjustment.

The case of another unhappy and unloved boy comes next. Those who should have loved him built up most deliberately a bad reputation for him. Of all the boys I have seen in the Judge Baker Foundation, I have felt the most sympathy for this lad. Many of the touching incidents in his life I have not recorded in this history. One does not like to fail with a boy like Dale.

Case No. 54
DALE ROCKWELL

Dale has been known in the clinic for three years. He is now fourteen years old. He is a healthy, well-developed, dynamic, pugnacious, self-assertive lad. Mentally when first tested, at a time of great emotional upset, he was rated as of low normal ability. Tests recently given credit him with an intelligence quotient of 95.

The situation: Dale was originally referred to the clinic by a social agency in a neighbouring state. Excessive and long-continued truancy from school, street stealing, and more serious delinquency, including several breakings and enterings with much older companions, made it seem impossible for the agency to keep him from being committed to an institution for delinquent children.

Because the agency felt that the lad's environment was largely to blame for his trouble, they were eager to make some adjustment other than this. His school report was so poor and it was so difficult for his teachers to control and understand him that the possibility of admission to an institution for the education of the feeble-minded was to be considered, though at that time he was not considered feeble-minded.

Dale was an unloved boy, without any home or person to call his own. His mother had died when he was six years old. His stepfather, who had legally adopted him, was a delinquent and a drunkard. He tried in every possible way to avoid any responsibility for Dale's care or behaviour. His brothers and sisters were all older. Some of them had homes of their own. They all had their own family problems, and none of them welcomed Dale in his home.

Earlier a church home had tried to care from him, but he ran away so frequently and was so disobedient, dishonest, and disturbing that he was no longer welcome there.

When I first knew Dale and became his friend, he had been temporarily confined in an institution for delinquent children. When he was discharged from there, without any social adjustment having been made, he was returned to his old environment. He immediately ran away, travelled nearly a hundred miles by walking and catching rides, and came back to the clinic in the night-time, asking to be readmitted. He gave the fact that he wished to see me as his reason for coming back.

Thinking about the boy: There are few boys I have ever known whom I have thought about more than about Dale, because the lad almost immediately and without any encouragement became dependently attached to me. Very little of this thinking has been theoretical.

Three years' acquaintance has convinced me that theories are not what will help Dale.

Thinking for him: After this rather remarkable running away, Dale was placed in a truant-school in his home state and remained there more than a year. Here his record was excellent after the first few weeks. During this year I saw him four times. His superintendent's reports at these times were always good. He said Dale was one of the best-behaved boys and one of the best workers he had ever had. He soon came to believe that the boy did not belong in the group, which was composed mostly of boys of rather poor intelligence who were difficult to supervise. The boy frankly said he was being good because I wished him to and because he wanted me to like him. He hoped he might some time live near me or that I might be his guardian.

During this year he earned a double promotion in school. He attempted no runaways after the first week. He did not steal during this time, though he had many opportunities to do so.

He was discharged and returned to his family, who were even more unwilling than ever before to receive him. Because of my absence from the clinic at the time, I had not seen him for several months before his discharge and I did not know of his new situation. Owing to his change in address, my letters had failed to reach him. After two months of non-delinquent behaviour in a most undesirable environment, he became convinced that I had forgotten him. At that time a young man who had earlier used this lad as an accomplice in breaking and entering came to live in the home of the relatives who were giving the boy shelter. Under this young man's influence Dale again became delinquent and was involved in three serious car-barn robberies.

I finally learned where Dale was and went to see him, arriving a few hours after his arrest and confinement in jail.

For fourteen months, under trying circumstances, Dale had been non-delinquent, and he had tried during this time to overcome his quarrelsome and pugnacious habits. He had done these things for no other reason than his loyalty to me. In his discouragement, when he felt he had misplaced his loyalties, he had reverted to his old delinquency. Dale was completely unhappy when I found him in jail. Arrangements were made for him to be temporarily cared for near the clinic, and it finally became possible for me to see him under circumstances more favourable for study.

Thinking with him: For months this lad had been in the rapport

328 FIFTY-FIVE "BAD" BOYS

of dependent attachment. He was now encouraged to be entirely frank. Several hours spent *thinking with* him failed to reveal anything in his mental life that I did not already know and that he did not freely admit to himself.

He was unloved and unwanted, and he knew and accepted these facts. His emotional responses to me were so immediate and frank because no one else liked him. He had been dishonest and delinquent. He said that while others had first taught him to steal, he needed very little encouragement. Most of his pleasures in life had come from delinquency. Dale had a bad temper. His father's behaviour in his contacts with society had already furnished Dale an example. When Dale was small, older boys had often amused themselves by making him angry, so that they could hear him swear and see him fight. Dale did not wish to overcome his temper. He believed it served him well in his kind of life. He recognized that his early teachings and experiences would make it hard for him to control his pugnaciousness. He had met his sex problems very well. His early experiences and knowledge had been so disgusting to him that he had no sex temptations, but he recognized that he soon would have. There seemed to be no way in which I might help him through any further knowledge of his mental life.

Results: The boy was placed in an excellent foster-home. A very sincere and patient visitor became interested in him. The lad was sincere in his determination to be the kind of a boy I admired. But I made a very serious mistake. A plan was made for him that included my suddenly dropping out of his life, and I agreed to the plan. We assumed that a much better environmental situation than he had ever had, the excellent people who were interested in him, including the psychiatrist of the agency which was placing him, would be able to win him and supplant the loyalties he had to me.

A year has passed. At first the boy did fairly well. He has gradually slipped until now he is almost a complete failure. He has been expelled from school three times, has lost his foster-home, and is now in an institution. He is dishonest and deceitful in many ways. He fights and makes himself disagreeable. He is, however, faithful and efficient in any work given him, and this helps greatly in his present adjustments.

Recently I have seen him a few times. His old respect for me and his desire for my approbation is gone. He is not frank and does not wish me to understand him. He tries to capitalize our old friendship by asking me for money and other favours. He assumes that my former interest was a matter of routine to me, and he rather ridicules himself for having responded to it. I believe that even though I were to know this boy as long as I live, and even if I were to provide all the physical comforts for him, I should never again be able to establish the positive rapport I once had with him. It is quite possible that had I continued to treat the boy, I might have been able successfully to transfer to other people or ideals the loyalties that once were responsible for his improved behaviour, and that a permanent success might have been accomplished.

*   *

The last case is an unhappy boy who has been very eagerly reaching out for someone to love and to care for him. Ultimately he will probably make a successful adjustment. The case is as yet unfinished.

Case No. 55
HAROLD LEWIS

Harold was nine years old when we first knew him in the clinic, three years ago. He was an erect, well-developed, healthy little boy.

His friendly expression and his regular, well-formed features made him attractive.

Because of his stubborn and unco-operative attitude his mental tests were not considered representative of his ability. They rated him as having very good average general ability.

The situation: Harold has experienced a good many of life's hard knocks. He had been placed as an infant in an unsupervised foster-home. Here he had lived until five years of age, visited frequently by both of his quarrelling parents. He was then taken to his own home, which had been temporarily re-established on the basis of the serious illness of his father, who died a few weeks afterwards. A period of intense family quarrelling followed, involving many of his relatives, most of whom seemed to have been as stubborn as Harold was reported to be at that time. Again he was placed, this time with a maternal relative, where he was fairly well cared for and strictly supervised, but not loved. In this home he heard much criticism of his dead father.

Shortly after he entered this relative's home, he rather suddenly became a very disturbing little boy. He would not mind. He ran away, had temper tantrums, got into all sorts of minor mischief with other children. His relatives considered him so thoroughly bad a boy that they not only gave him up in despair, but discouraged others from attempting to care for him. Among other behaviour difficulties reported at this time (he was then seven years old) were constant soiling himself while in school, at play, and at home and both diurnal and nocturnal enuresis. As a little child Harold had been praised by his foster-mother for gaining sphincter-control very early. Of all his behaviour the temper tantrums were reported as the worst. These would come on suddenly without much cause, but would leave very slowly. In fact, each one seemed to make him more stubborn than the one before.

A child-placing agency then took him, at his mother's request. This was one year before I first knew him. During this year he had lived in three different foster-homes. In each his unfortunate habits and his disturbing behaviour continued. His personality traits were said to be gradually growing worse. The composite report of these foster-parents was that Harold was stubborn, grudgeful, extremely quarrelsome, unappreciative, uncommunicative, distractible, and uninterested in school-work. He was careless about his appearance. He was suspected of bad sex habits and seemed to be perpetually unhappy. The lad was brought to the clinic to be studied and given psychotherapeutic help if possible.

Thinking about the boy: Harold was a boy who in his early years had been a normal, lovable, and loving child. Now he was showing exactly the opposite personality responses. The change had occurred soon after the serious emotional stress that resulted from his sudden removal from a good environment, the death of his father, and the subsequent references to the history of violent quarrelling between his parents, whom he had loved. Since it was evident from the history and the reports of the boy's behaviour that a constructive plan must include an exploration of his mental life, there was little reason to do theoretical thinking about Harold and the dynamisms in his mental life. These things could not be understood except by *thinking with* the boy himself about them.

Thinking for him: It was recommended in staff conferences that the boy come for regular psychotherapeutic interviews and an attempt be made to change his personality responses. He came regularly for these interviews. His foster-home seemed socially unsuitable for him, but since so little was known of his mental problems, a change was inadvisable at the time of the first treatments.

Thinking with him: Harold had developed the very unhappy habit of shutting other people out of his life. He was suspicious and deceitful. He liked to make people think he was being friendly and frank with them when he was not. He was skilful in deceiving strangers in this respect. It was evident early in the treatment that no rapport could be established on the basis of discussing his behaviour. That was what he expected and what he was prepared to resist.

He had a good memory of his earlier years. By discussing with me those happy days and describing his feelings of hate and resentment for others, he developed an interest in my opinions and a belief that I knew a good deal about how a boy felt. I succeeded in reaching a place with Harold where he sincerely wanted me to help him. He apparently liked me and wanted me to like him, but a good personality contact was not yet established. For, although he was frank and truthful about his emotional responses, he did not like to tell me about his faults. (He later told me that it was because he was afraid I should not like him if he did.)

Harold and I thought about many of his past experiences and finally about his present behaviour. He enjoyed coming for the interviews. During the period of treatment his behaviour improved. The enuresis and soiling ceased suddenly. I give in the order of their apparent importance the things that I found in his mental life.

He resented and tried to forget the charges of misbehaviour that his parents had made against each other. An older brother of whom he was very fond had run away from home because of his own problems, which were probably very similar to Harold's. He admired this brother's behaviour and tried to copy it. He had been punished and frightened because of sex habits of which he had been accused. He had not been told the facts he wished to know about these things. To frighten him he had been told things that he knew were lies. He said he had been involved in unfortunate filthy excretory play with other children and had witnessed their sex habits, though he had not indulged in them himself. I was rather inclined to believe his statements, though I knew he was failing to confess other misbehaviour.

His mother did not see him very often. It was known that she did not take him into her confidence when she did visit him. He insisted to me that she always did and clung to these statements. From this, one was justified in believing that he wanted her to be more frank. Harold did not believe that anyone loved or trusted him, and he did not think that he wanted them to.

His responses to me were ambivalent. He was both stubborn and friendly. He usually wanted to talk to me, but at times he refused to.

Because his behaviour had improved so much and because it seemed best socially to place him in an available country home some distance from the clinic, the treatments were discontinued. This seemed best, because I had accomplished all I could for him, though I certainly had not reached the bottom of his problems or helped him to face them entirely. I did not believe that his personality responses had been changed.

Results: I saw him a year later. Although the family situation had failed to improve in any way and the foster-home had been in some ways undesirable, the improvement in his behaviour had been maintained. He remained in the same foster-home for a year. He no longer had temper tantrums. The enuresis had almost ceased. Occasionally he soiled himself. This happened always at times of emotional upset. Now the complaints about the boy were that he was boisterous and careless, had poor table manners, and disobeyed his foster-mother in small matters. The change that had occurred in his personality reactions accounted for most of his improved behaviour. These changes occurred because Harold was taking people into his life and being loyal to them.

I had written him a few letters in the year following his first treatment and had called once on him at his foster-home, but failed to see him. I have been seeing him occasionally in the past year.

Harold is a very interesting boy to think about, when considering the depth of rapport that develops between the child and the psychiatrist. When I met him for the first time after the first year's period, he was pleased to see me and evidently had something he wished to say. He began to cry, a thing I had never seen him do before, and told me that he had for a long time wanted to see me to tell me how sorry he was that he had lied about his behaviour. He then made a free confession of many childish sex experiences and other misbehaviour. These things in themselves were not important or serious, but the failure to confess them had stood between the boy and me before. He is now in excellent personality contact with me. I have helped him to understand himself, and my praise for his developing loyalties to his visitor in particular and to others in his environment has been of constructive value to him. He says that the only thing that makes him unhappy now is that his foster-mother, whom he says he loves and from whom he craves response, cares more for another boy, who has been in the home much longer than he. The treatments the boy is receiving now are of much more value to him than the earlier ones, but undoubtedly the earlier contacts prepared the way for what is happening now.

Harold's visitor considers him a success already. His mother says she is proud of him. His companions in school like him, but his foster-mother believes that the improvement is only temporary, that he is really a bad boy, and that he will never be a success. There is no foster-father in the home and no man in his immediate environment. His intelligent, co-operative teacher sees some improvement in his behaviour and in his effort. I consider him well on the way to a successful adjustment to life, but in order to make this success certain his environment must be changed so that there will

be some sympathetic adult in it, possibly a man, who will understand him and to whom he may become thoroughly loyal. If I fail
to help this boy transfer to someone else the loyalties he now has to
me, I shall continue to keep in touch with him as long as he
needs me.

*　　*

For a period of more than three years I have known and *thought
about* these boys. Some I no longer see, some I am still treating.
None of them have I forgotten. Many of them I shall never forget.
I wish very much that I could predict with certainty the ultimate
successful outcome of the boys who have apparently responded to
my efforts to help them. I regret intensely the boys whom I have
failed to help. We really know very little about the therapeutic
value of the exact things we do or say to help the children who
need help, but possibly in recording our opinions of their problems, in taking stock of what we say to children and of their responses to us, we may be blazing the trail towards a more exact
knowledge of this very vital mystery—human behaviour and human personality.

CHAPTER XV

AS THE PSYCHIATRIST SEES IT

HE child comes into the world in much greater need of help than do the young of animals. The difference is not only physical, but mental. Young animals can quite well take care of themselves, and usually reach a similar normal maturity under similar normal environmental circumstances. It does not follow that children will do the same thing. Though the young fledgling's mother is killed, it knows, when the next season comes, how to build a nest and rear young. The daughter who has no mother or mother substitute does not have this knowledge.

As a child is developing, all his responses, both simple and complex, are influenced, directed, and altered by his association with his parents and with others in his dynamic environment. Their behaviour, beliefs, and responses have a most profound influence on the child's development and mental life. Moulding individuals in the casts of civilization, religion, morality, and progress are thus made possible.

To understand a child in his response to others and to his environment and constructively to utilize knowledge obtained through this understanding are the most important problems facing the world today. For on the general success achieved in this rests the future success of the race. It is very essential that those interested in understanding and helping children in their character-training, education, and mental health should face their problems and admit their limitations.

Among these is the fact that we have no measure for the relative importance of the various things we do for the child. We find it difficult to decide which thing we do is to be given the most credit, or whether any particular effort should be given any credit at all.

The child's companions, the social worker, the psychiatrist, the school, the church, the home, and the parents, all have perhaps had their influence on his character and personality. To divide this proportionately and to give credit exactly where it is due are impossible. To attempt to do this often confuses the understanding of the results and may easily interfere with their attainment. It is unavoidable that those attempting in different ways to give the child guidance and help should have different opinions as to what constitutes success in helping him adjust to life. We should try to understand one another's view-points. Before attempting to classify the results obtained in this series of cases a brief statement of the views of the psychiatrist may well be given.

The psychiatric approach to this subject is only one of many, and the results the psychiatrist obtains are at best only partial. This fact should not be forgotten in attempting to evaluate psychiatric efforts.

Disregarding methods entirely, the psychiatrist attempts to understand the child's personality and the environment in terms of how the child reacts to it. He tries to interpret both in such a way as to bring about in the child a better social and mental adjustment to life in its entirety. The psychiatrist attempts to give counsel, advice, and encouragement, to the end that the child may make these adjustments.

While there may seem to be some disagreement as to what constitutes a normal mental life, on analysis this is largely disagreement about the terms used to *express* the ideas rather than about the ideas themselves. Whether one accepts any part of the Freudian psychological theory or not, one can afford to admit that some psychoanalytic terms, such as are used below, are very useful in expressing ideas about mental life and mental hygiene.

Possibly the ultimate goal towards which the psychiatrist works as he attempts deliberately to change the life responses of the child may best be described in terms of what he considers desirable for the child's personality and behaviour.

1. A Child should Face the Reality of Life.

A child should understand his environment and the realities of life as they actually are. He should seek to become a part of his environment in such a way that, if he cannot be happy in it as he finds it, he will try to alter it or to change himself to fit in with it better. When he does this, he should understand and admit to himself what he is doing. Children who do this have good loyalties and ambitions. They will respond to other people and enjoy life in an active way. They thus avoid the denial, repression, or distortion of their emotional responses. Their behaviour is usually social or "good." On the other hand, the child who previously failed to face reality and who under treatment is now making an *effort* to do so may temporarily show unsocial or "bad" behaviour.

2. A Child should Express Himself.

A child should be able to express himself so that he develops self-confidence and a physical and emotional pleasure in living. He should actually have pleasurable value for those who give him similar emotional response. He should love those by whom he is loved. He should have outlets for his instinctive impulses. He should not feel inferior, unloved, unwanted, or afraid. To have avoided these tragedies he must have had the encouragement of a friendly environment, of loving and understanding parents, and of normal companions.

3. *The Child should Understand Himself.*

The child should be helped to understand his own body and mind, as far as possible. This instruction must come early in his life. He must learn the necessity and desirability of emancipating himself from those on whom he has been dependent. At an early age he should learn what his emotions are, and he should learn this from the people in his dynamic environment. Inevitably he feels love, hate, fear, anger. If he does not understand these emotions, his interpretation of them may overwhelm him.

4. *The Child should Understand his Experiences.*

The child should so understand his experiences, both mental and environmental, that he will not be burdened by the inevitable worries and fears that follow their inadequate liquidation. Everyone has certain experiences and thoughts about life about which he is apt to acquire garbled, incomprehensible, indigestible information. He cannot accept such information without in some way distorting or denying its real affective value. This is obviously unfortunate, and even dangerous if repetition gives it the power of a mental habit. The greatest single contribution of psychology and clinical psychiatry to our knowledge of children and of adults is the revelation of the fact that if experiences carrying great emotional value be forgotten, repressed, distorted, or denied, they are very likely to cause unwholesome mental and behaviour trends.

The psychiatrist, if he is to help the child, must consider the question: *"Why* does the child think and behave as he does?" And if he is to interpret his results, he must answer the question: *"Why* have the changes in the child occurred?" If he has established a good rapport with a child, he may interpret intelligently, for he, of all persons, best understands both the old and the new mental life and personality.

The psychiatrist should know in advance what changes he thinks are desirable in the mental life of the child. He should judge the value of behaviour changes by the actuality of change in the child's beliefs, feelings, and ideas. It is entirely possible that even behaviour ordinarily called "bad" may be a symptom of desirable changes in mental attitudes. Fortunately for the reputation of the psychiatrist, this is not often true.

Behaviour always has its mental equivalent. Improved behaviour that has as its mental equivalent the child's better understanding of life's problems, loyalties to desirable people, good ideals and ambitions, and normal responses to parents means much when one is measuring success. When the improved behaviour is based on such mental equivalents as fear of punishment, expectation of a premium for good behaviour, dependence on or excessive affection for some other person (especially if that person be only temporarily in the child's environment), it is to be quite differently evaluated as a measure of success.

Often when desirable personality changes seem to have come as a result of change in the child's environment alone, they will be found on close investigation to have occurred because some person in the new environment is able to interpret life and life's situations to the child in such a way that he understands, accepts, and faces them and learns to get satisfaction in so doing.

Perhaps the psychiatrist may be justified in believing that mental health and normal emotional responses are the most important things in life. But he is *not* justified, either by theory or by experience, in believing that the mere correction of abnormalities in thinking and in emotional responses will always result in improved social behaviour or even be the most important thing in attaining that goal. He is justified, however, in believing that it very often is.

Results obtained by efforts to give personality help are estimated largely by changes in behaviour. We judge others by what they do, ourselves by the way we feel. To a certain extent the psychiatrist who has been in good rapport with a child is able to, and does, judge his results by the way his patient feels and mentally responds rather than by the things he does.

The psychiatrist, therefore, must not expect others to measure his results by the same scales which he applies. In the social adjustment of the child he should seldom have the last word. He should be content to add to the solution of the total problem whatever he can by means of his study and treatment. While he is doing this, he can be doing a much more important thing; he may be understanding the mental responses of children to the end that more may be known about mental health and hygiene. Theorizing alone does not establish facts. We shall never know more about helping children to face life or to express and understand themselves until we have more *facts* about what mental habits and what environmental situations cause trouble, and why different children seem to respond to life in such devious ways.

The psychiatrist's interpretation of certain behaviour·in a certain child, even though it may be more nearly correct than that of others, is often rejected and is often unacceptable socially. There should be no failure in co-operation between the psychiatrist and others because this is true. The psychiatrist's task is much too important for him to feel discouraged or consistently in the wrong simply because his interpretations are not always accepted. On the other hand, he should not allow himself to believe that he in infallible if his ideas are readily accepted.

It is not relevant here to contrast the *psychiatric* interpretation of behaviour problems in children with their interpretation by people who are dealing with them in their usual environment. This is not because such a contrast is unimportant. Many unhappy children become unhappy adults because no one in their environment correctly interpreted their childhood behaviour. Many delinquent children remain delinquent all their lives because no one understood the mental drives behind their early delinquencies. To teach these facts to all is the child-psychiatrist's greatest duty.

A single example may be cited to illustrate the point that misbehaviour will be evaluated in quite different ways by different people interested in a child's welfare. Some children, especially those who have reached only a superficial rapport with the psychiatrist, will later say to others that they lied to the psychiatrist and succeeded in deceiving him throughout the period of their acquaintance. It is quite natural for the child's friends to feel, when the child makes such statements, that the treatment was a failure and that the psychiatrist did not understand or help the child in any way. There are several things that the psychiatrist who has been studying the child may know about that particular child, or children in general, which may cause him to disagree with this opinion.

The psychiatrist may not have been certain whether or not the child was being frank when he treated him. But he was seeking primarily to understand the child and his mental life, and not to know of his behaviour as such. Whatever the child said came from the child's mind, and no matter how far from the truth it was, if correctly interpreted it would reveal the contents of his mind to some extent.

There are several possible explanations of the child's lying. Under the influence of his personal responses to the psychiatrist he may have been truthful with him, but later, losing faith and fearing that the things he had said would be repeated and used against him, he may build up a defence for himself by saying that he lied to the doctor from the start, when in fact he told the truth. Or, again, the psychiatrist may know that, whether or not the child was truthful about *all* his behaviour and problems, he certainly was frank about some of them. He knows that often the sex problems of a delinquent and deceitful boy are frankly met during the treatment, and that in this, at least, the treatment has been of permanent and lasting value to him.

Finally, the psychiatrist knows that he will reach the depths of children's minds and help them more if he adopts a credulous rather than a suspicious attitude towards what they say.

It is quite the same when interpreting all other behaviour of problem children. But while the psychiatrist is justified in pointing to these facts, he should never forget that even though his interpretation may show that the child is not to "blame" for his behaviour, this interpretation does not remove the necessity of dealing practically with the child.

CHAPTER XVI

AS OTHERS SEE IT

I N the final analysis, the results for which the psychiatrist is striving are entities not measurable by definite standards and not recordable numerically. Character, love, affection, kindness, industry, and happiness cannot be expressed in percentages.

When an art reaches the developmental stage where its exponents become very sure of its facts, principles, and results, it becomes a potential science, which may be expressed in quantitative terms. Such numerical expression is especially useful to prevent those interested in that science from becoming too sure of themselves. No one who is sincerely and carefully thinking about problem children and attempting to give them personality help, and who, at the same time, is honestly trying to estimate what results have been obtained and how these have been brought about, is as yet sure enough about any of these things to need the restraining influence of statistics.

Possibly future generations will understand so well the mental responses of the infant and the influence his environment has upon him that they will believe it desirable to control these things rigidly and to pattern children so that they will all be alike. When that happens (if adults have also been standardized regarding what they believe is desirable), the psychiatrist may become an exact scientist, and he may then report his results in a definite and statistical way.

347

Social workers, who are dealing largely with the more measurable factors of the child's environment, find it difficult to tabulate their results. There is always the important personal element, which cannot appear in the tables. The psychiatrist is dealing almost entirely with this elusive thing.

The social worker, always in part the psychiatrist if a true social worker, sees the boy that she has known for many years finally become a social failure. Rough places in his childhood pathway have been smoothed; many times the boy has tried to be the kind of boy he knew he should be, and these efforts, though possibly brief, have been sincere. At some periods of his life he was a success; at times he has been a happier and better boy because of understanding and patient efforts on the part of the social worker.

The statistician says that the case is a failure. If the social worker accepts this decision as final, discouragement and loss of faith occur. The attitude of the social worker is thus changed and this in turn changes her responses to the next child. On the other hand, if the failure, in so far as it was one, is not admitted, neither the child who has finally failed nor the efforts that have been made for him are understood.

Success in the field of psychiatry, education, and training is relative. We have no exact measure of what constitutes success in social or psychiatric efforts with problem children. Perhaps all could agree on some such expression as "good adjustment to life situation," but there the agreement would end.

Some feel that the success of psychiatric efforts should be measured largely by an improvement in behaviour. Among these there is a difference of opinion as to what constitutes good behaviour and as to how much improvement there should be before success may be claimed.

Some believe that to help a child successfully to understand

and adjust to his own emotional responses in a way that will avoid a later mental disease or neurosis is the goal of the psychiatrist and a measure of his success.

Some feel that the psychiatrist should strive to develop in a child a lifelong devotion to parents or others and a willingness to conform entirely to their ideals, wishes, and theories.

Some believe that so to influence a child as to get him to understand and accept some certain system of philosophy and standards of morality, regardless of the child's own opinions and fundamental responses, is the necessary requisite of psychiatric success. Among these there are some who believe that mere acceptance without understanding is enough.

Some feel that the best success is to have helped the child to a better and more permanent happiness without in so doing making others unhappy.

Other beliefs and feelings held by sincere people furnish other standards by which to measure success and failure.

Besides the lack of standards and measurements there are two other important factors that tend to render valueless any efforts to apply definite standards to the measurement of success. One is the relativity of the whole situation. Children are "good" or "bad" only as compared with other children or adults, and a good child who has made undesirable changes in his behaviour may still be good as compared with a bad child who has made excellent changes in his. The other is that if results are to be measured, they must be measured at a definite time. They do not always appear at once, and the influence one person has on another, even after they have passed from each other's life, often continues and may even increase with time and experience.

Behaviour, however, is objective; changes in mental life that do not have overt behaviour equivalents are known only to those who have the child's confidence, and only in the degree that the confidence is given.

Any estimate of results, whether it be made by an unprejudiced observer, parents, social workers, teachers, or the psychiatrist, is conditioned by the personal standards and personality of the estimator and by the degree of rapport existing between him and the child and the investigator.

There is a very good reason why people disagree as to what is good and bad behaviour in children. No two people understand a child in exactly the same way or, at least, exactly as well. One's interpretation of the child's behaviour changes, not only as one's understanding improves, but also as one's own responses change. The general statement that it is more important to know *why* a child does things than to know *what* he does is corroborated by nearly every intelligent person. But when one is thinking of a *particular* child who is behaving in a *particular* way, it is not easy to remember this obvious fact. This accounts for many of the failures correctly to estimate the value of methods used in educational and in character training, as well as in psychiatric efforts. It represents the very essence of the problem of the evaluation of methods.

But all problem children must be dealt with in some way. We should try to understand why the undesirable behaviour or personality responses have appeared. When these things may be determined within a reasonable certainty, plans may be laid for social and psychiatric treatment, and methods of treatment may be definitely selected and be judged by their results. When we do not know the reason for a child's misbehaviour, we may, of course, conclude that its causation is unimportant and that the vital consideration is to render swift, uniform punishment to every child who misbehaves in this way. Or we may, by probing, reasoning, and assumption, construct a theoretical reason for the mis-behaviour and base treatment on this assumption. If we are correctly to evaluate the results of any course of treatment, we must consider whether this treatment was a definite and planned procedure based on a known total situation or whether it was theoretically determined or whether it was selected purely by chance.

CHAPTER XVII

SUMMARY

LARGE part of the interest and value of these case reports as a series lies in the individual cases themselves and in the fact that certain definite methods were used in them all. "Methods" seem to have no interest or value, however, unless they effect good results. Here is presented a summary of the results of my methods.

The cases have no statistical value as compared with all problem boys, or even with all those who were seen at the Judge Baker Foundation during the same period. The series merely represents all the boys whose treatment I began during a period of about five months. They represent about twenty per cent of all the cases at the clinic during this time.

The cases were selected for treatment primarily because of the seriousness or the importance of the problem. The selection was usually contingent upon the possibility of the boy's returning regularly for treatment, thought in a few critical cases this factor was ignored. Most of those with mental defect or recognized neurological or mental diseases were not treated, because they were considered institutional cases.

It is evident, therefore, that the frequency of any definite problem is not maintained in this series to compare with its proportionate frequency in any large group appearing in a clinic. In this series the more serious problems appear with greater frequency than in the average clinical group, the simpler ones with less, and those originally considered as unsuitable for anything but institutional treatment do not appear at all.

No attempt to present the summary of results in the form of tabulations or tables will be made.

In the individual case reports I have given my own estimate of the results obtained. In making these final estimates three general factors have entered in. They are arranged in the order of their importance for the estimate:

First, what the child himself said about his treatment and acquaintance with me; second, my own opinion of the results, considered both from a social and from a psychiatric standpoint; third, the opinions of others who know the child well.

Concerning the first it may be said that in nearly every case the child has either spontaneously told me or others his opinion of what has been done for him, or has shown very clearly by his behaviour how he evaluates my efforts. In a few cases it has been necessary to inquire. Statements obtained in this last way are not considered so reliable.

As to my own estimations the sources of possible error are of course great. In the first place, I have been trying, when *thinking about* these boys, to understand *why* and *how* changes have occurred rather than what has actually happened, either before or after the period of treatment. Secondly, try as a psychiatrist will, if he is interested in and likes children, he may not be able to avoid entirely the tendency to excuse them a little on the basis of dynamisms which he knows exist in their mental lives. Or the psychiatrist may see in the history of the child's unfortunate experiences or unhappy environment an excuse for his socially bad behaviour. When considering the child from a behaviour standpoint, the psychiatrist is never an unprejudiced observer. Partly to offset these and other sources of optimistic error, I never feel entirely satisfied with my own side of the child-psychiatrist equation. In none of the cases reported do I feel that I made no mistakes, and in very few of them do I feel that I might not have done better.

In nearly every case the collective opinion of those who know the child agrees in a general way with my own. The exceptions are noted in the cases themselves. As a matter of record I state the following fact: when disagreement occurs regarding results obtained by psychiatric effort, this disagreement comes more frequently from foster-parents of children than from the parents, teachers, social workers, or relatives of the child.

*   *

What follows is a brief summary of details noted in collecting and in correlating the facts and conclusions found in the case reports of these fifty-five boys.

SOCIAL SUMMARY

Source of the Cases

Fifteen were referred to the clinic from various juvenile courts.

Seven were referred by their families. (Of these, four were on the advice of school authorities.)

Thirty-three were referred by various social agencies dealing with children.

Environmental Situation

Twelve of the boys came to the clinic from homes where no economic stress had ever existed.

Twenty-one of the boys came from homes at least fairly comfortable. Of this group some experienced economic stress at times; none had received public charity.

Twenty-two of the boys came from homes of the poorer class. Economic stress existed in all of these, and they were, as a group, homes where crowded and unhygienic conditions prevailed.

Parental Situation

Thirty-two of the children had lived all or the major part of their lives with both parents. Of this number, twenty-one of them had been in homes where quarrelling and discord between the parents had in some definite way entered into the child's problems.

In eight of the cases the father was dead at the time the child was first seen.

In eleven cases the mother was dead.

Four of the boys were orphans when first known to us. Boys whose parents were entirely unknown are included in this group.

In nine of the families represented by these boys the parents were divorced or permanently separated before their contact with the clinic.

THERAPEUTIC SUMMARY

The Time Spent in the Treatment

The approximate time spent by the psychiatrist with these boys in therapeutic interviews and in other contacts was as follows:

The shortest time with any boy was three hours; the longest, two hundred hours; the average for the entire group was thirty-three hours.

Successes and Failures

In forty-three of the fifty-five cases modifications have occurred in the mental life of the child that have in some way helped him.

Of these forty-three cases, twenty-eight show a successful outcome. By this I mean that therapeutic efforts have effected personality changes that I believe will be permanent. These changes are manifested by better behaviour, more normal habits, better general adjustment to life and environment; and they have been definitely appreciated by all who know the boys.

In this group of forty-three children who have seemingly been helped by the treatment, there are three who are not included with those classed as successful, because I believe the apparent good results will be but temporary. In each of these three the behaviour of the child is and has been for some time satisfactory, but I feel that the mental life is still too abnormal to permit a good lifelong adjustment.

In twelve of the forty-three cases some definite personality help has been given. Permanent beneficial changes have been accomplished in the child's mental life, but these are not, to any large degree, directly and objectively obvious to others in their environment. In most of these cases this is because only a part, and usually not the most important part, of the problem has been solved.

*   *

The remaining twelve cases are psychiatric failures.

Of these, eight show no change of personality traits or of mental life resulting from the treatment.

In four cases the treatment has effected changes that in some way make the child's problems greater.

The Depth of Rapport

The following summary is a brief statement of the depth of rapport reached with these boys while treating them, correlated with the results obtained. This, in my opinion, is the most important thing to be found in this informally written book. These are statements founded on the validity of experience. I pretend to offer no scientific proof. I assume that these degrees of rapport are readily recognized and classified.

Of the entire series of fifty-five cases:

There are two with whom no positive rapport whatever was established.

In nine cases the superficial degree of friendly belief was reached.

In nine cases the degree of personal trust was reached.

In thirty-two cases the therapeutic degree of personality contact was reached.

In three cases the child became dependently attached to me.

Psychiatric Correlation

In thirty-eight cases I felt that I reached and held the therapeutically desirable rapport.

In fourteen cases I failed to reach the depth of rapport that I desired.

Three cases went further than I intended them to go or was then necessary.

Therapeutic Correlation

A correlation between the depth of rapport and results shows the following:

Of the nine cases that reached only the rapport of friendly belief, one was a success, four were partial successes, and four were failures.

Of the nine cases that reached the rapport of personal trust, five were successes, one was a partial success, two were failures, and one was made worse.

Of the thirty-two cases reaching the rapport of personality contact, twenty were permanent successes, three were temporary successes, seven were partial successes, one was a failure, and one was made worse.

Of the three who became dependently attached to me, two were successes, and one was a failure, finally, after being a very good temporary success at first.

Of the two with whom no positive rapport could be established, both were failures; one of these had his problems made more difficult.

Correlation of Rapport-Failure and Results

Of the fourteen with whom I failed to reach the degree of rapport which I thought would be therapeutically advisable, eight were failures, five were partial successes, and one was successful.

Of the three who entered a degree of rapport deeper than necessary, one was a success, one was a partial success, and one was made worse.

In other words, with nearly all of those boys with whom I failed entirely, or with whom my success was slight, I had failed to reach or to hold the degree of rapport that I believed to be the most desirable one.

*   *

Some of the boys classified as successes, especially those classified as partial successes, are boys who will probably continue to have life-problems and unhappiness conditioned either by their irremediable environments or their mental and unaltered personality responses. Some of them I might have helped more had I understood them better, or had I been able to inspire in them belief and trust in me, and develop a desire to have me understand them.

May I repeat that the foregoing statements of results are not presented as dogmatic facts scientifically established? They represent only my attempt to understand and to classify not only that vague but vitally important thing, the interaction between two human minds, but also what can be effected by the use of this interaction as a psychotherapeutic instrument.